Advanced Placement* Calculus AB/BC Instructor's Resource Guide

to accompany

Calculus: Early Transcendental Functions

Third Edition

Robert T. Smith
Roland B. Minton

Prepared by
Gail Duering Thomas
Mary Thomas
Larry Peterson

Boston Burr Ridge, IL Dubuque, IA New York San Francisco St. Louis
Bangkok Bogotá Caracas Kuala Lumpur Lisbon London Madrid Mexico City
Milan Montreal New Delhi Santiago Seoul Singapore Sydney Taipei Toronto

The McGraw-Hill Companies

Advanced Placement Instructor's Resource Guide to accompany
CALCULUS: EARLY TRANSCENDENTAL FUNCTIONS, THIRD EDITION
ROBERT T. SMITH AND ROLAND B. MINTON

Published by McGraw-Hill Higher Education, an imprint of The McGraw-Hill Companies, Inc., 1221 Avenue of the Americas, New York, NY 10020.

1 2 3 4 5 6 7 8 9 0 QPD / QPD 0 9 8 7

ISBN-13: 978-0-07-723627-4
ISBN-10: 0-07-723627-0

www.mhhe.com

About the Authors

Gail Duering Thomas is currently an adjunct instructor for the Mathematics Department at Montana State University. For nineteen years, Gail taught mathematics at Weber High School in Ogden, Utah. She served as a reader and table leader for the Advanced Placement Calculus Exam for seven years. As a College Board Consultant, she conducted many one-day workshops for the Western Region of the College Board. She also conducted many one-week summer institutes. Gail also presented workshops at Teachers Teaching with Technology (T^3) and NCTM conventions.

Mary Thomas teaches Advanced Placement Calculus at Ross High School in Ross, Ohio. A veteran teacher, with over thirty years of classroom experience, Mary has served as an Advanced Placement Calculus exam reader for the last five years. She was recognized as the Outstanding Secondary Mathematics Classroom Teacher for Southwest Ohio in 2002. She is currently the mathematics department chair at Ross High School.

Larry Peterson has taught AP Calculus since 1976 and is currently teaching at Northridge High School in Layton, Utah. He is a regular presenter at state, regional, national, and international conventions in mathematics and technology. His Advanced Placement experience ranges from Calculus to Computer Science to Statistics. He was a reader for the AP Calculus exam for 13 years, serving as a Table Leader for six years. In 2003 and 2004 Larry was also a Question Leader. In addition to his work as a College Board consultant, Larry served a six year term as a member of the Board of Directors of the National Board for Professional Teaching Standards. His awards include: Milken Educator, Tandy Scholar, Disney American Teacher Award winner, and Utah Teacher of the Year. Larry and his wife, Lynette, live in Roy, Utah.

Table of Contents

Topic Outline for AP Calculus AB
With correlations to
Smith and Minton, *Calculus Early Transcendental Functions,* Third Edition

I. Functions, Graphs, and Limits

AP Topic	Chapter.Section	Pages
Analysis of Graphs With the aid of technology, graphs of functions are often easy to produce. The emphasis is on the interplay between the geometric and analytic information and on the use of calculus both to predict and to explain the observed local and global behavior of a function.	3.3 3.4 3.5 3.6	265-277 277-286 286-296 296-307
Limits of functions (including one-sided limits)		
• An intuitive understanding of the limiting process	1.2	79-87
• Calculating limits using algebra	1.3	87-97
• Estimating limits from graphs or tables of data	1.2 and throughout the rest of the text	79-87
Asymptotic and unbounded behavior		
• Understanding asymptotes in terms of graphical behavior	1.5	110-121
• Describing asymptotic behavior in terms of limits involving infinity	1.5	110-121
• Comparing relative magnitudes of functions and their rates of change (for example, contrasting exponential growth, polynomial growth, and logarithmic growth)	Student Activity: "Order of Magnitude of a Function"	
Continuity as a property of functions		
• An intuitive understanding of continuity. (The function values can be made as close as desired by taking sufficiently close values of the domain.)	1.4	97-109
• Understanding continuity in terms of limits	1.4	97-109

• Geometric understanding of graphs of continuous functions (Intermediate Value Theorem and Extreme Value Theorem)	1.4 3.3	97-109 265-277

II. Derivatives

AP Topic	Chapter.Section	Pages
Concept of the derivative		
• Derivative presented graphically, numerically, and analytically	2.1 2.2	146-158 159-170
• Derivative interpreted as an instantaneous rate of change	2.1	146-158
• Derivative defined as the limit of the difference quotient	2.2	159-170
• Relationship between differentiability and continuity	2.2	159-170
Derivative at a point		
• Slope of a curve at a point. Examples are emphasized, including points at which there are vertical tangents and points at which there are no tangents.	1.1 2.2 3.3	74-79 159-170 265-277
• Tangent line to a curve at a point and local linear approximation	2.1 3.1	146-158 242-255
• Instantaneous rate of changes as the limit of average rate of change	2.1	146-158
• Approximate rate of change from graphs and tables of values	2.2 and throughout the rest of the text	159-170
Derivative as a function		
• Corresponding characteristics of graphs of f and f'	2.2	159-170
• Relationship between the increasing and decreasing behavior of f and the sign of f'	3.4	277-286

• The Mean Value Theorem and its geometric consequences	2.9	226-235
• Equations involving derivatives. Verbal descriptions are translated into equations involving derivatives and vice versa.	7.1	566-577
Second derivatives		
• Corresponding characteristics of the graphs of f, f', f''	3.5	286-296
• Relationship between the concavity of f and the sign of f''	3.5	286-296
• Points of inflection as places where concavity changes	3.5	286-296
Applications of derivatives		
• Analysis of curves, including the notions of monotonicity and concavity	3.4 3.5 3.6	277-286 286-296 296-307
• Optimization, both absolute (global) and relative (local) extrema	3.3 3.7	265-277 308-320
• Modeling rates of change, including related rates problems	3.8 3.9	321-327 327-338
• Use of implicit differentiation to find the derivative of an inverse function	2.8	216-226
• Interpretation of the derivative as a rate of change in varied applied contexts, including velocity, speed, and acceleration	2.1 2.3 and throughout the rest of the text	146-158 170-180
• Geometric interpretation of differential equations via slope fields and the relationship between slope fields and solution curves for differential equations	7.3	587-599

Computation of derivatives		
• Knowledge of derivatives of basic functions, including power, exponential, logarithmic, trigonometric and inverse trigonometric functions	2.3 2.6 2.7 2.8 4.8	170-180 196-206 206-215 216-226 416-426
• Basic rules for the derivatives of sums, products, and quotients of functions	2.3 2.4	170-180 180-188
• Chain rule and implicit differentiation	2.5 2.8	189-195 216-226

III. Integrals

AP Topic	Chapter.Section	Pages
Interpretations and properties of definite integrals		
• Definite integrals as a limit of Riemann sums	4.4	369-383
• Definite integral of the rate of change of a quantity over an interval interpreted as the change of the quantity over the interval: $\int_a^b f'(x)\,dx = f(b) - f(a)$	4.4 4.5 5.1	369-383 383-393 432-441
• Basic properties of definite integrals (examples include additivity and linearity)	4.4	369-383
Applications of integrals Appropriate integrals are used in a variety of applications to model physical, biological, or economics situations. Although only a sampling of applications can be included in any specific course, students should be able to adapt their knowledge and techniques to solve other similar application problems. Whatever applications are chosen, the emphasis is on using the method of setting up an approximating Riemann sum and representing its limit as a definite integral. To provide a common foundation, specific applications should include using the integral of a rate of change to give the accumulated change, finding the area of a region, the volume of a solid with known cross sections,	4.1 4.3 4.4 4.5 5.1 5.2 5.3 5.6 5.7	344-354 362-369 369-383 383-393 432-441 441-456 456-464 484-496 496-505

the average value of a function, and the distance traveled by a particle along a line.		
Fundamental Theorem of Calculus		
• Use of the Fundamental Theorem to evaluate definite integrals	4.5	383-393
• Use of the Fundamental Theorem to represent a particular antiderivative, and the analytical and graphical analysis of functions so defined.	4.5	383-393
Techniques of antidifferentiation		
• Antiderivatives following directly from derivatives of basic functions	4.1 6.1 6.3	344-354 510-514 521-530
• Antiderivatives by substitution of variables (including change of limits for definite integrals)	4.6 6.1 6.3	393-402 510-514 521-530
Applications of antidifferentiation		
• Find specific antiderivatives using initial conditions, including applications to motion along a line	4.1 5.5	344-354 472-484
• Solving separable differential equations and using them in modeling (in particular, studying the equation $y' = ky$ and exponential growth)	7.1 7.2	566-577 577-587
Numerical approximations to definite integrals Use of Riemann sums (using left, right, and midpoint evaluation points) and trapezoidal sums to approximate definite integrals of functions represented algebraically, graphically, and by tables of values	4.3 4.4 4.7	362-369 369-383 402-416

Topic Outline for AP Calculus BC
With correlations to
Smith and Minton, *Calculus Early Transcendental Functions,* Third Edition

Sections containing topics unique to Calculus BC are in bold type

I. Functions, Graphs, and Limits

AP Topic	Chapter.Section	Pages
Analysis of Graphs With the aid of technology, graphs of functions are often easy to produce. The emphasis is on the interplay between the geometric and analytic information and on the use of calculus both to predict and to explain the observed local and global behavior of a function.	3.3 3.4 3.5 3.6	265-277 277-286 286-296 296-307
Limits of functions (including one-sided limits)		
• An intuitive understanding of the limiting process	1.2	79-87
• Calculating limits using algebra	1.3	87-97
• Estimating limits from graphs or tables of data	1.2 and throughout the rest of the text	79-87
Asymptotic and unbounded behavior		
• Understanding asymptotes in terms of graphical behavior	1.5	110-121
• Describing asymptotic behavior in terms of limits involving infinity	1.5	110-121
• Comparing relative magnitudes of functions and their rates of change (for example, contrasting exponential growth, polynomial growth, and logarithmic growth)	Student Activity: "Order of Magnitude of a Function"	
Continuity as a property of functions		
• An intuitive understanding of continuity. (The function values can be made as close as desired by taking sufficiently close values of the domain.)	1.4	97-109
• Understanding continuity in terms of limits	1.4	97-109

• Geometric understanding of graphs of continuous functions (Intermediate Value Theorem and Extreme Value Theorem)	1.4 3.3	97-109 265-277
***Parametric, polar, and vector functions** The analysis of planar curves includes those given in parametric form, polar form and vector form.	**9.1** **9.4** **10.1** **11.1**	**716-725** **742-754** **786-796** **854-864**

II. Derivatives

AP Topic	Chapter.Section	Pages
Concept of the derivative		
• Derivative presented graphically, numerically, and analytically	2.1 2.2	146-158 159-170
• Derivative interpreted as an instantaneous rate of change	2.1	146-158
• Derivative defined as the limit of the difference quotient	2.2	159-170
• Relationship between differentiability and continuity	2.2	159-170
Derivative at a point		
• Slope of a curve at a point. Examples are emphasized, including points at which there are vertical tangents and points at which there are no tangents.	1.1 2.2 3.3	74-79 159-170 265-277
• Tangent line to a curve at a point and local linear approximation	2.1 3.1	146-158 242-255
• Instantaneous rate of changes as the limit of average rate of change	2.1	146-158
• Approximate rate of change from graphs and tables of values	2.2 and throughout the rest of the text	159-170
Derivative as a function		

• Corresponding characteristics of graphs of f and f'	2.2	159-170
• Relationship between the increasing and decreasing behavior of f and the sign of f'	3.4	277-286
• The Mean Value Theorem and its geometric consequences	2.9	226-235
• Equations involving derivatives. Verbal descriptions are translated into equations involving derivatives and vice versa.	7.1	566-577
Second derivatives		
• Corresponding characteristics of the graphs of f, f', f''	3.5	286-296
• Relationship between the concavity of f and the sign of f''	3.5	286-296
• Points of inflection as places where concavity changes	3.5	286-296
Applications of derivatives		
• Analysis of curves, including the notions of monotonicity and concavity	3.4 3.5 3.6	277-286 286-296 296-307
+ Analysis of planar curves given in parametric form, polar form, and vector form, including velocity and acceleration	**9.2** **9.5** **11.2** **11.3** **11.5**	**726-734** **755-763** **864-875** **876-877** **895-896**
• Optimization, both absolute (global) and relative (local) extrema	3.3 3.7	265-277 308-320
• Modeling rates of change, including related rates problems	3.8 3.9	321-327 327-338
• Use of implicit differentiation to find the derivative of an inverse function	2.8	216-226
• Interpretation of the derivative as a rate of change in varied applied contexts, including	2.1 2.3 and	146-158 170-180

velocity, speed, and acceleration	throughout the rest of the text	
• Geometric interpretation of differential equations via slope fields and the relationship between slope fields and solution curves for differential equations	7.3	587-599
+ Numerical solution of differential equations using Euler's method	**7.3**	**587-599**
+ L'Hopitals Rule, including its use in determining limits and convergence of improper integrals and series	**3.2** **6.6** **8.3** **8.5**	**255-265** **546-561** **636-648** **656-664**
Computation of derivatives		
• Knowledge of derivatives of basic functions, including power, exponential, logarithmic, trigonometric and inverse trigonometric functions	2.3 2.6 2.7 2.8 4.8	170-180 196-206 206-215 216-226 416-426
• Basic rules for the derivatives of sums, products, and quotients of functions	2.3 2.4	170-180 180-188
• Chain rule and implicit differentiation	2.5 2.8	189-195 216-226
+ Derivatives of parametric, polar, and vector functions	**9.2** **9.5** **11.2**	**726-734** **755-764** **864-875**

III. Integrals

AP Topic	Chapter.Section	Pages
Interpretations and properties of definite integrals		
• Definite integrals as a limit of Riemann sums	4.4	369-383
• Definite integral of the rate of change of a quantity over an interval interpreted as the change of the quantity over the interval:	4.4 4.5 5.1	369-383 383-393 432-441

$\int_a^b f'(x)\,dx = f(b) - f(a)$ • Basic properties of definite integrals (examples include additively and linearity)	4.4	369-383
***Applications of integrals** Appropriate integrals are used in a variety of applications to model physical, biological, or economics situations. Although only a sampling of applications can be included in any specific course, students should be able to adapt their knowledge and techniques to solve other similar application problems. Whatever applications are chosen, the emphasis is on using the method of setting up an approximating Riemann sum and representing its limit as a definite integral. To provide a common foundation, specific applications should include using the integral of a rate of change to give the accumulated change, finding the area of a region (including a region bounded by polar curves), the volume of a solid with known cross sections, the average value of a function, and the distance traveled by a particle along a line, and the length of a curve (including a curve given in parametric form).	4.1 4.3 4.4 4.5 5.1 5.2 5.3 5.6 5.7 **1.1** **5.4** **9.3** **9.5**	344-354 362-369 369-383 383-393 432-441 441-456 456-464 484-496 496-505 **74-79** **464-472** **734-742** **755-764**
Fundamental Theorem of Calculus • Use of the Fundamental Theorem to evaluate definite integrals • Use of the Fundamental Theorem to represent a particular antiderivative, and the analytical and graphical analysis of functions so defined.	4.5 4.5	383-393 383-393
Techniques of antidifferentiation • Antiderivatives following directly from derivatives of basic functions + Antiderivatives by substitution of variables (including change of limits for definite integrals), parts, and simple partial fractions (nonrepeating linear factors only)	4.1 6.1 6.3 4.6 6.1 **6.2** 6.3 **6.4**	344-354 510-514 521-530 393-402 510-514 **514-521** 521-530 **530-538**

+ Improper integrals (as limits of definite integrals)	**6.6**	**546-561**
Applications of antidifferentiation • Find specific antiderivatives using initial conditions, including applications to motion along a line • Solving separable differential equations and using them in modeling (in particular, studying the equation $y' = ky$ and exponential growth) + Solving logistic differential equations and using them in modeling	 4.1 5.5 7.1 7.2 **3.9** **7.2**	 344-354 472-484 566-577 577-587 **327-338** **577-587**
Numerical approximations to definite integrals Use of Riemann sums (using left, right, and midpoint evaluation points) and trapezoidal sums to approximate definite integrals of functions represented algebraically, graphically, and by tables of values	4.3 4.4 4.7	362-369 369-383 402-416

*IV. Polynomial Approximations and Series

AP Topic	Chapter.Section	Pages
***Concept of series** A series is defined as a sequence of partial sums, and convergence is defined in terms of the limit of the sequence of partial sums. Technology can be used to explore convergence or divergence	**8.1** **8.2**	**612-626** **626-636**
***Series of constants** + Motivating examples, including decimal expansion + Geometric series with applications + The harmonic series + Alternating series with error bound + Terms of series as areas of rectangles and their relationship to improper integrals, including the integral test and its use in testing the convergence of p-series	 **8.2** **8.2** **8.2** **8.4** **8.3**	 **626-636** **626-636** **626-636** **648-655** **636-648**

+ The ratio test for convergence and divergence	**8.5**	**656-664**
+ Comparing series to test for convergence or divergence	**8.3**	**636-648**
***Taylor series**		
+ Taylor polynomial approximation with graphical demonstration of convergence (for example, viewing graphs of various Taylor polynomials of the sine function approximating the sine curve)	**8.7**	**672-685**
+ Maclaurin series and the general Taylor series centered at $x = a$	**8.7**	**672-685**
+ Maclaurin series for the functions $e^x, \sin x, \cos x,$ and $\frac{1}{1-x}$	**8.7**	**672-685**
+ Formal manipulation of Taylor series and shortcuts to computing Taylor series, including substitution, differentiation, and antidifferentiation, and the formation of new series from known series	**8.6** **8.7** **8.8**	**664-672** **672-685** **685-694**
+ Functions defined by power series	**8.6**	**664-672**
+ Radius and interval of convergence of power series	**8.6**	**664-672**
+ Lagrange error bound for Taylor polynomials	**8.7**	**672-685**

Introduction

Calculus: Early Transcendental Functions, Third Edition by Robert Smith and Roland Minton was designed to be used in a three or four semester college calculus course. It includes many chapters and topics that are not part of the Advanced Placement* Program Calculus Course Description. The curriculum of Calculus AB corresponds closely with that of most first semester college calculus courses. Calculus BC corresponds with the curriculum of the first two semesters of college calculus.

The Topic Outline for Calculus AB and the Topic Outline for Calculus BC are guidelines for teachers. They list those topics that students should master if they are to be successful on the appropriate AP Calculus Exam. Many teachers believe that other topics (such as integration by parts or L'Hopital's Rule for finding the value of limits) should be part of their students' calculus experience and all teachers should design a course that includes those topics they feel are necessary for student success in college calculus. Because of the vagaries of most high school teaching schedules, many teachers often find it helpful to teach those topics not found on the Topic Outlines after the AP Calculus Exam has been administered in May.

Every teacher should have a copy of the College Board® publication "Calculus Course Description". This booklet is invaluable because it discusses such topics as the philosophy of the courses, goals, prerequisites, the Topic Outlines for Calculus AB and Calculus BC, appropriate uses for the graphing calculator, exam formats, sample multiple-choice and free-response questions, and many other useful topics.

Another excellent source of information about AP Calculus is AP Central®. AP Central (apcentral.collegeboard.com) is a compilation of Web resources for AP Calculus teachers (free registration required). Users can find the following:

- "AP Course Descriptions, AP Exam questions and scoring guidelines, sample syllabi, research reports, and feature articles.
- A searchable Institutes and Workshops database, providing information about professional development events. AP Central offers online events that participants can access from their home or school computers.
- The Course Home Pages (apcentral.collegeboard.com/coursehomepages), which contain insightful articles, teaching tips, activities, label ideas, and other course specific content contributed by colleagues in the AP community.
- Links to AP publications and products (some available for immediate download) that can be purchased online at the College Board Store (store.collegeboard.com).
- Moderated electronic discussion groups (EDGs) for each AP course to facilitate the exchange of ideas and practices.
- Teachers' Resource database—click on the "Teachers' Resources" tab to search for reviews of textbooks, reference books, documents, Web sites, software, videos, and more. College and high school faculty write the reviews with specific reference to the value of the resources in teaching AP courses.
  ("Calculus Course Description", College Board, p.62)

The Philosophy of the AP Calculus Courses

It may be helpful to think of Calculus AB as divided into four broad concepts; 1) limits, 2) derivatives, 3) indefinite integrals, and 4) definite integrals. The exam will focus on broad concepts and applicable methods. Although students will be expected to be competent in manipulation and computation, the test does not emphasize manipulation or memorization. The content of Calculus AB is similar to most first semester college calculus courses.

Calculus BC is an extension of Calculus AB. Both courses contain the same core of required topics, but Calculus BC also includes advanced integration techniques, analysis of functions presented in polar, parametric and vector form, and the study of infinite series. Calculus BC is equivalent to the first two semesters of college calculus.

The AP Calculus Exam tests these concepts in several ways. Functions will be presented in a variety of ways: graphical, numerical, analytical, or verbal. Students need to be able to work with any of the representations and see the connections between them. They may be asked to explain in writing what these concepts mean in the context of an application.

The College Board and the Calculus Test Development Committee support and encourage the use of graphing technology as a way to increase understanding of calculus concepts. It is important that students be familiar with the operation of the graphing calculator. It will be used on part of the exam. While they may be very good at using the calculator to do a range of things, students will only be tested on the following calculator functionalities:

1. Graph a function in specified viewing window.
2. Find the roots of functions or the intersection of two functions.
3. Find a numerical approximation for the derivative of a function.
4. Find a numerical approximation for the value of a definite integral.

No other skills using the graphing calculator will be required. In fact, if students use other features, such as curve fitting, they will lose points on the exam. The test is written so that there is no advantage in using one calculator over another. Students may store any information they want in calculator memory. They will not be required to clear the memory before the test begins.

The Philosophy of the Instructor's Resource Guide

This book is an attempt to make it easier to teach an AP Calculus course with Calculus: Early Transcendental Functions, Third Edition as the main text. The authors have tried to include answers to commonly asked questions about any calculus book. Some of the material for each chapter will include:

- Correlations between the text and the Topic Outline for Calculus AB and the Topic Outline for Calculus BC. Those sections not necessary for each course will be listed so teachers may decide whether to include them in their course.
- Required vocabulary and theorems
- Correlation to the Calculus Concepts Videos that explain essential concepts through dynamic animations.
- Activities for student enrichment
- Teacher notes for AP topics that require further development than what is given in the text
- Sets of multiple-choice and free-response questions (including complete solutions) focusing on the topics in that chapter as well as spiraled questions using topics from previous chapters that can be used for testing, exercises or preparation for the AP Calculus Exam

CHAPTER 0: PRELIMINARIES

In their introduction to Chapter 0, Robert T. Smith and Roland B. Minton, the authors of Calculus (3ed) write, "We have primarily included material that we consider essential for the study of calculus that you are about to begin. We must emphasize that understanding is always built upon a solid foundation. While we do not intend this chapter to be a comprehensive review of precalculus mathematics, we have tried to hit the highlights and provide you with some standard notation and language that we will use throughout the text."

Students in a high school calculus class should have taken the standard prerequisites: algebra, geometry, trigonometry, analytic geometry and analysis of functions. They should have studied linear, polynomial, rational, exponential, logarithmic, trigonometric, inverse trigonometric and piecewise functions. Their study of the listed functions should include, but not be limited to, the domain, range, graph, how to find zeros, and ways to combine functions, such as addition, subtraction, division and composition. They should know the value of the trigonometric functions for the numbers $0, \frac{\pi}{6}, \frac{\pi}{4}, \frac{\pi}{3}, \frac{\pi}{2}$ and their multiples. For a more complete list of suggested topics, be sure to read the prerequisites on page 6 in the "Calculus Course Description" booklet.

Chapter 0 is an excellent review of those topics.

Section 0.2 "… presents a general framework for using technology to explore the graphs of functions" (Calculus (3ed), Smith/Minton, page 20). The authors demonstrate the strengths and pitfalls when using calculators to generate graphs of functions.

Student Activity: Introductory Assignment

Teacher's Notes:

In preparing to teach calculus most teachers must make a decision about Chapter 0. It is a good review of the precalculus topics that students should be familiar with before they take a calculus class. However, many teachers are on a very tight timeline and, therefore, do not like to take the time to thoroughly review every topic in Chapter 0. Many teachers choose to begin with new material and then incorporate review topics as they become necessary. This activity can be used in the first days of class and can serve as a review.

The problems can be assigned as individual homework. However, as a group assignment this activity can introduce students to each other and reduce a student's anxiety about his/her preparation. Teachers can learn about their students by roaming about the classroom and listening in on individual groups as they solve the problems.

Questions (a), 5, 6, 7, and 19 represent common student errors and can generate a lot of discussion about proper mathematics. Each student should turn in for grading, the proper forms of the problems and this paper should be kept handy for quick reference throughout the course.

Student Worksheet

Which of the following statements are true for all numbers? If a statement is not true, write a new statement using either the left or right side that is true. For example:

a. $(x+2)^2 = x^2 + 4$

This statement is false: $(x+2)^2 = x^2 + 4x + 4$

1. $2x^{-1} = \dfrac{1}{2x}$

2. $\dfrac{x+3}{x+4} = \dfrac{3}{4}$

3. $\dfrac{a+b}{c} = \dfrac{a}{c} + \dfrac{b}{c}$

4. $\dfrac{a}{b+c} = \dfrac{a}{b} + \dfrac{a}{c}$

5. $|x| = x$

6. $\sqrt{x^2} = x$

7. $\sqrt{x^2 + y^2} = x + y$

8. $\sqrt{xy} = \sqrt{x} \cdot \sqrt{y}$

9. $\sqrt{\dfrac{x}{y}} = \dfrac{\sqrt{x}}{\sqrt{y}}$

10. $\log \dfrac{x}{y} = \dfrac{\log x}{\log y}$

11. $\log x \cdot \log y = \log x \cdot \log y$

12. $\log(x+y) = \log x + \log y$

13. $\ln x^2 = (\ln x)^2$

14. $\sin(A \pm B) = \sin A \pm \sin B$

15. $\cos A \cos B \pm \sin A \sin B = \cos(A \mp B)$

16. $2\sin 8x \cdot \cos 8x = \sin 16x$

17. $\sin^2 x = (\sin x)^2$

18. $\sin^{-1} x = (\sin x)^{-1}$

19. $e^{A \pm B} = e^A \pm e^B$

20. $e^{x^2} = (e^x)^2$

21. $e^{2\ln x} = 2x$

22. The graphs of these two functions are the same:

$f(x) = \dfrac{x^2 - 1}{x - 1}$ and $g(x) = x + 1$

23. Solve: $x^2 = 3x$
$x = 3$

Solutions

1. F $2x^{-1} = \frac{2}{x}$ or $(2x)^{-1} = \frac{1}{2x}$

2. F $\frac{x(3)}{x(4)} = \frac{3}{4}$

3. T $c \neq 0$

4. $\frac{ac+ab}{bc} = \frac{a}{b} + \frac{a}{c}$

   $b, c \neq 0$

5. F $|x| = \begin{cases} x & \text{if } x \geq 0 \\ -x & \text{if } x < 0 \end{cases}$

6. F $\sqrt{x^2} = |x|$

7. F $\sqrt{(x+y)^2} = |x+y|$

8. T As long as $x, y \geq 0$

9. T As long as $x \geq 0,\ y > 0$

10. F $\log \frac{x}{y} = \log x - \log y$

11. F $\log xy = \log x + \log y$

12. F $\log(x+y)$ cannot be simplified

13. F $\ln x^2 = 2 \ln x$

14. F $\sin(A \pm B) = \sin A \cos B \pm \cos A \sin B$

15. T

16. T

17. T (right side is how to enter expression on the calculator)

18. F $\sin^{-1} x$ is $\arcsin(x)$

    $(\sin x)^{-1} = \frac{1}{\sin x} = \csc x$

19. F $e^{A+B} = e^A e^B; e^{A-B} = \frac{e^A}{e^B}$

20. F $e^{2x} = (e^x)^2$

21. F $e^{2\ln x} = e^{\ln x^2} = x^2$

22. F $f(x)$ is a line with a hole at $x = 1$
    $g(x)$ is a line

23. F $x^2 = 3x$
    $x^2 - 3x = 0$
    $x(x-3) = 0$
    $x = 0,\ x = 3$

CHAPTER 1: LIMITS AND CONTINUITY

Correlations

The section by section correspondence to the Topic Outline for Calculus AB and the Topic Outline for Calculus BC (*Calculus BC topics are in italic type*) is:

AP Topic	Chapter.Section	Pages
I. Functions, Graphs, and Limits		
Limits of functions (including one-sided limits)		
• An intuitive understanding of the limiting process	1.2	79-87
• Calculating limits using algebra	1.3	87-97
• Estimating limits from graphs or tables of data	1.2 and throughout the rest of the text	79-87
I. Functions, Graphs, and Limits		
Asymptotic and unbounded behavior		
• Understanding asymptotes in terms of graphical behavior	1.5	110-121
• Describing asymptotic behavior in terms of limits involving infinity	1.5	110-121
• Comparing relative magnitudes of functions and their rates of change (for example, contrasting exponential growth, polynomial growth, and logarithmic growth)	Student Activity: "Order of Magnitude of a Function"	
I. Functions, Graphs, and Limits		
Continuity as a property of functions		
• An intuitive understanding of continuity. (The function values can be made as close as desired by taking sufficiently close values of the domain.)	1.4	97-109
• Understanding continuity in terms of limits	1.4	97-109
• Geometric understanding of graphs of continuous functions (Intermediate Value Theorem …)	1.4	97-109

AP Topic	Chapter.Section	Pages
II. Derivatives **Derivative at a point** • Slope of a curve at a point. Examples are emphasized, including points at which there are vertical tangents and points at which there are no tangents.	1.1	74-79
III. Integrals **Applications of integrals** *Appropriate integrals are used in a variety of applications to model physical, biological, or economics situations. Although only a sampling of applications can be included in any specific course, students should be able to adapt their knowledge and techniques to solve other similar application problems. Whatever applications are chosen, the emphasis is on using the method of setting up an approximating Riemann sum and representing its limit as a definite integral. To provide a common foundation, specific applications should include… the length of a curve*	*1.1*	*74-79*

<table>
<tr><th>Textbook Section</th><th>AP Topic</th></tr>
<tr><td>1.1 A Brief Preview of Calculus: Tangent Lines and the Length of a Curve</td><td>II. Derivatives

Derivative at a point<ul><li>Slope of a curve at a point. Examples are emphasized, including points at which there are vertical tangents and points at which there are no tangents.</li></ul>III. Integrals

Applications of integrals Appropriate integrals are used in a variety of applications to model physical, biological, or economics situations. Although only a sampling of applications can be included in any specific course, students should be able to adapt their knowledge and techniques to solve other similar application problems. Whatever applications are chosen, the emphasis is on using the method of setting up an approximating Riemann sum and representing its limit as a definite integral. To provide a common foundation, specific applications should include... the length of a curve</td></tr>
<tr><td>1.2 The Concept of Limit</td><td>I. Functions, Graphs, and Limits

Limits of functions (including one-sided limits)<ul><li>An intuitive understanding of the limiting process</li><li>Estimating limits from graphs or tables of data</li></ul></td></tr>
<tr><td>1.3 Computation of Limits</td><td>I. Functions, Graphs, and Limits

Limits of functions (including one-sided limits)<ul><li>Calculating limits using algebra</li></ul></td></tr>
<tr><td>1.4 Continuity and its Consequences</td><td>I. Functions, Graphs, and Limits

Continuity as a property of functions<ul><li>An intuitive understanding of continuity. (The function values can be made as close as desired by taking sufficiently close values of the domain.)</li><li>Understanding continuity in terms of limits</li><li>Geometric understanding of graphs of continuous functions (Intermediate Value Theorem ...)</li></ul></td></tr>
<tr><td>1.5 Limits Involving Infinity</td><td>I. Functions, Graphs, and Limits

Asymptotic and unbounded behavior<ul><li>Understanding asymptotes in terms of graphical behavior</li><li>Describing asymptotic behavior in terms of limits involving infinity</li></ul></td></tr>
</table>

Vocabulary and Section Notes

Vocabulary used in the Topic Outline for Calculus AB and the Topic Outline for Calculus BC (*Calculus BC topics are in italic type*) include:

Arc Length
Continuous function
Discontinuous function
Horizontal asymptote
Indeterminate form
Infinite limit
Intermediate Value Theorem
Limit
One-sided limit
Piecewise-defined functions
Removable discontinuity
Secant line
Slant or oblique asymptotes
Slope of a curve
Squeeze Theorem
Vertical asymptote

Section notes for the Calculus AB Course:

Section 1.4 (Continuity and Its Consequences): Method of Bisections is not part of the Topic Outline for Calculus AB.

Section 1.6 (Formal Definition of the Limit): The $\varepsilon - \delta$ proof is not part of the Topic Outline for Calculus AB.

Section 1.7 (Limits and Loss-of-Significance Errors): Although not a specific part of the Topic Outline for Calculus AB, awareness of the limitations of calculator representations of numbers is essential to wise use of technology in studying functions.

Section notes for the Calculus BC Course:

Section 1.4 (Continuity and Its Consequences): Method of Bisections is not part of the Topic Outline for Calculus BC.

Section 1.6 (Formal Definition of the Limit): The $\varepsilon - \delta$ proof is not part of the Topic Outline for Calculus BC.

Section 1.7 (Limits and Loss-of-Significance Errors): Although not a specific part of the Topic Outline for Calculus BC, awareness of the limitations of calculator representations of numbers is essential to wise use of technology in studying functions.

Student Activity: How Many Fish in the Lake

Teacher's Notes:

Limits are a common mathematical construct found in the everyday world that your students inhabit. This exercise is one way to introduce them to the idea of a numerical limit and to help them become familiar with some of the features of their calculators.

The idea that the number of fish in the lake will stabilize is the same as the limit of the number of fish in the lake as the stocking program continues over time. You can use limit vocabulary as you discuss this activity with your students. In mathematical notation, it is necessary to define some terms:

t: the number of years the stocking program has been in existence

$f(t)$: the number of fish in the lake in year t

$\lim_{t \to \infty} f(t)$: the limit or the stable number of fish in the lake

After completing this exercise your students should be ready to pursue a more formal study of limits in their mathematical context.

Student Worksheet

Biologists speculate there are 10000 fish in a small lake. Over the past several years, surveys of angler's catches and the natural mortality rate show that the number of fish decreases by 20% per year. The biologists would like to raise the number of fish in the lake to about 15,000 and maintain that figure into the future. The number of years it will take to achieve this goal depends on how many fish they stock each year. How long will it take the number of fish to reach 99% of the goal or about 14,850 fish?

1. If the biologists stock 1000 fish per year, how long will it take the number of fish to reach 99% of the goal or about 14,850 fish? If they continue to stock fish at this rate, is there a stable amount of fish in the lake? How long does it take to be within 1% of this number?

Solution:

If there were 10,000 fish in the lake, with 20% decrease per year and 1000 fish stocked, the number of fish after one year would be 9000 and if this were repeated one more year, the number of fish would be 8200.

```
10000-.2*10000+1
000
                9000
█
```

```
10000-.2*10000+1
000
                9000
9000-.2*9000+100
0
                8200
```

Rather than re-typing the expression every time, replace the number of fish with ANS and now, just by pressing ENTER, the calculator can continue the calculation until the user is finished.

```
9000-.2*9000+100
0
                8200
Ans-.2*Ans+1000
                7560
                7048
              6638.4
```

It would seem that if the biologists were only stocking 1000 fish per year, the number of fish in the lake declines. Why? Will the number of fish in the lake stabilize? Finish the table for the fish-stocking program for 1000 fish per year.

Stocking 1000 fish per year

Year	Number of Fish	Year	Number of Fish
0	10000	13	
1	9000	14	
2	8200	15	
3	7560	16	
4	7048	17	
5	6638.4	18	
6	6310.7	19	
7	6048.6	20	
8		21	
9		22	
10		23	
11		24	
12		25	

2. If the biologists stock 2000 fish per year, how long will it take the number of fish to reach 14,850 fish? If they continue to stock fish at this rate, is there a stable amount of fish in the lake? How long does it take to be within 1% of this number?

Stocking 2000 fish per year

Year	Number of Fish	Year	Number of Fish
0	10000	13	
1		14	
2		15	
3		16	
4		17	
5		18	
6		19	
7		20	
8		21	
9		22	
10		23	
11		24	
12		25	

3. If the biologists stock 3000 fish per year, how long will it take the number of fish to reach 14,850 fish? If they continue to stock fish at this rate, is there a stable amount of fish in the lake? How long does it take to reach 99% of this number?

Stocking 3000 fish per year:

Year	Number of Fish	Year	Number of Fish
0	10000	13	
1		14	
2		15	
3		16	
4		17	
5		18	
6		19	
7		20	
8		21	
9		22	
10		23	
11		24	
12		25	

4. If the biologists stock 4000 fish per year, how long will it take the number of fish to reach 14,850 fish? If they continue to stock fish at this rate, is there a stable amount of fish in the lake? How long does it take to be within 1% of this number?

Stocking 4000 fish per year

Year	Number of Fish	Year	Number of Fish
0	10,000	13	
1		14	
2		15	
3		16	
4		17	
5		18	
6		19	
7		20	
8		21	
9		22	
10		23	
11		24	
12		25	

Student Activity: Order of Magnitude of a Function

Teacher's Notes:

This activity demonstrates the relative order of magnitude between two functions using a limit of the ratio of the two. Since students have not learned L'Hopitals' Rule yet, we will use both graphical and numerical modes to view the problem.

It is helpful to have the teacher demonstrate the first two examples of the effect of the graphing window on the behavior of the two functions.

The solutions to the questions are

1. The values of $f(x)$ get larger.
2. The values of $g(x)$ get larger.
3. The values get smaller and close to zero.
4. The values get large without bound.
5. $g(x)$ has the higher order of magnitude.
6. The ratio gets large without bound.
7. The ratio gets small and close to zero.
8. $g(x) = 2^x$ has the higher order of magnitude.
9. logarithmic, power, exponential
10. The limit gets large without bound.
11. The limit is zero.
12. The limit is zero.
13. $g(x)$ has the higher order of magnitude.
14. $f(x)$ has the higher order of magnitude.
15. Both functions appear to be of the same magnitude.

Student Worksheet

One of the competencies listed in the Topic Outline for Calculus AB and the Topic Outline for Calculus BC is "Comparing relative magnitudes of functions and their rates of change (for example, contrasting exponential growth, polynomial growth, and logarithmic growth)." Using technology, we can explore functions and their rates of change through graphs and tables.

Ask students to use a calculator to solve the equation $x^2 = 2^x$. Most students will draw a graph in the standard viewing window and only report two solutions ($x = 2$ and $x = -0.7666647$). There is a third solution, $x = 4$, but it isn't apparent in the standard viewing window.

We can view this relationship between the two functions by changing the viewing window to emphasize one function over another. If we focus on the behavior near the origin, we see two points of intersection, but miss the third point.

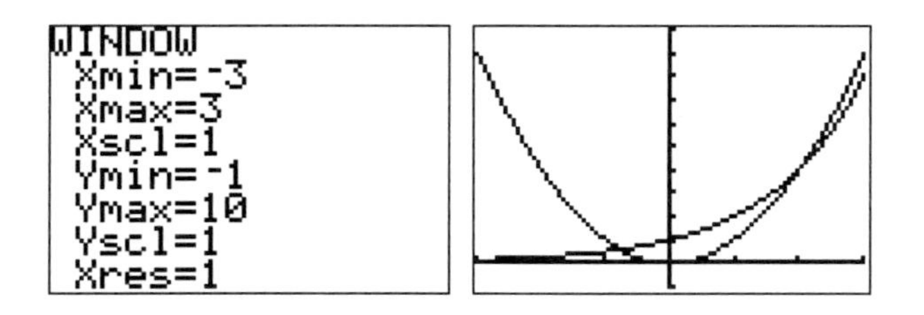

Enlarging the vertical direction, it is easier to note the third point of intersection.

WINDOW
Xmin=-2
Xmax=6
Xscl=1
Ymin=-1
Ymax=30
Yscl=5
Xres=1

However, the end behavior of each function is easier to detect when both the vertical and horizontal directions are enlarged.

WINDOW
Xmin=0
Xmax=20
Xscl=5
Ymin=-1
Ymax=400
Yscl=50
Xres=1

From this view, we can see that the exponential function increases much more rapidly than the quadratic function.

One way to classify functions according to order of magnitude is by taking limits of quotients of functions. Suppose L is the $\lim_{x \to \infty} \frac{f(x)}{g(x)}$.

Let us examine how the two functions behave.

Let $Y_1 = f(x) = x^2$, $Y_2 = g(x) = 2^x$, $Y_3 = \frac{Y_1}{Y_2}$, and $Y_4 = \frac{Y_2}{Y_1}$.

Go to **TBLSET** and use the initial values shown

```
TABLE SETUP
 TblStart=0
 ΔTbl=1
Indpnt: Auto Ask
Depend: Auto Ask
```

Use **TABLE** to fill in the values below.

X	Y_1	Y_2	Y_3	Y_4
0				
1				
2				
3				
4				
5				
8				
10				
15				

1. What happened to the values of *f(x)* as you chose larger values for *x*?

2. What happened to the values for *g(x)* as you chose larger values for *x*?

3. What happened to the values for Y_3 as you chose larger values for *x*?

4. What happened to the values for Y_4 as you chose larger values for *x*?

5. Which function, *f(x)* or *g(x)*, appears to have the larger magnitude?

6. What can you say about the ratio $\lim_{x \to \infty} \frac{f(x)}{g(x)}$ if the function with the larger magnitude is the numerator?

7. What can you say about the ratio $\lim_{x\to\infty}\frac{f(x)}{g(x)}$ if the function with the larger magnitude is the denominator?

Let us generalize your conclusions.

If $\lim_{x\to\infty}\frac{f(x)}{g(x)}$ is infinite, then *f(x)* has a higher order of magnitude than *g(x)*.

If $\lim_{x\to\infty}\frac{f(x)}{g(x)}$ is zero, then *f(x)* has a lower order of magnitude than *g(x)*.

If $\lim_{x\to\infty}\frac{f(x)}{g(x)}$ is a finite, nonzero number, then *f(x)* has the same order of magnitude as *g(x)*.

You are probably familiar with this idea using polynomial functions in determining horizontal asymptotes. The function with the higher degree controls the overall behavior of the ratio.

Consider the two functions $f(x)=x^2+3x$ and $g(x)=x^2+1$. Since the $\lim_{x\to\infty}\frac{x^2+3x}{x^2+1}=1$, the two functions are of equal magnitude. As the graph shows, the limit appears to be a non-zero constant.

```
WINDOW
 Xmin=0
 Xmax=20
 Xscl=5
 Ymin=-1
 Ymax=5
 Yscl=1
 Xres=1
```

This indicates that the functions have the same order of magnitude.

Looking at the two functions, $f(x)=x^2$ and $g(x)=2^x$, we can take the limit of the ratio of the two functions. If we write the ratio as $\lim_{x\to\infty}\frac{x^2}{2^x}$, sketch the graph of the ratio in the following window.

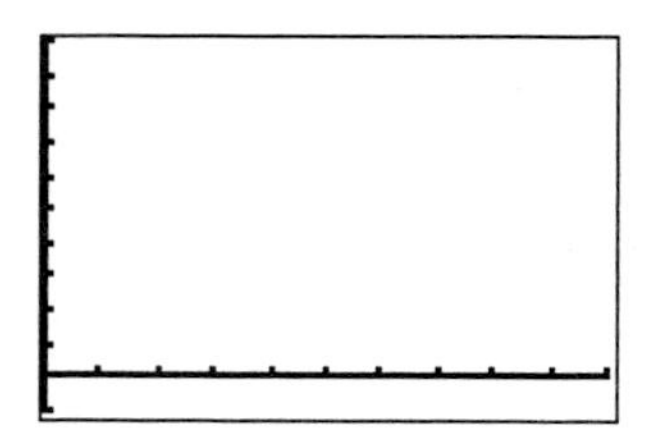

8. Based on your graph, which function, $f(x)=x^2$ or $g(x)=2^x$, has the higher order of magnitude?

9. List the following classes of functions in order of increasing magnitude
   a) exponential function
   b) logarithmic function
   c) power function ($y = x^n$).

From your results and the rules for limits of ratios of functions, determine the limits of the following:

10. $\lim\limits_{x\to\infty} \dfrac{x^3 + 2x - 5}{\ln x}$

11. $\lim\limits_{x\to\infty} \dfrac{x^{10}}{3^x}$

12. $\lim\limits_{x\to\infty} \dfrac{x^{100}}{e^{0.01x}}$

The graphs of the ratio of $\dfrac{f(x)}{g(x)}$ are shown. Determine from the graph whether *f(x)* or *g(x)* has the higher order of magnitude.

13. 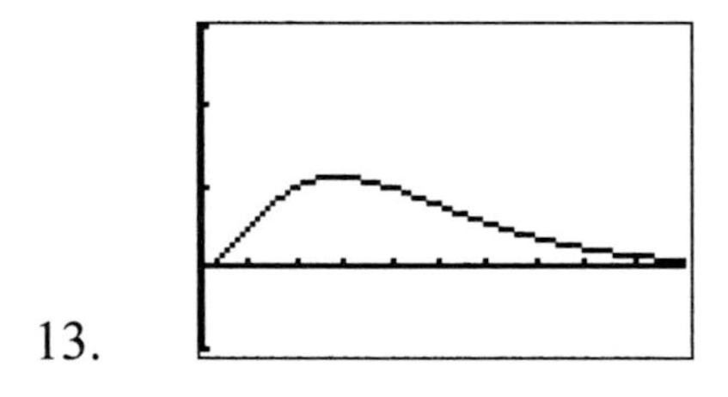

14. 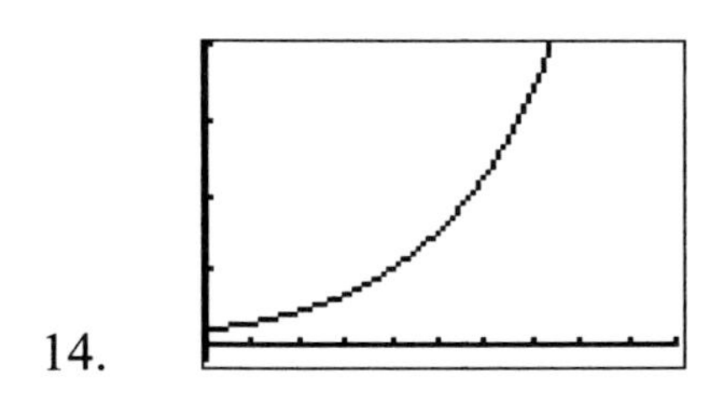

15. 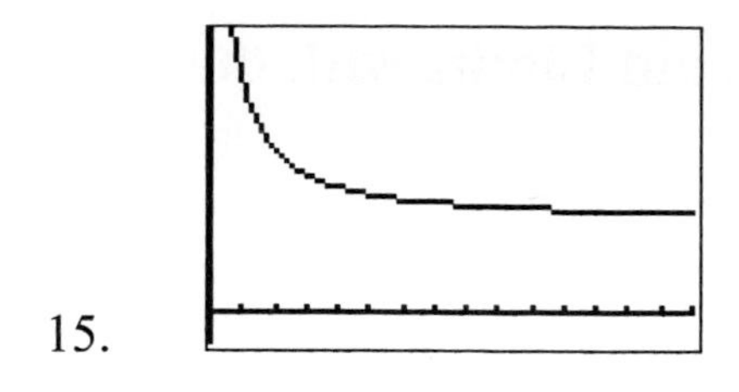

Remember the relative magnitudes of the different types of functions. The four classes of functions tested on the AP Calculus Exam, listed in order of increasing magnitude: logarithmic, polynomial, exponential, and factorial. The first three are part of the Topic Outline for Calculus AB. Factorials are only part of the Topic Outline for Calculus BC.

Teacher's Notes: Using the Calculator to Find Limits with the Rule of Three

Teacher's Notes:

One of the important principles supported by the Advanced Placement Calculus Course Description is the use of the Rule of Three to investigate functions. The Rule of Three states that a function can be investigated from a graphical, numerical or analytical perspective. However, conclusions can only be verified analytically.

Consider the function $f(x) = \dfrac{x-2}{x^2-4}$.

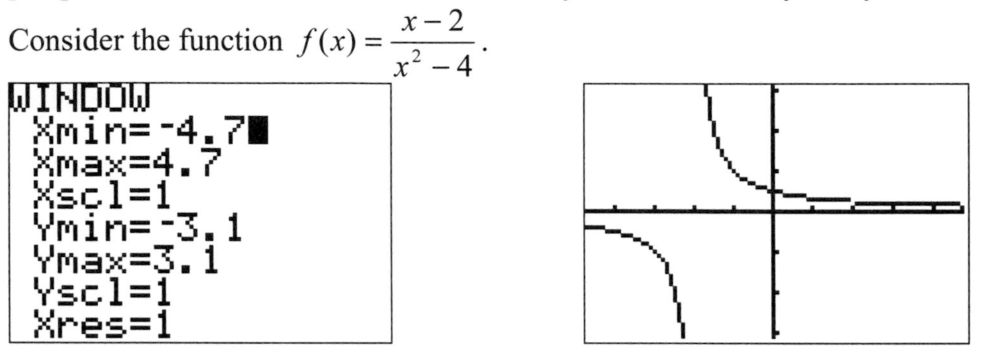

We know the function is undefined at $x = -2$ and $x = 2$. At $x = -2$ we can see a vertical asymptote. We can use a graphing calculator to support this contention.

Verifying a Vertical Asymptote (Numerically)

Using the TI 83/84, go to **(2nd WINDOW) TBLSET**. Set the variables as shown, then press **(2nd GRAPH) TABLE**.

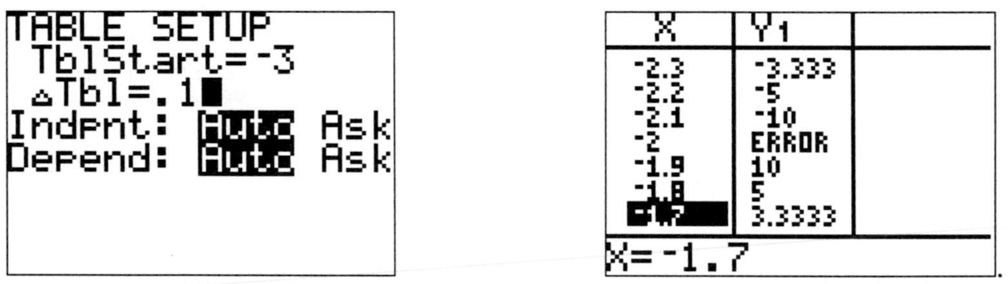

You can scroll down the X column to see the values for the function in Y1. At x = -2 the table correctly reports an error. Notice the y-values on either side of x = -2. When x < -2, the values are negative. When x > -2, the values are positive.

Now, go back to **TBLSET** and change the values as shown, then press **TABLE**. Notice that we have narrowed the domain and decreased the step size.

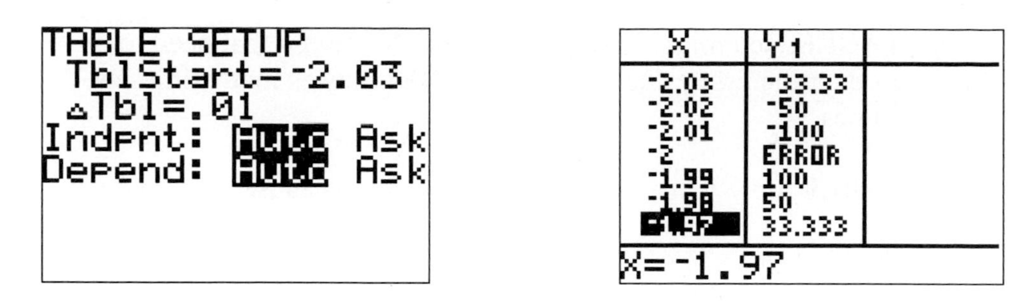

Once again, we see the y-values change from negative to positive as x passes through -2. Notice that the y-values are getting larger in both the positive and negative directions.

We can refine our window once more by changing the domain and shrinking the step size as shown.

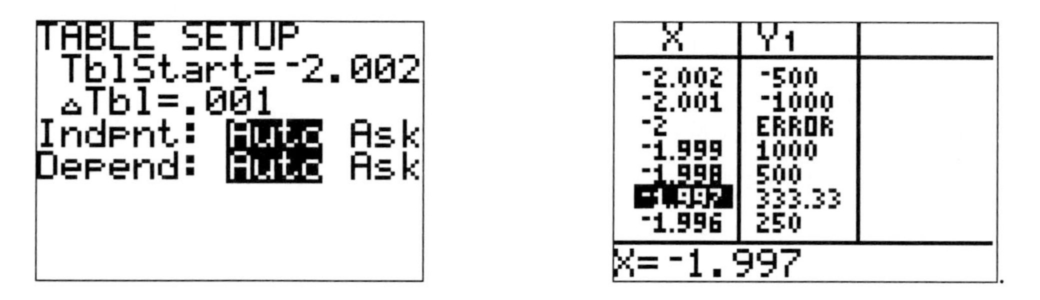

We can see that, as the x-values get closer to -2, the y-values diverge, getting further and further apart.

We can use this to verify that $\lim_{x \to -2} \frac{x-2}{x^2-4}$ does not exist. The end behavior goes to $\pm\infty$ which indicates a vertical asymptote at x = -2.

Verifying a Removable Discontinuity (Numerically)

While the vertical asymptote is obvious at x = -2, the behavior of the function at x = 2 is more difficult to determine. We can once again use the **TABLE** feature of the calculator to investigate the behavior of the function. This time change the **Indpnt** line to **Ask** in the **TBLSET** window as shown.

The first time you use **TABLE**, you might have values in the X column that need to be deleted. Place the cursor over the first value and press the **DEL** key as many times as necessary to delete all values.

Now, when you press **TABLE**, no y-values appear in the window because you have not **ASK**ed for any x-values.

X	Y1	

X=

Enter some values in the x column that are larger than 2, but get closer to 2.

X	Y1	
2.5	.22222	
2.1	.2439	
2.01	.24938	
2.001	.24994	
2.0001	.24999	
2	ERROR	

X=

Notice that the y-values get slightly larger each time until $x = 2$ when the function becomes undefined again. Once again, delete all the values in the x-column and repeat the exercise with values smaller than x = 2 but that get closer to 2.

X	Y1	
1	.33333	
1.5	.28571	
1.9	.25641	
1.999	.25006	
1.999	.25006	
2	.25	

X=1.99999

Notice the x-value at the bottom of the window is 1.99999 but it is rounded to x = 2 since the column width is fixed. Move the cursor to the same row in the Y column.

X	Y1	
1	.33333	
1.5	.28571	
1.9	.25641	
1.999	.25006	
1.999	.25006	
2	.25	

Y1=.250000625002

The actual value is shown at the bottom of the window even though the value in the column is rounded to y = 0.25.

You should notice that as x approached 2, the y-values approached 0.25. This supports, but does not verify, the conclusion $\lim_{x \to 2} \frac{x-2}{x^2-4} = 0.25$.

Graphical Support

Graph the function in a **DECIMAL** window. Use the **TRACE** button to move the cursor from its position on the y-axis leftward to x = -2. Notice the coordinates that appear at the bottom of the screen. At first, the y-values grow larger. But at x =-2, we

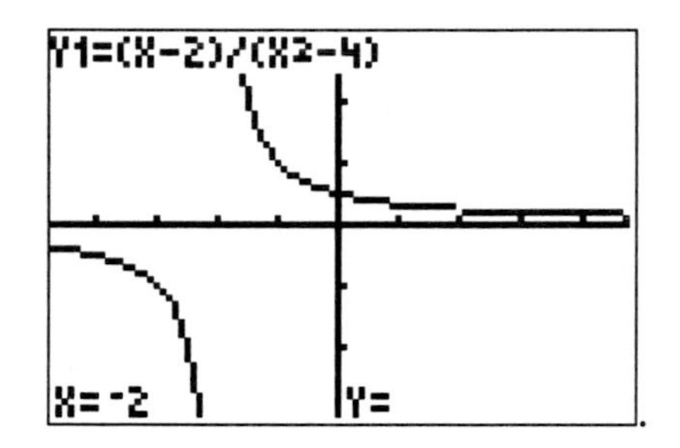

see no value is shown for y since the function is undefined. Continue to move the cursor to the left. Now, large negative y-values show at the bottom of the window.

Repeat the process at x = 2. This time you should see that the y-coordinates are clustering about y = 0.25

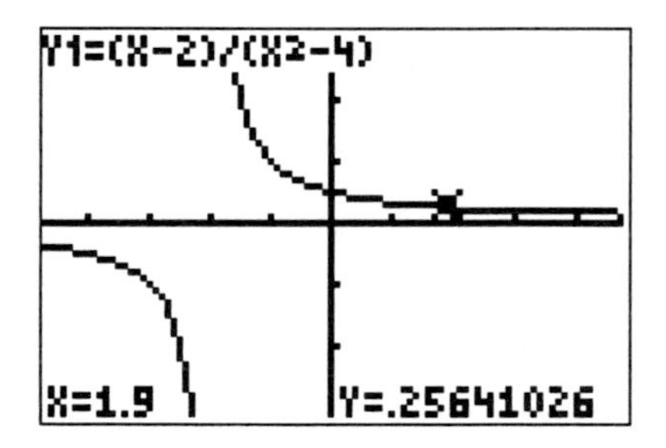

similar to the values that appeared in the **TABLE**. As you move the cursor to x = 2, we see that the y-value again disappears.

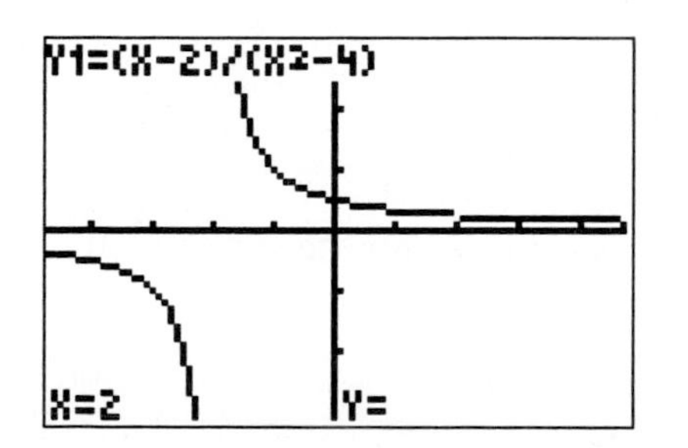

You should have noticed that the y-values did not move away from each other as they did at x = -2. As you move the cursor to the right of x = 2, the y-values again appear and are close to y = 0.25. This supports the notion that the $\lim_{x \to 2} \frac{x-2}{x^2-4} = 0.25$.

When we try to substitute x = 2, the function is undefined. Since direct substitution gives $\frac{0}{0}$, the limit is said to be *indeterminate*. We say that there is a "hole" in the graph. The y-value of the "hole" is 0.25 when x = 2.

The Rule of Three allows us to investigate functions graphically, numerically, or analytically. Nevertheless, remember, we can only *verify* results analytically. You should conclude this demonstration with algebraic analysis.

Verifying a Limit that Leads to a Vertical Asymptote

Once again, we look at the function $f(x) = \frac{x-2}{x^2-4}$ as $x \to -2$.

$$\lim_{x \to -2} \frac{x-2}{x^2-4} = \lim_{x \to -2} \frac{x-2}{(x-2)(x+2)} = \lim_{x \to -2} \frac{1}{x+2} =$$

$$\lim_{x \to -2^-} \frac{1}{x+2} = \frac{1}{0} \to -\infty; \quad \lim_{x \to -2^+} \frac{1}{x+2} = \frac{1}{0} = \infty$$

This shows the limit of the function does not exist as x approaches -2. The function increases without bound in both the positive and negative directions, which shows the presence of a vertical asymptote.

When we give +/- infinity for an answer, it is understood that the limit does not exist. Many authors use this notation to indicate unbounded behavior. It is important for students to understand the difference between these two forms of the answer.

Verifying a Limit that Leads to an Indeterminate Value

Let us now look at the same function $f(x) = \frac{x-2}{x^2-4}$ as $x \to +2$

$\lim_{x \to 2} \frac{x-2}{x^2-4} = \lim_{x \to 2} \frac{x-2}{(x-2)(x+2)} = \lim_{x \to 2} \frac{1}{x+2} = \frac{1}{4}$. We can see that, although the function has an indeterminate limit at $x = 2$, the limit of the function is 0.25.

Multiple-Choice Questions–Calculus AB/BC Topics

1. $\lim\limits_{x\to\infty} \dfrac{x^3 - x^2 + 5x + 8}{2x^3 + 6x^2 - 2} =$

   A. -4
   B. 0
   C. $\frac{1}{2}$
   D. 1
   E. 3

2. $\lim\limits_{x\to-\infty} \dfrac{4x - 6}{\sqrt{x^2 - x - 6}} =$

   A. -4
   B. 0
   C. 1
   D. 4
   E. Does not exist

3. If $f(x) = \dfrac{2x^2 - 2}{x^2 + 3x + 2}$, which of the following statements are true?

   I. $\lim\limits_{x\to-1} f(x) = -4$
   II. $\lim\limits_{x\to-2} f(x) = -6$
   III. $\lim\limits_{x\to\infty} f(x) = 2$

   A. I only
   B. II only
   C. III only
   D. I and III only
   E. II and III only

*4. Which two functions grow at different rates?

   A. $\ln(2x)$ and $\ln(x^2)$
   B. $\log_2(x)$ and $\log_3(x)$
   C. $4x^5$ and $100x^5$
   D. $\sqrt{x^6 + x^4 + x^2}$ and x^3
   E. e^{2x} and e^{3x}

5. The graph of function f is shown below.

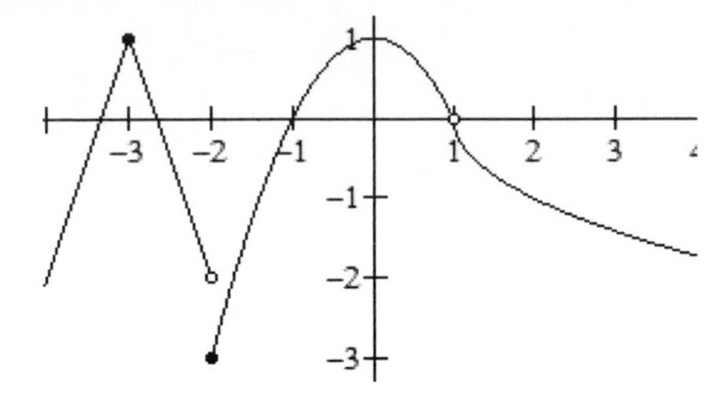

Which of the following statements are true?

I. $\lim_{x \to -3} f(x) = 1$

II. $\lim_{x \to -2^-} f(x) = -3$

III. $\lim_{x \to 1} f(x) = 0$

A. I only
B. II only
C. III only
D. I and II only
E. I and III only

6. Let $f(x) = \begin{cases} e^x & -\infty < x \le 0 \\ |x-2| + k & 0 < x < \infty \end{cases}$. Find k so that f is continuous everywhere.

A. -1 B. 0 C. $\frac{1}{2}$ D. 1 E. e

7. If $f(x) = \dfrac{1-x}{x-2}$, then $\lim_{x \to 2^-} f(x)$ is

A. $-\frac{1}{2}$ B. $\frac{1}{2}$ C. $-\infty$ D. ∞ E. -1

8. $\lim_{x \to -6} \dfrac{x^2 - 36}{x^2 + 36} =$

A. -1 B. 0 C. 1 D. 2 E. Does not exist

9. Given: $f(x) = 4 + \dfrac{1}{x-2}$. Which of the following statements is true?

A. $\lim\limits_{x \to 2^-} f(x) = \lim\limits_{x \to 2^+} f(x)$

B. $\lim\limits_{x \to 2} f(x)$ exists

C. $\lim\limits_{x \to -\infty} f(x) = \lim\limits_{x \to \infty} f(x)$

D. $\lim\limits_{x \to 2} f(x) = -\infty$

E. $\lim\limits_{x \to 2} f(x) = \infty$

10. Let $h(x) = \begin{cases} \dfrac{x^2-4}{x-2}, & if \ \ x \neq 2 \\ 0 & , if \ \ x = 2 \end{cases}$. Which of the following statements is true?

I. The function is continuous everywhere.

II. $\lim\limits_{x \to 2^+} h(x) = \lim\limits_{x \to 2^-} h(x)$.

III. The graph of $h(x)$ has a vertical asymptote at $x = 2$.

A. I only
B. II only
C. III only
D. II and III only
E. I and III only

Solutions to Sample Questions

1. C $\lim_{x\to\infty}\frac{x^3}{2x^3}=\frac{1}{2}$

2. A $\lim_{x\to-\infty}\frac{4x}{|x|}=-4$

3. D $\lim_{x\to-1}\frac{2(x+1)(x-1)}{(x+2)(x+1)}=\lim_{x\to-1}\frac{2(x-1)}{x+2}=-4$

   $\lim_{x\to\infty}\frac{2x^2}{x^2}=2$

*4. E $\lim_{x\to\infty}\frac{e^{2x}}{e^{3x}}=0$

5. E

6. A $e^0=|0-2|+k$

   $k=-1$

7. D

8. B $\lim_{x\to-6}\frac{(-6)^2-36}{(-6)^2+36}=0$

9. C $\lim_{x\to-\infty}f(x)=\lim_{x\to\infty}f(x)=4$

10. B $\lim_{x\to2}\frac{x^2-4}{x-2}=\lim_{x\to2}\frac{(x-2)(x+2)}{(x-2)}=\lim_{x\to2}x+2=4$

Connect2Calculus Videos for Chapter 1

The Calculus Concepts Video's for Chapter 1: *(Calculus BC topics are in italic type)*
Some of the topics on the videos go beyond the scope of Calculus AB/BC, but would be worth watching as an application of calculus.

1.0 Limits of Functions
1.1 The Meaning of the Limit of a Function
1.2 Limits and Continuity
1.3 A Precise Definition of the Limit (not in Topic Outline for Calculus AB/BC)

CHAPTER 2: DIFFERENTIATION

Correlations

The section by section correspondence to the Topic Outline for Calculus AB and the Topic Outline for Calculus BC (*Calculus BC topics are in italic type*) is:

AP Topic	Chapter.Section	Pages
II. Derivatives		
Concept of the derivative		
• Derivative presented graphically, numerically, and analytically	2.1 2.2	146-158 159-170
• Derivative interpreted as an instantaneous rate of change	2.1	146-158
• Derivative defined as the limit of the difference quotient	2.2	159-170
• Relationship between differentiability and continuity	2.2	159-170
II. Derivatives		
Derivative at a point		
• Slope of a curve at a point. Examples are emphasized, including points at which there are vertical tangents and points at which there are no tangents.	2.2	159-170
• Tangent line to a curve at a point …	2.1	146-158
• Instantaneous rate of changes as the limit of average rate of change	2.1	146-158
• Approximate rate of change from graphs and tables of values	2.2 and throughout the rest of the text	159-170
II. Derivatives		
Derivative as a function		
• Corresponding characteristics of graphs of f and f'	2.2	159-170
• The Mean Value Theorem and its geometric consequences	2.9	226-235

AP Topic	Chapter.Section	Pages
II. Derivatives		
Applications of derivatives		
• Use of implicit differentiation to find the derivative of an inverse function	2.8	216-226
• Interpretation of the derivative as a rate of change in varied applied contexts, including velocity, speed and acceleration	2.1, 2.3 and throughout the rest of the text	146-158, 170-180
II. Derivatives		
Computation of derivatives		
• Knowledge of derivatives of basic functions, including power, exponential, logarithmic, trigonometric and inverse trigonometric functions	2.3, 2.6, 2.7, 2.8	170-180, 196-206, 206-215, 216-226
• Basic rules for the derivatives of sums, products, and quotients of functions	2.3, 2.4	170-180, 180-188
• Chain rule and implicit differentiation	2.5, 2.8	189-195, 216-226

Textbook Section	AP Topic
2.1 Tangent Lines and Velocity	**II. Derivatives** **Concept of the derivative** • Derivative presented graphically, numerically, and analytically • Derivative interpreted as an instantaneous rate of change **Derivative at a point** • Tangent line to a curve at a point … • Instantaneous rate of changes as the limit of average rate of change **Applications of derivatives** • Interpretation of the derivative as a rate of change in varied applied contexts, including velocity, speed and acceleration
2.2 The Derivative	**II. Derivatives** **Concept of the derivative** • Derivative presented graphically, numerically, and analytically • Derivative defined as the limit of the difference quotient • Relationship between differentiability and continuity **Derivative as a function** • Corresponding characteristics of graphs of f and f'
2.3 Computation of Derivatives: The Power Rule	**II. Derivatives** **Applications of derivatives** • Interpretation of the derivative as a rate of change in varied applied contexts, including velocity, speed and acceleration **Computation of derivatives** • Knowledge of derivatives of basic functions, including power, exponential, logarithmic, trigonometric and inverse trigonometric functions • Basic rules for the derivatives of sums, products, and quotients of functions
2.4 The Product and Quotient Rules	**II. Derivatives** **Computation of derivatives** • Basic rules for the derivatives of sums, products, and quotients of functions

Textbook Section	AP Topic
2.5 The Chain Rule	**II. Derivatives** **Computation of derivatives** • Chain rule and implicit differentiation
2.6 Derivatives of the Trigonometric Functions	**II. Derivatives** **Computation of derivatives** • Knowledge of derivatives of basic functions, including power, exponential, logarithmic, trigonometric and inverse trigonometric functions
2.7 Derivatives of the Exponential and Logarithmic Functions	**II. Derivatives** **Computation of derivatives** • Knowledge of derivatives of basic functions, including power, exponential, logarithmic, trigonometric and inverse trigonometric functions
2.8 Implicit Differentiation and Inverse Trigonometric Functions	**II. Derivatives** **Applications of derivatives** • Use of implicit differentiation to find the derivative of an inverse function **Computation of derivatives** • Knowledge of derivatives of basic functions, including power, exponential, logarithmic, trigonometric and inverse trigonometric functions • Chain rule and implicit differentiation
2.9 The Mean Value Theorem	**II. Derivatives** **Derivative as a function** • The Mean Value Theorem and its geometric consequences

Vocabulary and Section Notes

Vocabulary used in the Topic Outline for Calculus AB and the Topic Outline for Calculus BC (*Calculus BC topics are in italic type*) include:

Acceleration
Average rate of change
Average velocity
Chain rule
Derivative
Difference quotient
Differentiable
Implicit differentiation
Instantaneous rate of change
Logarithmic differentiation
Mean Value Theorem
Power rule
Product Rule
Quotient rule
Rolle's Theorem
Signed distance
Speed
Tangent line
Velocity

Section notes for the Calculus AB Course:

Section 2.1, 2.2, 2.3, 2.5, 2.6, 2.7: Each of these sections contain exercises related to position, velocity and acceleration and their relationships. These topics are discussed in more detail in the article, "Position, Velocity, and Acceleration" in the Teacher's Notes section in Chapter 4.

Section 2.7 (Derivatives of Exponential and Logarithmic Functions): Hyperbolic functions, by name, are not part of the Topic Outline for Calculus AB, but with the given definitions, students should be able to complete exercises 49-51. Exercise 52 is slightly more difficult.

Section notes for the Calculus BC Course:

Section 2.1, 2.2, 2.3, 2.5, 2.6, 2.7: Each of these sections contain exercises related to position, velocity and acceleration and their relationships. These topics are discussed in more detail in the article, "Position, Velocity, and Acceleration" in the Teacher's Notes section in Chapter 4.

Section 2.7 (Derivatives of Exponential and Logarithmic Functions): Hyperbolic functions, by name, are not part of the Topic Outline for Calculus BC, but with the given definitions, students should be able to complete exercises 49-51. Exercise 52 is slightly more difficult.

Student Activity: The 20 Minute Ride

Teacher's Notes:

This activity is designed to help students see the need for an instantaneous rate of change, which is the derivative. All previous activity they have done with velocity has been average rate of change. As they complete this worksheet, the last entry in the table (at precisely 10 minutes) cannot be computed using traditional algebra methods.

Since the time intervals are given in ordinal numbers, it is good to guide them through a few of the more challenging intervals. Otherwise, they will be off by one minute in their computations.

You can also use this activity as an introduction to the relationship between a function, its first derivative and its second derivative. The keystrokes for the TI-83/84 follow.

1. Clear Lists $\mathbf{L_1}$ through $\mathbf{L_4}$.

2. Enter the time values, 0-20, in $\mathbf{L_1}$.

3. Enter the cumulative distances in $\mathbf{L_2}$.

4. Use **StatPlot** to make a scatter plot of one student's data. Let $\mathbf{L_1}$ be the X list and $\mathbf{L_2}$ be the Y List. Choose **Plot1**. The plot should look like the student's hand drawn graph.

5. Place the cursor in the title bar of $\mathbf{L_3}$. Go to **(2nd Stat), OPS, 7 ΔList($\mathbf{L_2}$)**. This will find the differences in each value in $\mathbf{L_2}$ which gives the distance traveled each minute. Place the cursor in the first cell below the tile bar and press **2nd Insert**. This will pad the list so that there is an additional value to match up with the time values. Use **StatPlot** to make a scatter plot of $\mathbf{L_1}$ and $\mathbf{L_3}$. Use **Plot2**. Choose a different symbol for the graph (the + sign is good.) This plot is the graph of the individual velocities for each minute. Students should be able to see that when the value of the velocity is large, the graph of distance increases more steeply.

6. Repeat the process using $\mathbf{L_4}$. Find the **(2nd Stat), OPS, 7 ΔList($\mathbf{L_3}$)**. This will compute the acceleration for each minute. Remember to pad the values in $\mathbf{L_4}$ so there are an equal number of values when compared to time. Use **StatPlot** to make a scatter plot between $\mathbf{L_1}$ and $\mathbf{L_4}$. Choose **Plot3.** The period is too faint to be seen. Use the square as the symbol. Students should see that when the car was slowing down, the acceleration was negative. You can also point out that the distance graph is concave upward when the acceleration is positive. Similarly, the distance graph is concave downward when the acceleration is negative.

This is an introductory activity. It gives a graphical view of the relationship between the function and its derivatives. You can refer to this activity when you discuss the relationships. Students do not need to be proficient with the calculator skills in this activity.

Student Worksheet

As a passenger in a car, take a 20 minute ride with a responsible adult. At the end of each minute, record your cumulative distance traveled (to the nearest 0.1 miles). Spend no more than half your time on the freeway and observe all traffic laws.

Time	0	1	2	3	4	5	6
Distance							
Time	7	8	9	10	11	12	13
Distance							
Time	14	15	16	17	18	19	20
Distance							

Make a connected scatter plot of your results on the grid below. Let t (time) be the horizontal axis and s (distance) be the vertical axis. Let each horizontal unit represent 1 min and each vertical unit represent 2 miles.

FOLLOW-UP FOR THE TWENTY MINUTE RIDE

Fill in the table below using the values obtained and the graph of your data.

Let Δs represent the change in distance traveled. Let Δt represent the change in elapsed time. Calculate the velocity or speed of the car for the given interval.

Time Period	Δs	Δt	Velocity	
			Miles per minute	Miles per hour
Entire 20 minutes				
First 10 minutes				
Last 10 minutes				
5th minute through the 16th minute				
3rd minute through the 8th minute				
9th minute through the 10th minute				
During the 5th minute				
During the 10th minute				
During the 15th minute				
At precisely 10 minutes				

1. A. Circle the place on the graph when you traveling the fastest.

   B. What was your velocity?

   C. How far would you have traveled if you had maintained this velocity for the entire 20 minutes?

2. A. Box the place on the graph when you were traveling the slowest.

   B. What was your velocity?

   C. How far would you have traveled if you had maintained this velocity for the entire 20 minutes?

3. Why doesn't the graph ever decrease?

Student Activity: The Slope Function

Teacher's Notes:

It is important that students quickly gain an intuitive understanding of the slope of a curve. In most of their previous mathematics classes, students were interested in finding the slope of a line, which happens to be a constant. The slope of all other functions will vary depending upon the location you choose to consider. Choose any two points on a line and the slope between them never changes. However, if one were to look at the graph of $y = x^2$, it should quickly become clear that there are intervals of x values with positive slopes, intervals of x values with negative slopes, and even a point with zero slope. It is also true that within the interval of x values with positive slopes, there are points whose slope is larger than others are. There are similar relationships within the interval of x values with negative slopes.

The beauty and power of calculus is the ability to derive a formula to calculate the slope of the curve at any point. This activity lays a foundation for the formal derivation of the slope of a curve, tangent lines, and the derivative.

Use the large format grid (as a transparency) to point out the variability of the slope of the curve. Tangent lines are provided to help the student's eyes focus on one particular point and to be able to see the slope of the curve at that point. The tangent lines are drawn at $x = -2, -1, 0, 1,$ and 2. Use the tangent line to help students estimate the slope of the curve at that point and fill in the space in the table of values of $f'(x)$. After the completing the table of values for $f'(x)$ and plotting the points, make a rough sketch of the graph of the derivative.

You can use the vocabulary of calculus as you discuss this activity, but at this time, the only required skill is the ability to estimate the slope of the curve at the indicated points, using the tangent line as a visual aid. It might be helpful to have students use toothpicks or spaghetti to lie over the grid to help them in estimating their slopes. Of course, since students will be estimating the slopes and their skill in sketching a tangent line is rudimentary, there will be some variability in the student answers. Many of them will also be anxious about the accuracy of their answers. Encourage them to do their best and assure them that there is some flexibility in the accuracy of answers for this activity.

Have the students keep this worksheet and you can refer to it after establishing the Power Rule to help students make the connection between the degree of the function and the degree of the derivative.

Student Worksheet

<u>Questions 1-6</u>: For each function,

a. Draw the tangent to the curve at each x-value.
b. Estimate the slope of the tangent line and fill in the table.
c. Graph the derivative function for the given function.

1.

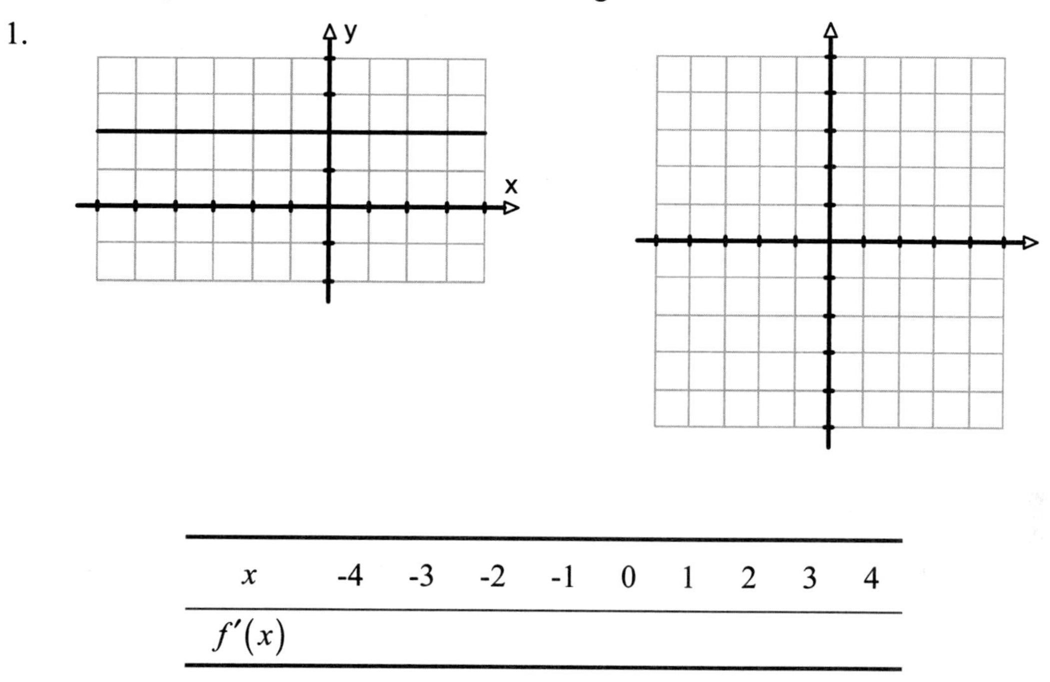

x	-4	-3	-2	-1	0	1	2	3	4
$f'(x)$									

2.

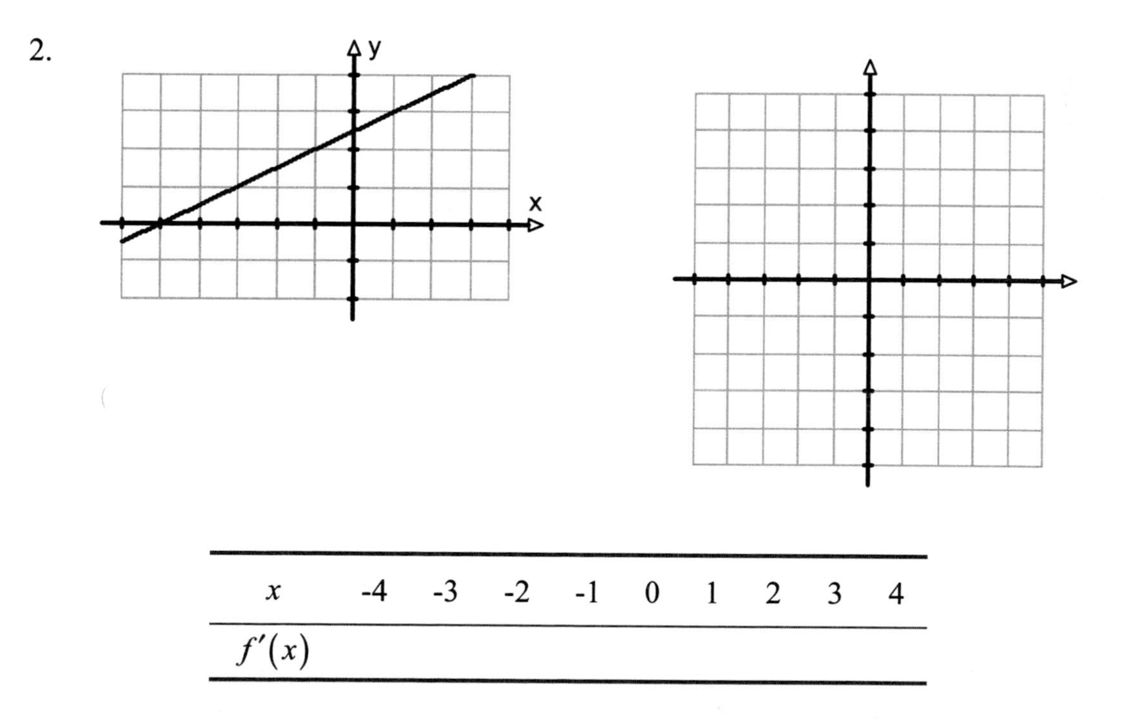

x	-4	-3	-2	-1	0	1	2	3	4
$f'(x)$									

3.

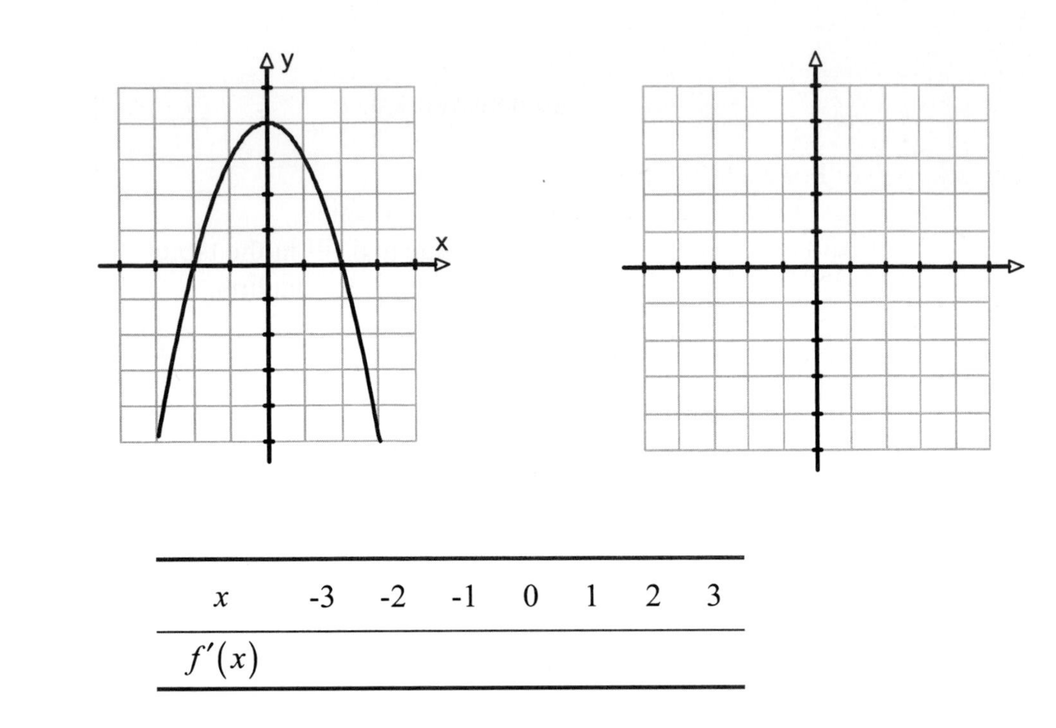

x	-3	-2	-1	0	1	2	3
$f'(x)$							

4.

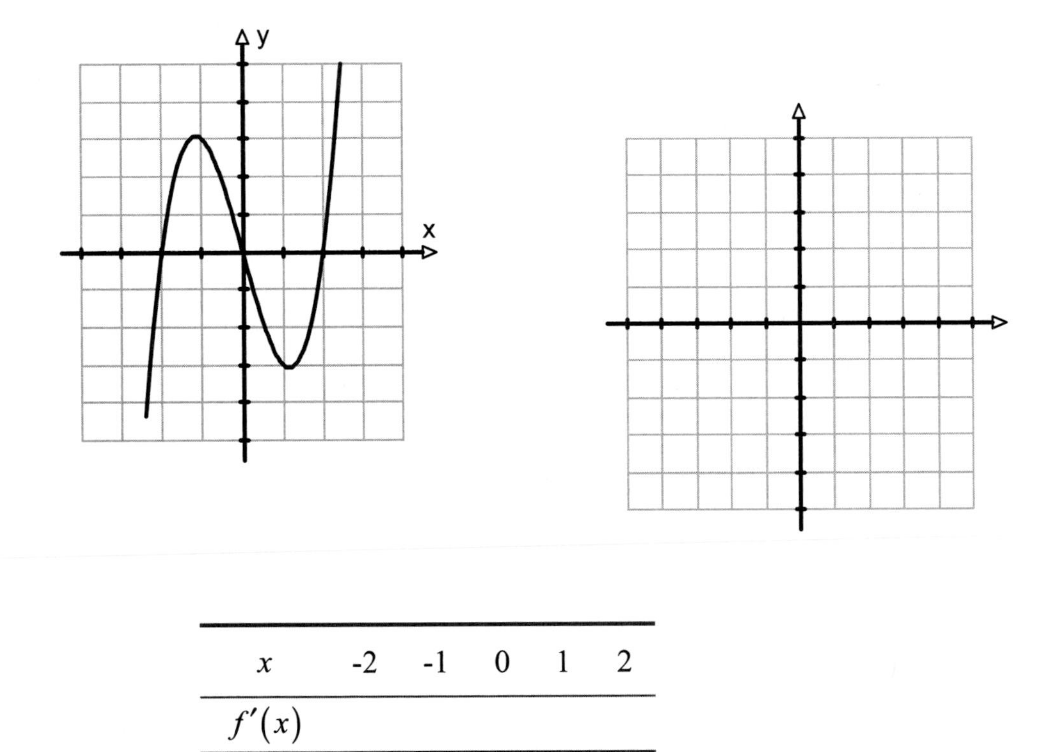

x	-2	-1	0	1	2
$f'(x)$					

5.

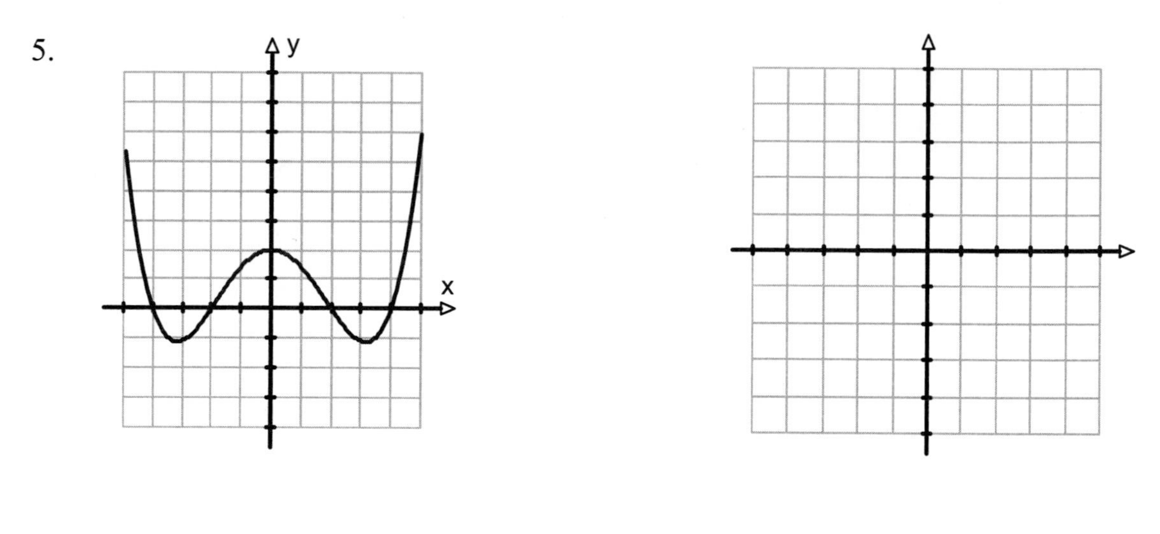

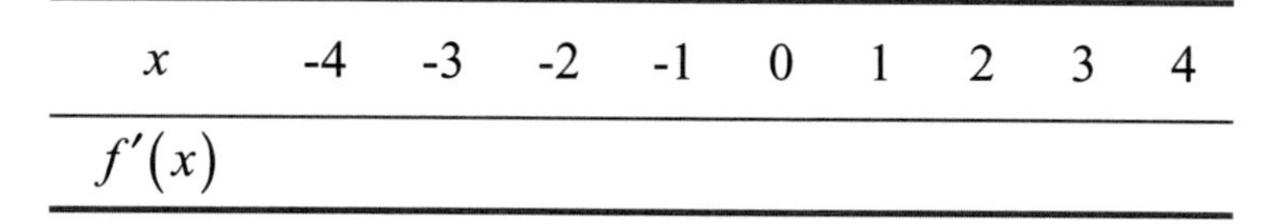

x	-4	-3	-2	-1	0	1	2	3	4
$f'(x)$									

6.

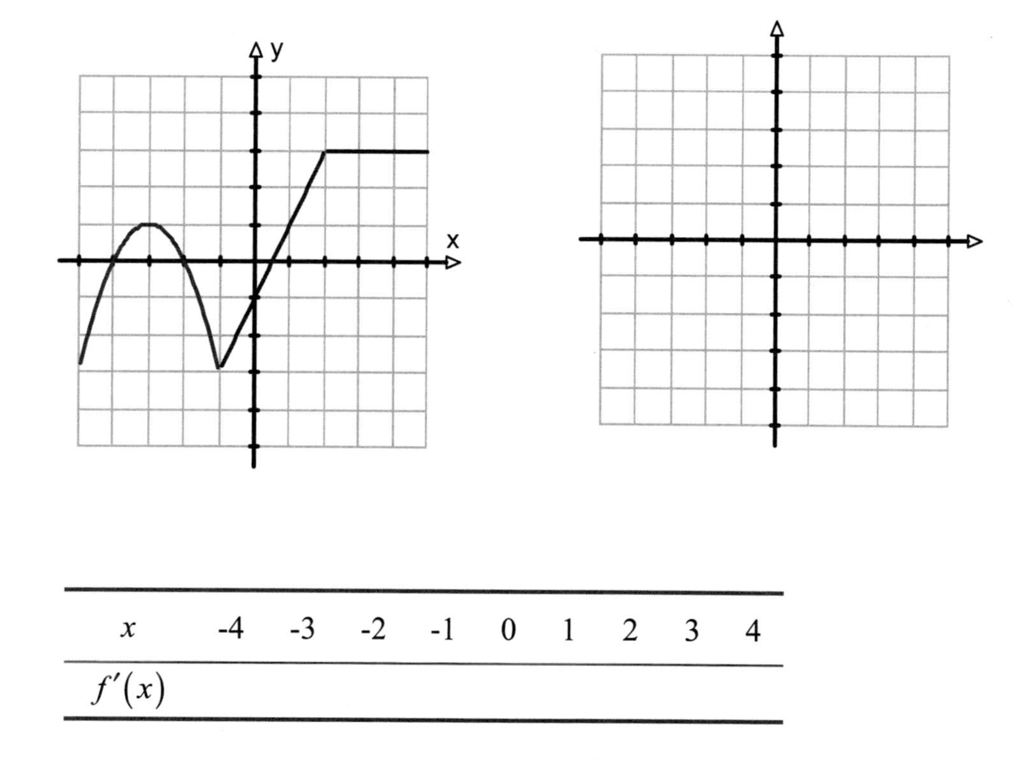

x	-4	-3	-2	-1	0	1	2	3	4
$f'(x)$									

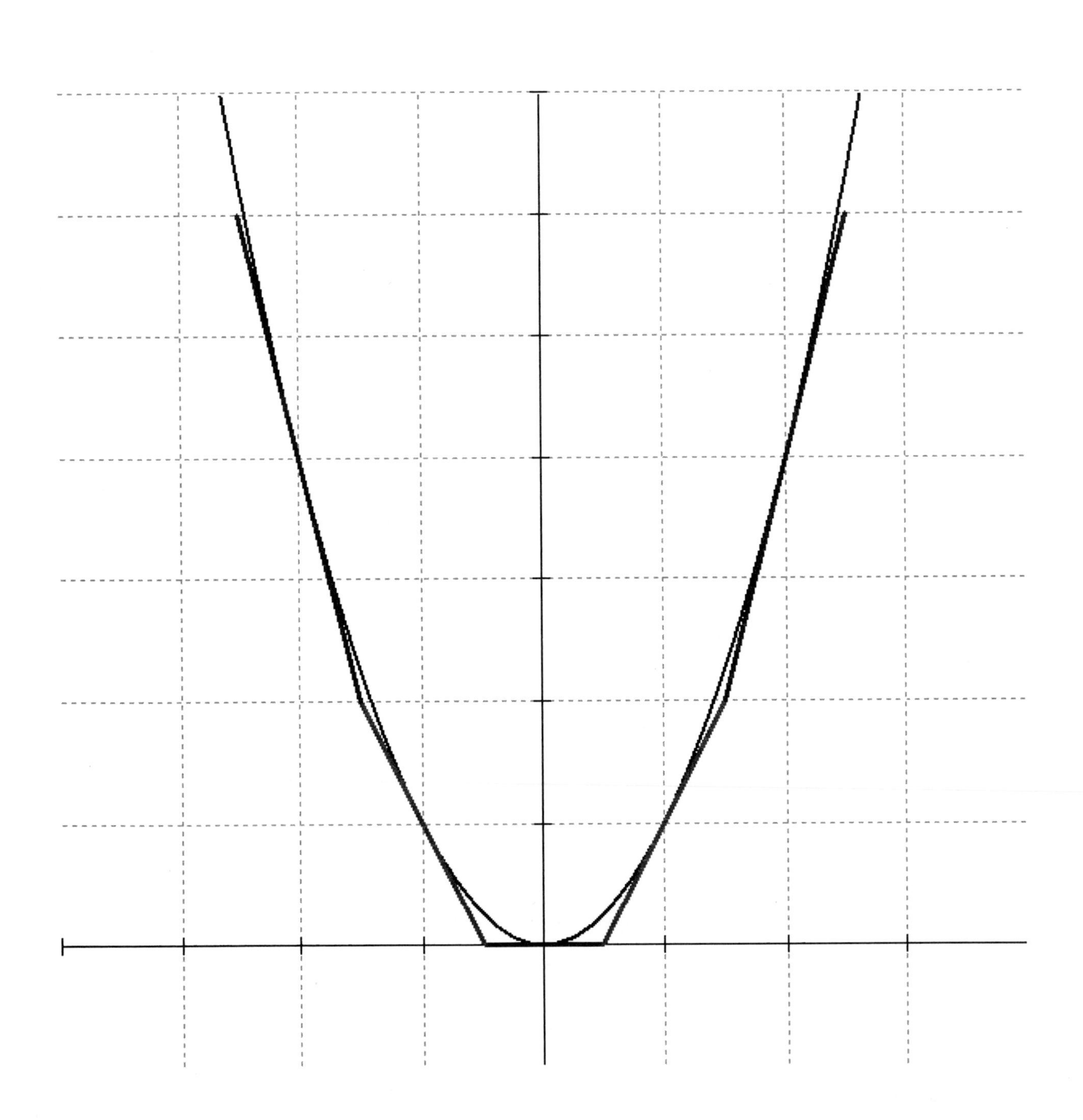

Answers:

Questions 1-6: For each function,

a. Draw the tangent to the curve at each x-value.
b. Estimate the slope of the tangent line and fill in the table.
c. Graph the derivative function for the given function.

1.

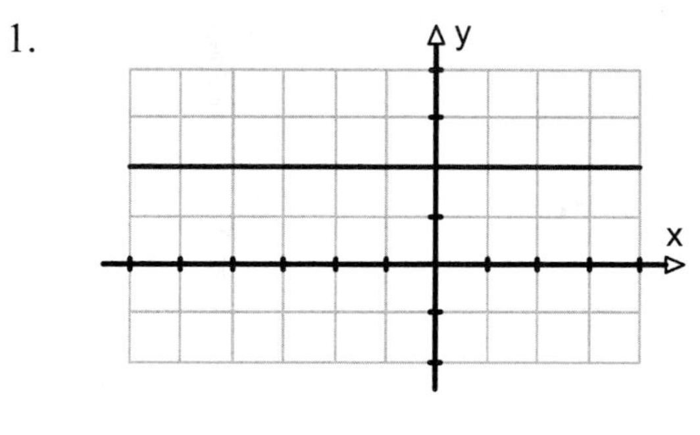

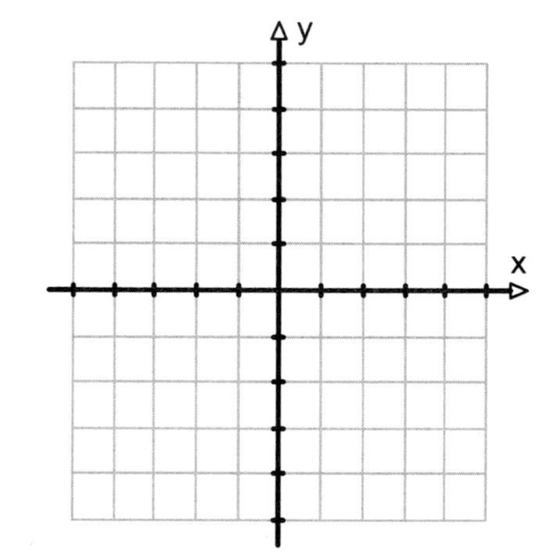

x	-4	-3	-2	-1	0	1	2	3	4
$f'(x)$	0	0	0	0	0	0	0	0	0

2.

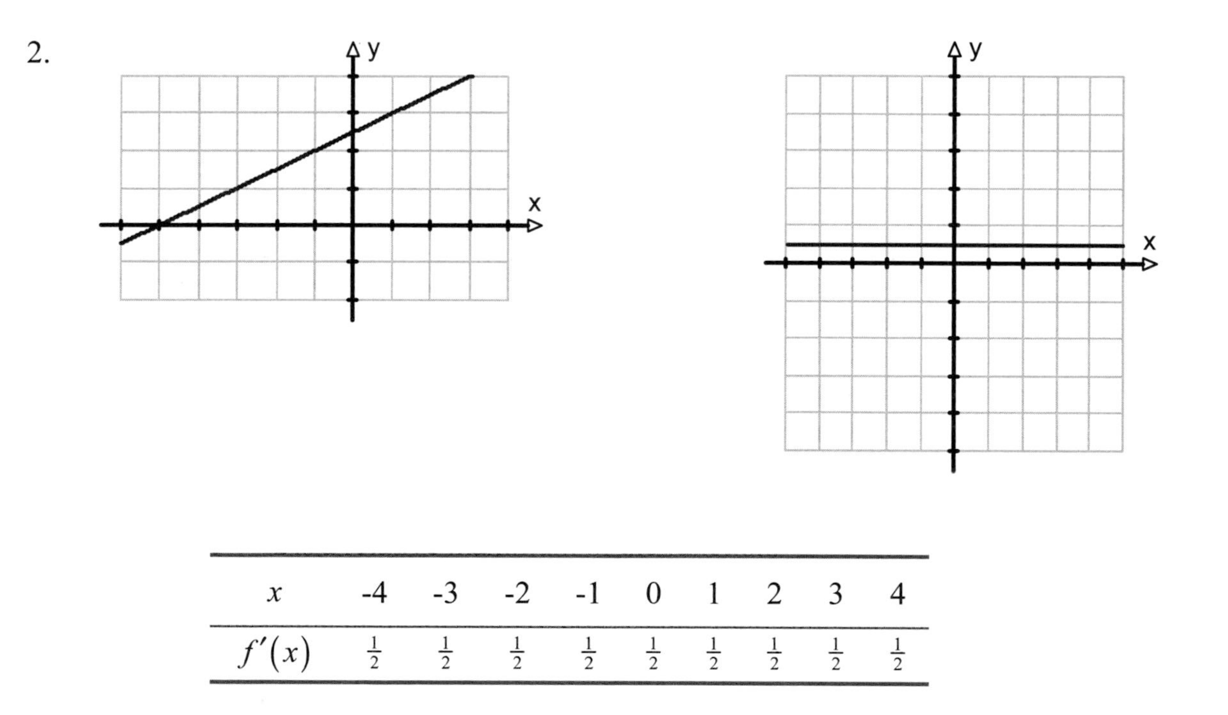

x	-4	-3	-2	-1	0	1	2	3	4
$f'(x)$	$\frac{1}{2}$	$\frac{1}{2}$	$\frac{1}{2}$	$\frac{1}{2}$	$\frac{1}{2}$	$\frac{1}{2}$	$\frac{1}{2}$	$\frac{1}{2}$	$\frac{1}{2}$

3.

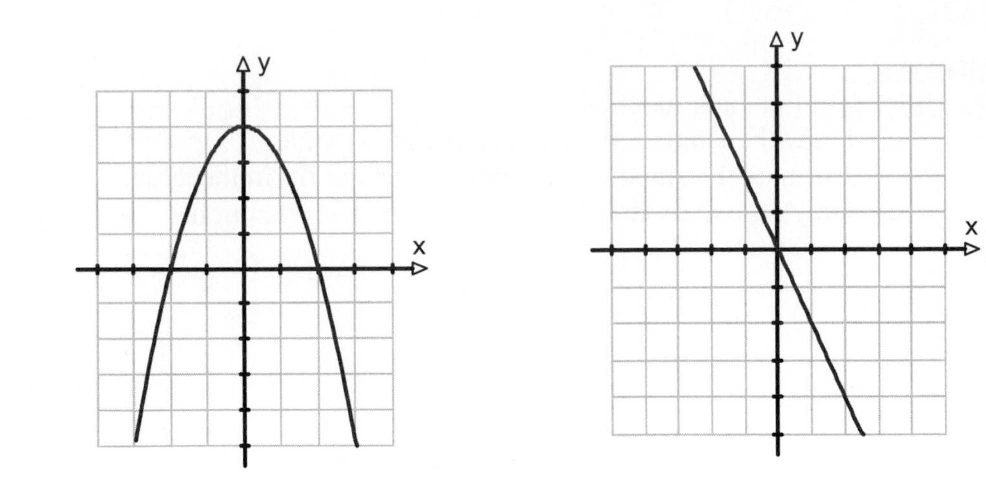

x	-3	-2	-1	0	1	2	3
$f'(x)$	6	4	2	0	-2	-4	-6

4.

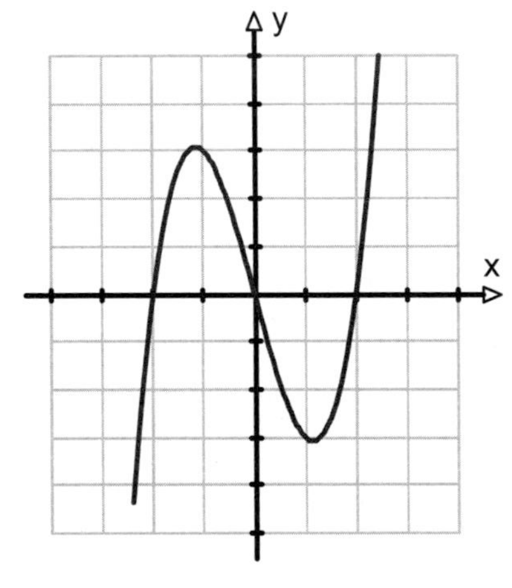

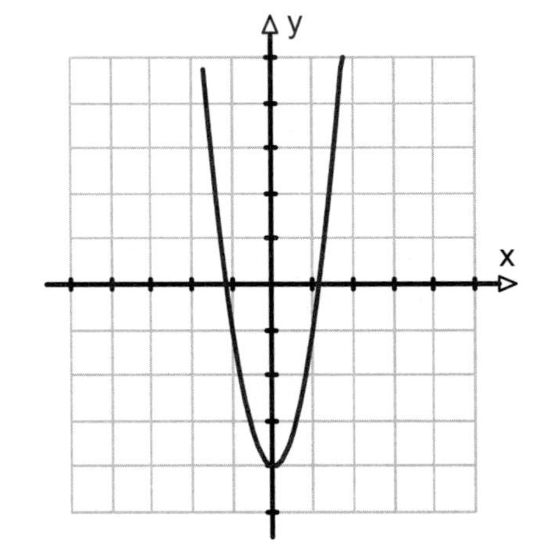

x	-2	-1	0	1	2
$f'(x)$	8	-1	-4	-1	8

5.

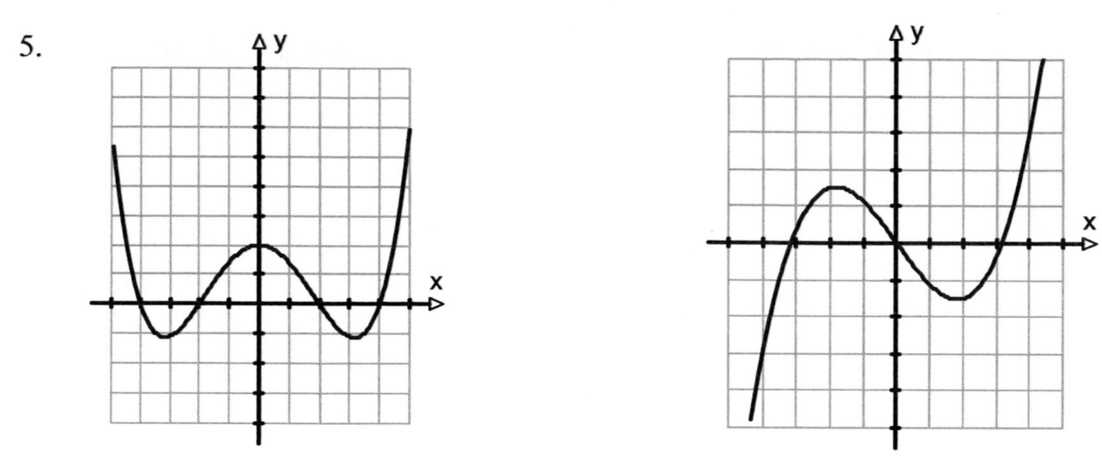

x	-4	-3	-2	-1	0	1	2	3	4
$f'(x)$	-3	$\frac{3}{8}$	$\frac{3}{2}$	$\frac{9}{8}$	0	$-\frac{9}{8}$	$-\frac{3}{2}$	$-\frac{3}{8}$	3

6.

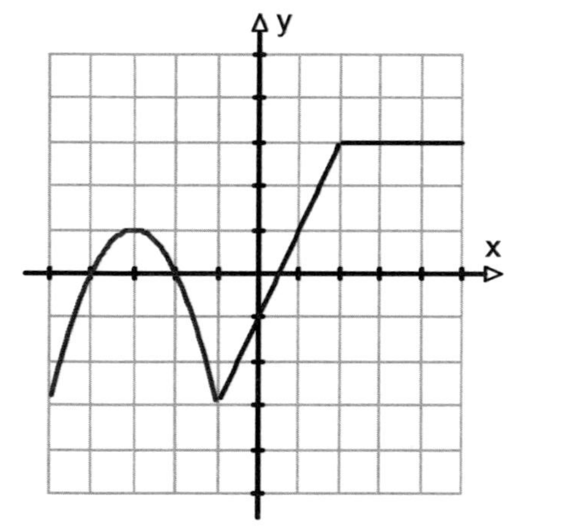

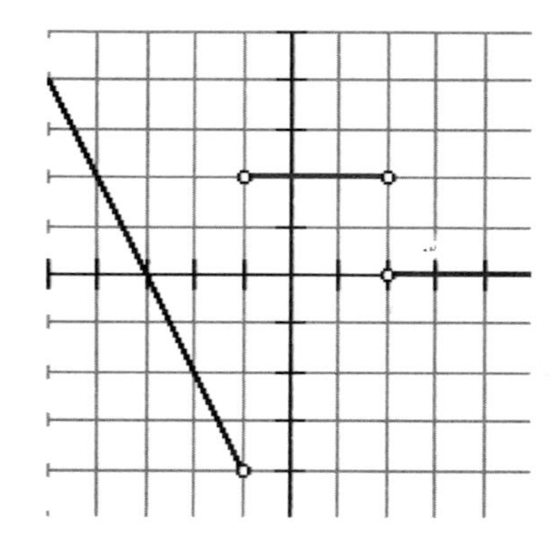

x	-4	-3	-2	-1	0	1	2	3	4
$f'(x)$	2	0	-2	d.n.e.	2	2	d.n.e.	0	0

Teacher's Notes: Visualizing Derivatives with a Calculator

Teacher's Notes:

The graphing calculator is a powerful tool to use to help students visualize major calculus concepts. To help students understand properties of a function and its derivative type a function in **Y1** and the definition of the derivative in **Y6** (I use **Y6** because it is usually in view, but can easily be turned on or off as needed. Be sure to notice the use of the graphing ball for the graph of **Y6**. It makes it easier to track the graph of the derivative as it is being drawn). Be sure to store a value for H near 0.

```
Plot1 Plot2 Plot3
\Y1=sin(X)
\Y2=
\Y3=
\Y4=
\Y5=
-0Y6=(Y1(X+H)-Y1(
X))/H
```

```
.0001→H
                1E-4
```

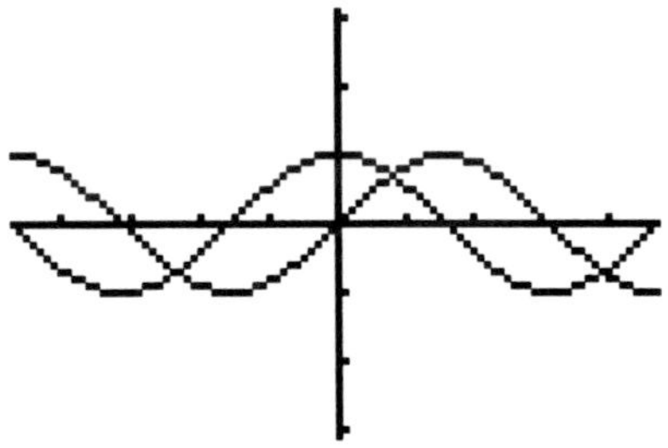

In a convenient window, the display will show the graph of the function and a reasonably accurate approximation for the derivative (depending on the value chosen for **H**). It is then easy to compare salient features of both functions such as:

1. When $f(x)$ has a local maximum or minimum, what is the value of $f'(x)$?

2. When $f(x)$ is increasing, where is the graph of $f'(x)$?

3. When $f(x)$ is decreasing, where is the graph of $f'(x)$

4. In some cases, it may be possible to ask students to speculate about the formula for $f'(x)$.

If desired, put the second derivative into **Y7**, and then it would be possible to discuss properties of concavity and inflection points. Initially, turn off the graph of **Y6** and just compare the graphs of the function and the second derivative.

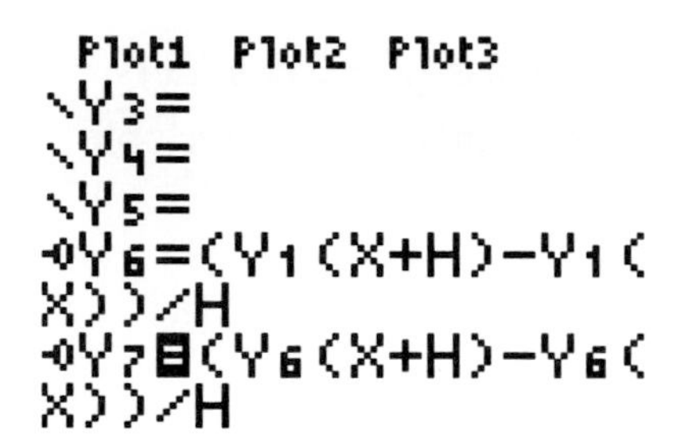

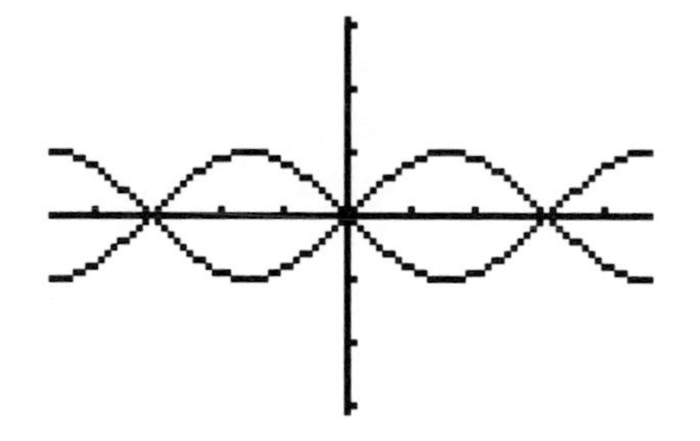

1. When $f(x)$ is concave down, where is the graph of $f''(x)$?

2. When $f(x)$ is concave up, where is the graph of $f''(x)$?

3. What is happing to the graph of $f(x)$ when the graph of $f''(x)$ crosses the x-axis?

Another perspective would show all three graphs and use them to discuss pertinent features from the perspective of any or all of the graphs.

4. Compare the graphs of $f(x)$, $f'(x)$, and $f''(x)$ at relative maxima, relative minima, and inflection points.

5. Compare the graphs of $f(x)$, $f'(x)$, and $f''(x)$ when the graph of $f(x)$ is increasing, decreasing, concave up or concave down.

Use easily interpreted functions such as $f(x)=x^2$ or $f(x)=x^3$ or $f(x)=\sin(x)$ and choose a window that clearly shows all features.

Before introducing the algebraic derivation of the derivative of common functions, graphing the function and the derivative allows the student to speculate on the derivative function before actually deriving the formula. If students guess a formula for the derivative, the teacher could enter that in an available space and compare the graph of the guess with the graph of the derivative. This is especially effective when discussing the derivative of an equation like $y=\sin(2x)$ which would be $y'=2\cos(2x)$.

```
Plot1 Plot2 Plot3
\Y1=sin(2X)
\Y2=
\Y3=
\Y4=
\Y5=
Y6=(Y1(X+H)-Y1(
X))/H
```

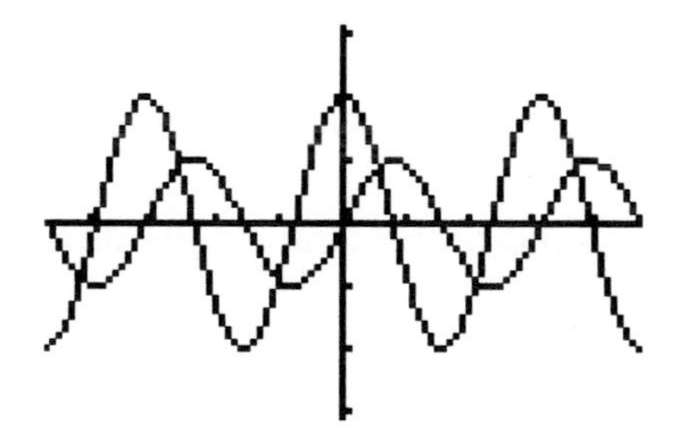

The students should be able to recognize the graph of the derivative as $y' = 2\cos(2x)$. Try several other examples of trigonometric functions until the students are comfortable with the basic role of the Chain Rule in calculating the derivative.

To explore the derivative of $y = e^x$, graph the function and the derivative.

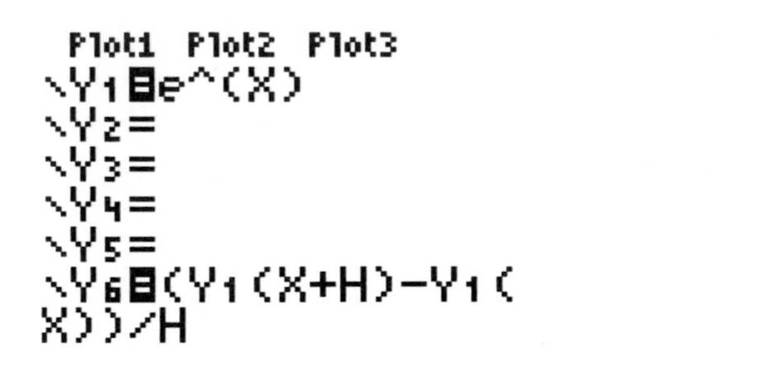

There is no apparent difference between the graphs of y and y'.
In **Y2** enter the ratio of the derivative and the function and then draw the graph:

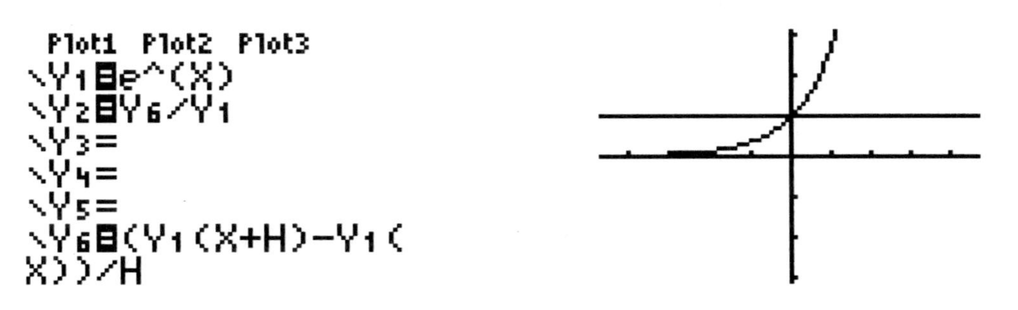

The ratio is approximately one, which implies $\frac{\frac{dy}{dx}}{y} = 1$ or $\frac{dy}{dx} = y$ or if $y = e^x$ then $y' = e^x$.

A formal proof of the relationship can now be pursued.

For exponentials like $y = 2^x$ or $y = 4^x$ or $y = b^x$, the ratio will be $\ln(b)$ as in:

If $y = b^x$, then $\frac{\frac{dy}{dx}}{y} = \ln(b)$ or $\frac{dy}{dx} = \ln(b)y$ or $\frac{dy}{dx} = \ln(b) \cdot b^x$

More specifically, if $y = 2^x$, then $y' = \ln(2) \cdot 2^x$

Tracing on the ratio equation yields a constant value that is approximately $(\ln(2))$

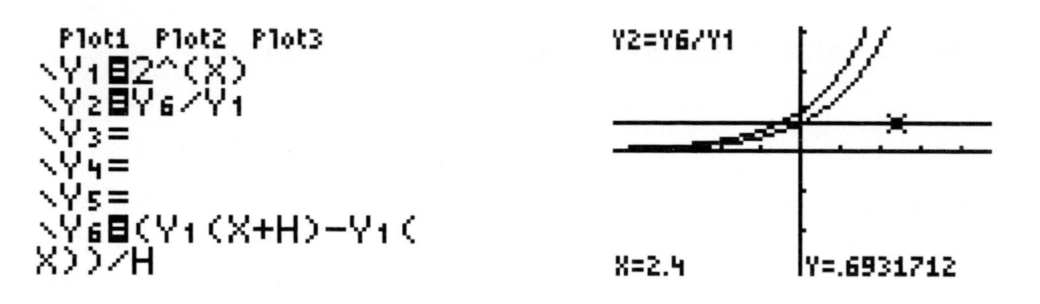

Again, after exploring these properties, it should be easier for students to understand the algebraic derivation of the derivative formula and to appreciate the connections between the visual aspects of the functions and their derivatives.

These are just a few ways to use the calculator to demonstrate important calculus properties before formal algebraic methods are employed. Taking the time, at the beginning of the course to lay a visual foundation will make it easier for students to understand later concepts.

Teacher's Notes: Differentiability and Local Linearity

Teacher's Notes:

Whether the derivative of a function exists or not, at a particular value of x, is what the topic of differentiability is all about. One way to demonstrate this to students is through the idea of local linearity. If one zooms in on the graph of the function at the point under consideration, and if the function is differentiable, then the graph will appear as a non-vertical line in the viewing window. If the graph is a vertical line, or the graph always shows a sharp change of direction, then the function is not considered differentiable at the point under consideration.

Graph $y = \sin(x)$ using the **(ZOOM) 4: ZDECIMAL** graphing window. **(ZOOM) 2: ZOOM IN** at the point on the graph where $x = 1$ and repeat this process until the graph appears as a straight line.

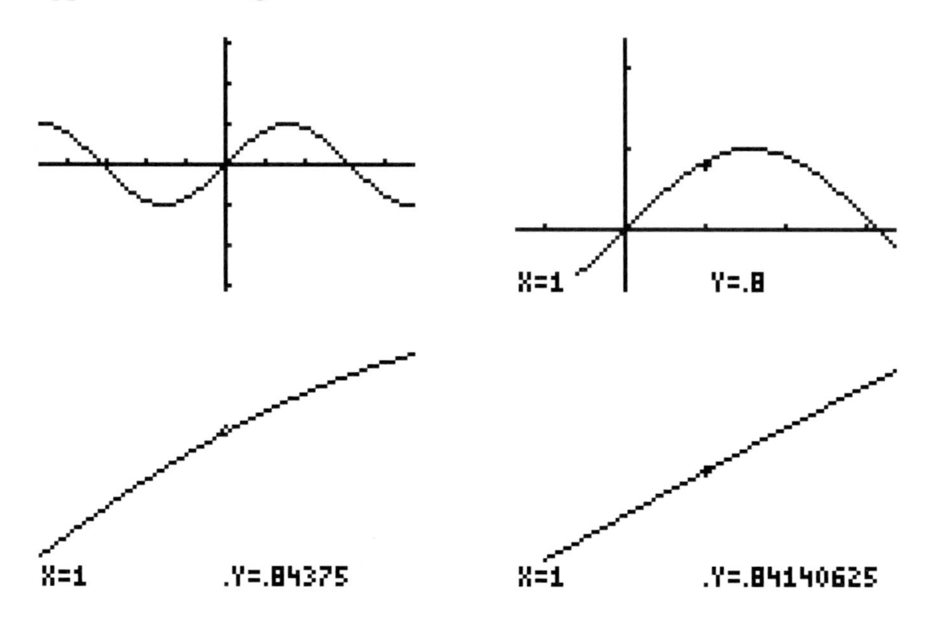

With default factory settings, it should take about 6 or 7 repetitions (Note: the default **ZOOM IN** factors are set at 2. If you wish to increase this value (and zoom in faster), go to **(2nd ZOOM) MEMORY** and choose the **SET FACTORS** option). This graph serves to demonstrate what is meant by local linearity: For a small interval of values of around $x = 1$ the graph appears to be a straight line and values of $y = \sin(x)$ could be approximated with the values obtained by evaluating the equation of the tangent line at the point $x = 1$. To emphasize that statement now include the equation of the tangent line at $x = 1$ and observe how closely the two graphs resemble each other.

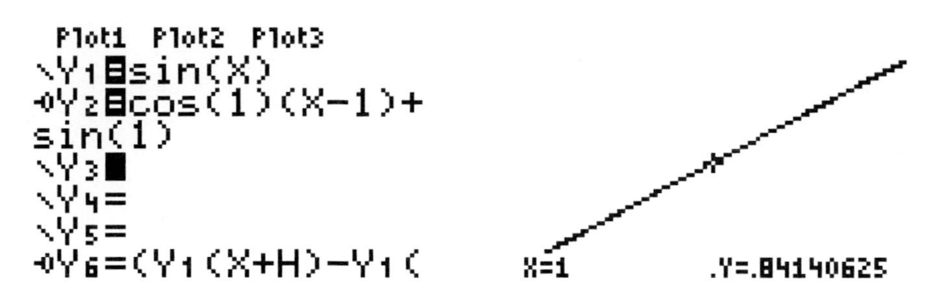

If you examine the **WINDOW** you can see an interval of values around $x = 1$ where the value obtained using the tangent line is a respectable approximation for the actual value of the function. Use the **TRACE** button to go to any point on the $y = \sin(x)$ graph and then use the "down arrow" to jump to the graph of the tangent line.

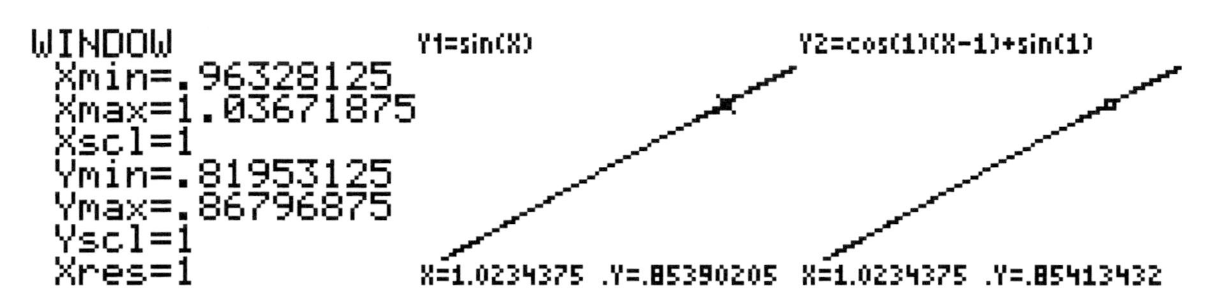

Compare how close the y-values are for any particular x. Students should be able to see, that as the evaluation points move away from $x = 1$, the tangent line approximation is less accurate and an informal discussion of error in the approximations could occur at this point.

Finally, have the calculator redraw the graph of the function and the tangent line in the **(ZOOM) 4: ZDECIMAL** graphing window. This last look at the two graphs should demonstrate, again, what is meant by local linearity.

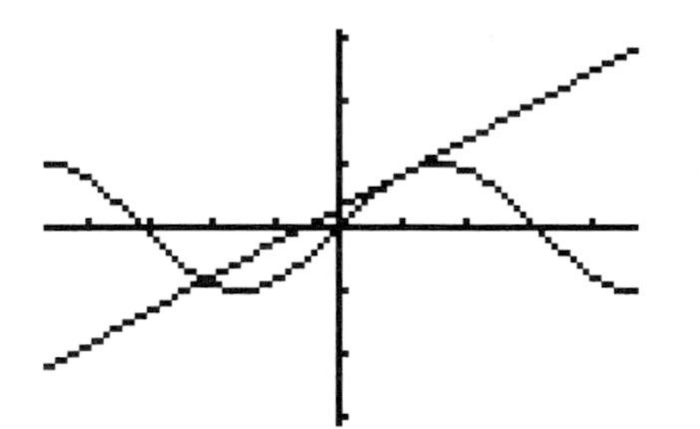

If a function is not differentiable at a point, repeated use of **ZOOM IN** will reveal a graph that either appears vertical at that point or the graph always shows a "sharp change of direction".

Consider the function $y = x^{\frac{1}{3}}$ at $x = 0$. After zooming in three times, the graph appears almost vertical.

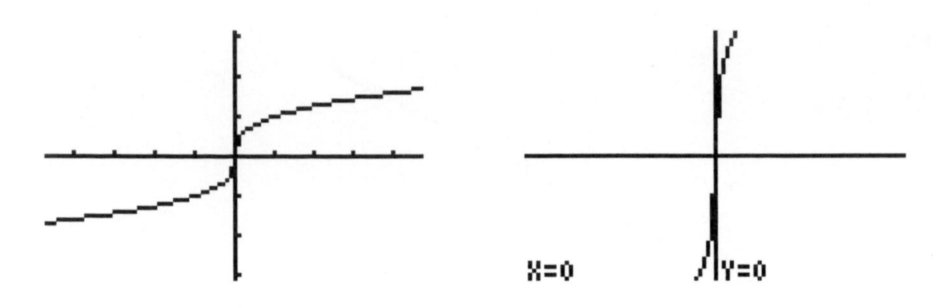

To clearly see what is happening at $x = 0$ it might be necessary to delete the axes from the graph **(2nd ZOOM) FORMAT** and choose **AXES OFF**. After zooming in six times the graph is essentially vertical and thus the derivative does not exist at $x = 0$ and $y = x^{\frac{1}{3}}$ is not differentiable there.

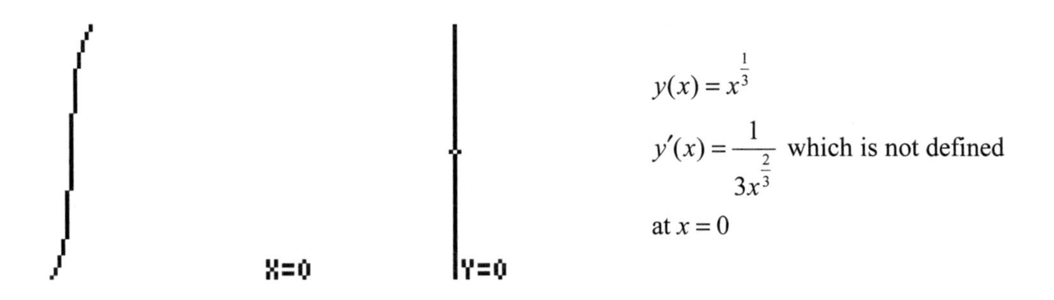

$y(x) = x^{\frac{1}{3}}$

$y'(x) = \dfrac{1}{3x^{\frac{2}{3}}}$ which is not defined

at $x = 0$

The classic example of a function with a "sharp change of direction" is $y = |x|$. The graph of the function in a Decimal window and the graph after using **ZOOM IN** five times appear to be identical (the difference is in the interval of values used in the graphing window). There is a "sharp change of direction" at $x = 0$ and the derivative does not exist at that point.

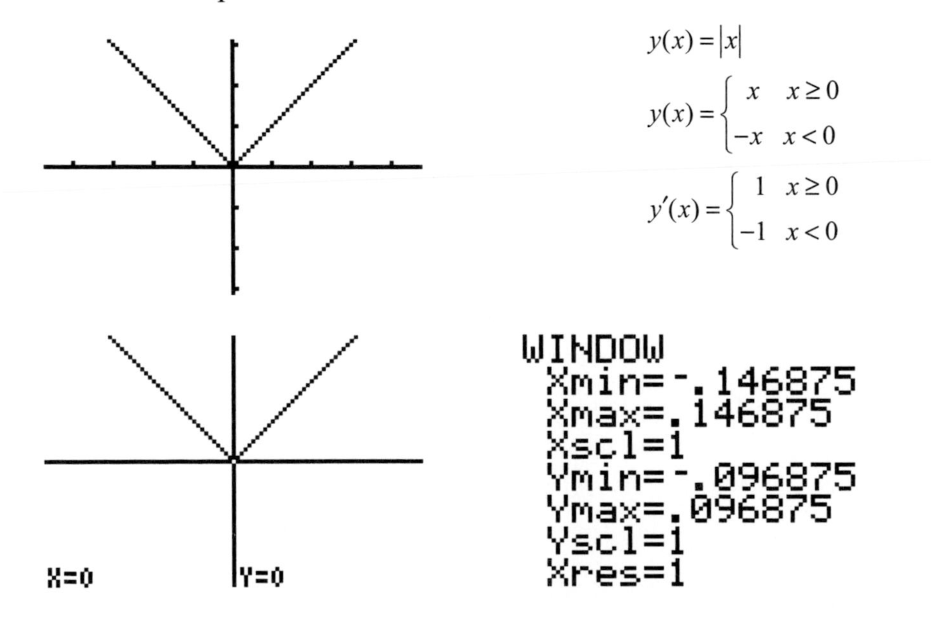

$y(x) = |x|$

$$y(x) = \begin{cases} x & x \geq 0 \\ -x & x < 0 \end{cases}$$

$$y'(x) = \begin{cases} 1 & x \geq 0 \\ -1 & x < 0 \end{cases}$$

A piecewise defined function is also an excellent example of differentiability and local linearity. Questions about differentiability arise at the values when the function changes from one interval to another.

$$y=\begin{cases} 3x+4, & x\le -1 \\ x^2+x+1, & -1<x<0 \\ e^x, & x\ge 0 \end{cases}$$

There are several ways to enter the equations for a piecewise function. One set of keystrokes for this function are:

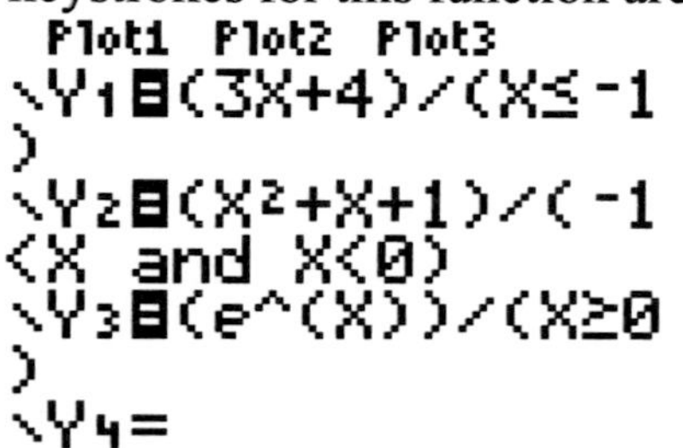

Is this function differentiable at $x=0$ or $x=-1$?

ZOOM IN at (-1, 1) and the graph looks like:

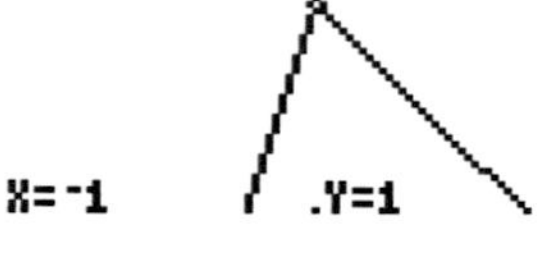

ZOOM IN at (0, 1) and the graph looks like:

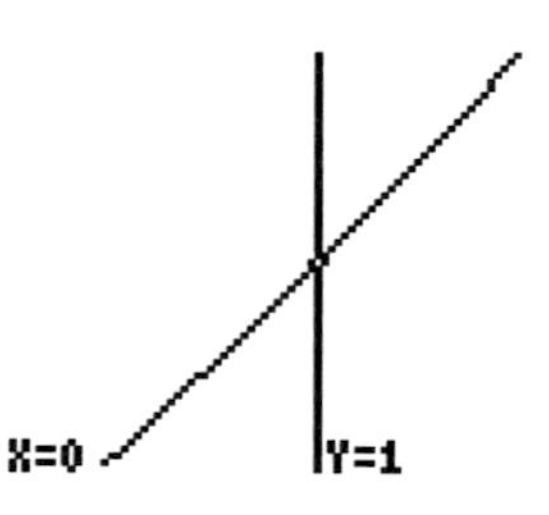

The function is differentiable at $x=0$ but not at $x=-1$.

$$y=\begin{cases} 3x+4, & x\le -1 \\ x^2+x+1, & -1<x<0 \\ e^x, & x\ge 0 \end{cases} \qquad y'(x)=\begin{cases} 3 & x\le -1 \\ 2x+1 & -1<x<0 \\ e^x & x\ge 0 \end{cases}$$

$$\lim_{x\to -1^-} y'(x) \neq \lim_{x\to -1^+} y'(x) \qquad\qquad \lim_{x\to 0^-} y'(x) = \lim_{x\to 0^+} y'(x)$$

$$\lim_{x\to -1^-} 3 \neq \lim_{x\to -1^+} 2x+1 \qquad \text{but} \qquad \lim_{x\to 0^-} 2x+1 = \lim_{x\to 0^+} e^x$$

$$3 \neq -1 \qquad\qquad 1 = 1$$

Multiple-Choice Questions–Calculus AB/BC Topics

1. Which of the following are asymptotes of $2y + xy - x + 3 = 0$?

I. $x = 3$
II. $x = -2$
III. $y = 1$

A. I only
B. III only
C. I and II only
D. II and III only
E. I, II, and III

*2. A particle moves along the x-axis so that at time t, $1 \le t \le 5$, its position is given by $x(t) = x^2 \cos\left(\frac{1}{3}x\right)$. During that time period, the particle's average velocity equals its instantaneous velocity when $t =$
A. 2.957
B. 3.042
C. 3.458
D. 4.880
E. 5.113

3. Function f, consisting of 2 line segments and 2 quarter circles, is graph below.

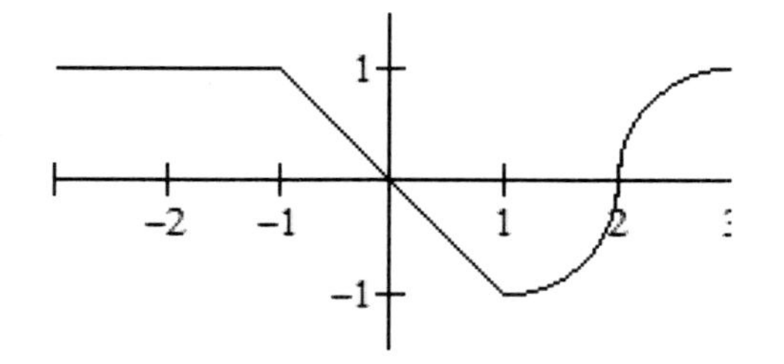

For which values of x, $-3 < x < 3$, is f not differentiable?

I. $x = -1$
II. $x = 1$
III. $x = 2$

A. I only
B. II only
C. I and II only
D. II and III only
E. I, II, and III

4. $\lim_{h \to 0} \dfrac{\cos\left(\frac{\pi}{6}+h\right)-\cos\left(\frac{\pi}{6}\right)}{h}$

A. Does not exist B. $\frac{1}{2}$ C. $\frac{-1}{2}$

D. $\frac{\sqrt{3}}{2}$ E. $-\frac{\sqrt{3}}{2}$

5. If $\dfrac{dy}{dx} = 2\cos(y)$ then $\dfrac{d^2y}{dx^2} =$

A. $-2\sin(y)$ B. $2\sin(y)$ C. $-2\sin(y)\cos(y)$
D. $-4\sin(y)\cos(y)$ E. $4\sin(y)\cos(y)$

6. If $h(x) = \dfrac{f(x)}{g(x)}$ and $h'(x) = \dfrac{g(x)(2x) - f(x)g'(x)}{(g(x))^2}$ then $f(x)$ could be

A. $x^2 - 3$ B. $2x$ C. x^3 D. 2
E. cannot be determined

*7. Let $f(x) = 2^x$, $g(x) = 3\sin(x)$ and $h(x) = f(g(x))$. For $0 < x < 1$, f and g intersect at point c. What is the value of $h'(c)$?

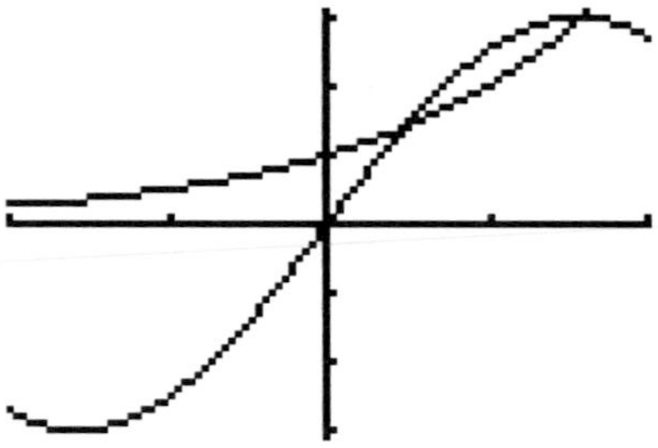

A. 0.486 B. 1.400 C. 2.575 D. 2.639

E. 4.854

8. The graph of $f'(x)$ is shown below. If $f(2) = -3$, what is the equation of the tangent line at $x = 2$?

the graph of $f'(x)$

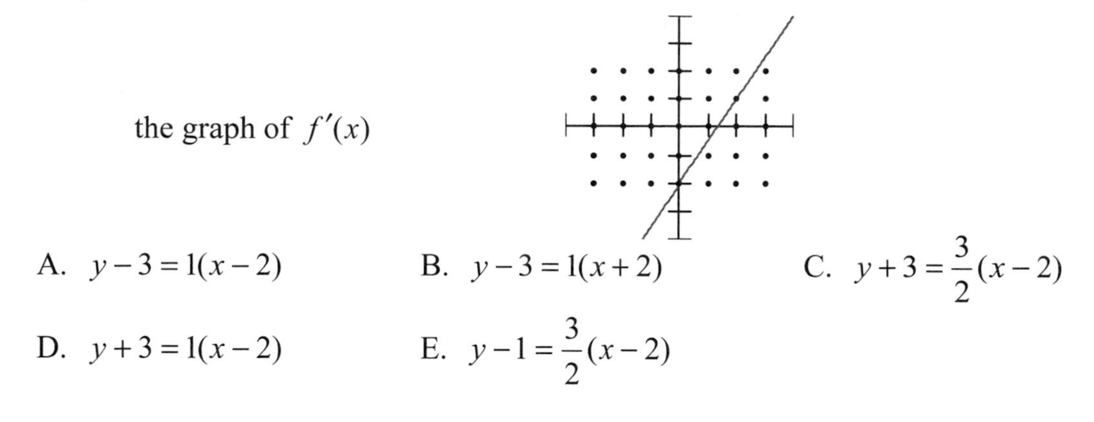

A. $y - 3 = 1(x - 2)$ B. $y - 3 = 1(x + 2)$ C. $y + 3 = \frac{3}{2}(x - 2)$

D. $y + 3 = 1(x - 2)$ E. $y - 1 = \frac{3}{2}(x - 2)$

Use the following information for questions 9-10

Let *f* and *g* be differentiable functions with values for $f(x), g(x), f'(x),$ and $g'(x)$

x	$f(x)$	$g(x)$	$f'(x)$	$g'(x)$
1	4	-4	12	-8
2	5	1	-6	4

9. Find the value of the derivative of $f(x) \cdot g(x)$ at $x = 1$.

A. -96 B. -80 C. -48 D. -32 E. 0

10. If $h(x)$ is the inverse function of $f(x)$, find $h'(4)$.

A. $-\frac{1}{8}$ B. $\frac{1}{12}$ C. $\frac{1}{8}$ D. 1 E. -4

11. Let $f(x) = \begin{cases} x^2 + 2; & x < 1 \\ 4 - x; & x \geq 1 \end{cases}$. Which is true?

I. $f(x)$ is continuous at $x = 1$

II. $f(x)$ is differentiable at $x = 1$

III. $\lim_{x \to 1^-} f(x) = \lim_{x \to 1^+} f(x)$

A. I only
B. II only
C. III only
D. I and III only
E. II and III only

Free-Response Questions–Calculus AB/BC Topics

1. Function $d(t)$ represents the distance, in feet, a car travels for time t, in seconds. Some values of d are listed in table below.

t, seconds	0	2	4	6	8	10
$d(t)$, feet	0	30	70	120	180	240

a. Use the data from the table to find the average velocity of the car for its first eight seconds. Show the computations used to arrive at your answer. Indicate units of measure.

b. Use the data from the table to estimate the velocity of the car at 4 seconds. Show the computations used to arrive at your answer. Indicate units of measure.

c. Use the data from the table to estimate the car's instantaneous rate of change at $t = 10$. Show the computations used to arrive at your answer. Indicate units of measure.

d. Use your answer from part *c* to write an equation for the line tangent to $y = d(t)$ at $t = 10$. Use this tangent line to estimate the distance traveled at $t = 11$.

2. Consider the curve given by $xy^2 - 2y = 3$.

a. Show that $\frac{dy}{dx} = \frac{y^2}{2 - 2xy}$.

b. Find all points on the curve where the slope is 0.

c. Find all points on the curve where the tangent line is vertical.

d. Find all points in the fourth quadrant whose x-coordinate is 1 and write an equation for the tangent line at each of these points.

3. Let f be the function given by $f(x)=(x+1)^2(x-3)$. As shown in the graph below, the function crosses the y-axis at point *P* (0,-3) and the *x*-axis at point *Q* (3, 0).

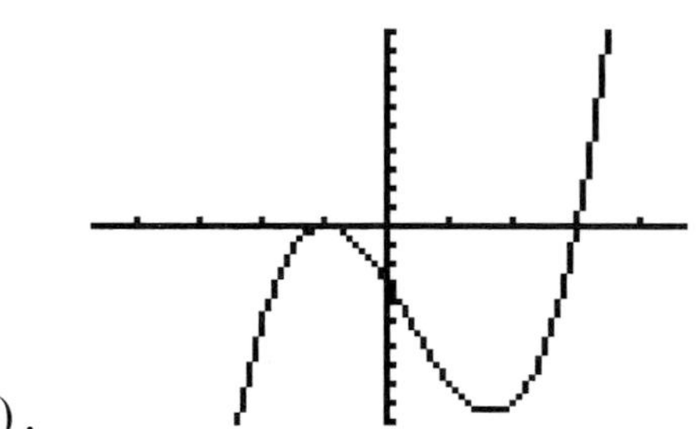

The graph of $f(x)$.

   a. Write an equation for the line passing through points *P* and *Q*.

   b. Write an equation for the line tangent to the function at point *P*.

   c. Find the coordinates of point *S*, the point on the graph of f, between points *P* and *Q* such that the line tangent to the function at point *S* is parallel to the line $\overleftrightarrow{PQ}$.

   d. Write the equation of the line tangent to f at point *S*.

4. Let *f(x)* and *g(x)* be the functions shown below.

   Let $h(x)=f(g(x))$ and $k(x)=f(x^4)$.

   a. Find $h(-3)$.
   b. Which is true? $h'(-1)>0$ or $h'(-1)=0$ or $h'(-1)<0$? Show the work that leads to your conclusion.
   c. Which is true? $h'(-2)>0$ or $h'(-2)=0$ or $h'(-2)<0$? Show the work that leads to your conclusion.
   d. Determine if *k* is increasing at *x* = -1. Justify your answer.

Graph of $f(x)$

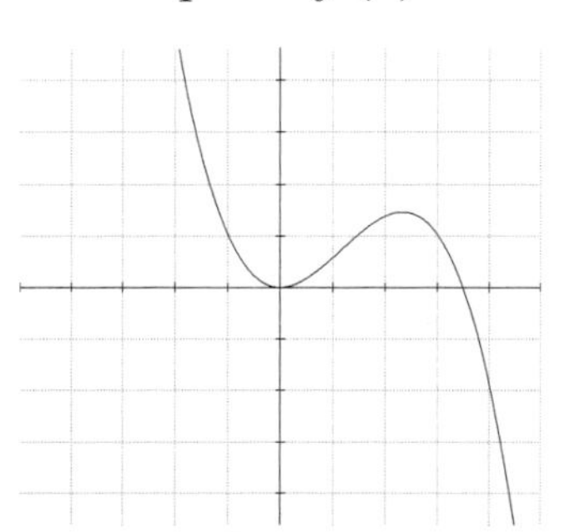

Graph of $g(x)$

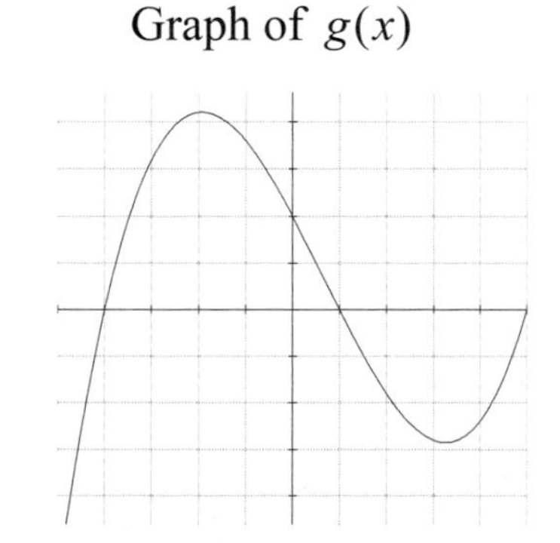

Solutions to Sample Questions

Solutions to Multiple-Choice Questions

1. D $y(2+x)=x-3$

$$y=\frac{x-3}{x+2}$$

*2. C $x'(t)=\frac{x(5)-x(1)}{4}$

$$x'(t)=-0.83451$$

3. E

4. C

$$\lim_{h\to 0}\frac{\cos(x+h)-\cos(x)}{h}=-\sin(x)$$

$$\lim_{h\to 0}\frac{\cos\left(\frac{\pi}{6}+h\right)-\cos\left(\frac{\pi}{6}\right)}{h}=-\sin\left(\frac{\pi}{6}\right)=-\frac{1}{2}$$

5. D.

$$\frac{d^2y}{dx^2}=-2\sin(y)\frac{dy}{dx}$$

$$\frac{d^2y}{dx^2}=-2\sin(y)2\cos(y)$$

$$\frac{d^2y}{dx^2}=-4\sin(y)\cos(y)$$

6. A.

$$h'(x)=\frac{g(x)f'(x)-f(x)g'(x)}{(g(x))^2}$$

$$f'(x)=2x$$

$$f(x)=x^2+C$$

$$f(x)=x^2-3$$

*7. E. The intersection of $f(x)$ and $g(x)$ is 0.48557

$$h(x)=2^{3\sin(x)}$$

$$h'(0.48557)=4.85382..$$

8. D. $f'(2) = 1$

$y - 3 = 1(x - 2)$

9. B $h(x) = f(x) \cdot g(x);\ \ h'(x) = f'(x) \cdot g(x) + f(x) \cdot g'(x)$

$h'(1) = f'(1) \cdot g(1) + f(1) \cdot g'(1) = 12 \cdot (-4) + 4 \cdot (-8) = -80$

10 B If $f(x)$ and $h(x)$ are inverse functions then $h(f(x)) = x$ and

$h'(f(x)) \cdot f'(x) = 1;\ \ \mathrm{h}'(f(1)) \cdot f'(1) = 1$

$h'(4) \cdot 12 = 1;\ \ h'(4) = \frac{1}{12}$

11. D

Solutions to Free-Response Questions

1. Function $d(t)$ represents the distance, in feet, a car travels for time t, in seconds. Some values of d are listed in table below.

t, seconds	0	2	4	6	8	10
$d(t)$, feet	0	30	70	120	180	240

a. Use the data from the table to find the average velocity of the car for its first eight seconds. Show the computations used to arrive at your answer. Indicate units of measure.
b. Use the data from the table to estimate the velocity of the car at 4 seconds. Show the computations used to arrive at your answer. Indicate units of measure.
c. Use the data from the table to estimate the car's instantaneous rate of change at $t = 10$. Show the computations used to arrive at your answer. Indicate units of measure.
d. Use your answer from part c to write an equation for the line tangent to $y = d(t)$ at $t = 10$. Use this tangent line to estimate the distance traveled at $t = 11$.

(a) $\frac{d(8)-d(0)}{8} = \frac{180-0}{8} = 22.5$ ft/sec

$2\begin{cases}1: \text{answer}\\1: \text{correct label}\end{cases}$

(b) $\frac{d(6)-d(2)}{4} = \frac{120-30}{4} = 22.5$ ft/sec, or

$\frac{d(6)-d(4)}{2} = \frac{120-70}{2} = 25$ ft/sec, or

$\frac{d(4)-d(2)}{2} = \frac{70-30}{2} = 20$ ft/sec

$2\begin{cases}1: \text{answer}\\1: \text{correct label}\end{cases}$

(c) $\frac{d(10)-d(8)}{2} = \frac{240-180}{2} = 30$ ft/sec

$2\begin{cases}1: \text{answer}\\1: \text{correct label}\end{cases}$

(d) $y = 30(t-10)+240$

$y = 30(11-10)+240$

$y = 270$

$d(11) \approx 270$ ft

$3\begin{cases}1: \text{tangent line}\\1: \text{computes } y \text{ on tangent line at } t = 11\\1: \text{answer}\end{cases}$

2. Consider the curve given by $xy^2 - 2y = 3$.

a. Show that $\dfrac{dy}{dx} = \dfrac{y^2}{2-2xy}$.

b. Find all points on the curve where the slope is 0.

c. Find all points on the curve where the tangent line is vertical.

d. Find all points in the fourth quadrant whose x-coordinate is 1 and write an equation for the tangent line at each of these points.

---

a. $y^2 + x2y\dfrac{dy}{dx} - 2\dfrac{dy}{dx} = 0$

$y^2 = (2-2xy)\dfrac{dy}{dx}$

$\dfrac{dy}{dx} = \dfrac{y^2}{2-2xy}$

2 { 1: implicit differentiation; 1: verifies expression for $\dfrac{dy}{dx}$ }

b. $\dfrac{dy}{dx} = 0$ when $y = 0$

but $x(0)^2 - 2(0) = 3;\ 0 \neq 3$
There are no points on the curve where the slope $= 0$

2 { 1: solves $\dfrac{dy}{dx} = 0$; 1: verifies there are no points on curve where the slope = 0 }

c. $\dfrac{dy}{dx}$ is undefined when

$2 - 2xy = 0; xy = 1$

$(1)y - 2y = 3$

$x = \dfrac{-1}{3}, y = -3$

2 { 1: $2-2xy=0$; 1: solves for x and y }

d. $1y^2 - 2y = 3$

$(y-3)(y+1) = 0$

$y = 3, y = -1$

at $(1,-1)$ $\dfrac{dy}{dx} = \dfrac{(-1)^2}{2-2(1)(-1)} = \dfrac{1}{4}$

$y + 1 = \dfrac{1}{4}(x-1)$

3 { 1: $y^2 - 2y = 3$; 1: point (1, -1); 1: equation of tangent line }

*3. Let f be the function given by $f(x)=(x+1)^2(x-3)$. As shown in the graph below, the function crosses the y-axis at point P (0,-3) and the x-axis at point Q (3, 0).

The graph of $f(x)$.

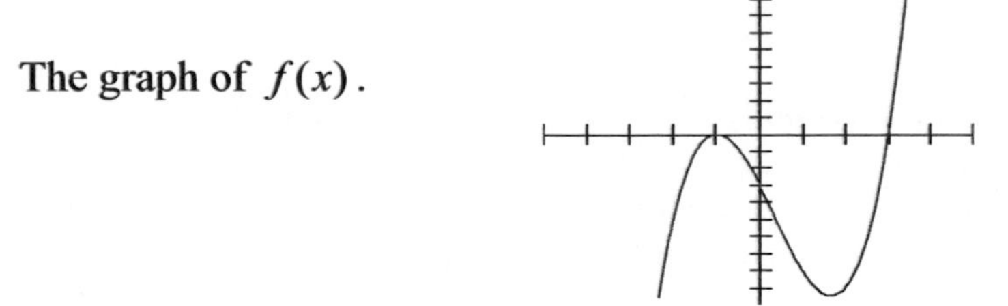

a. Write an equation for the line passing through points P and Q.

b. Write an equation for the line tangent to the function at point P.

c. Find the coordinates of point S, the point on the graph of f, between points P and Q such that the line tangent to the function at point S is parallel to the line $\overleftrightarrow{PQ}$.

d. Write the equation of the line tangent to f at point S.

Solution	Scoring
a. $m=\dfrac{0-(-3)}{(3-0)}=1$ $y-(-3)=1(x-0)$	2 $\begin{cases}1: \text{slope}\\1: \text{equation}\end{cases}$
b. $f'(0)=-5$ $y-(-3)=-5(x-0)$	3 $\begin{cases}1: \text{calculates } f'(x)\\1: f'(0)\\1: \text{equation}\end{cases}$
c. $2(x+1)(x-3)+(x+1)^2(1)=1$ $x=1.78629,\ y=-9.42252$	3 $\begin{cases}1: \text{sets } f'(x)=1\\1: \text{solves for } x\\1: \text{solves for } y\end{cases}$
d. $y-(-9.422521)=1(x-1.78629)$	1: equation

4. Let *f(x)* and *g(x)* be the functions shown below.

   Let $h(x) = f(g(x))$ and $k(x) = f(x^4)$.

   a. Find $h(-3)$.
   b. Which is true? $h'(-1) > 0$ or $h'(-1) = 0$ or $h'(-1) < 0$? Show the work that leads to your conclusion.
   c. Which is true? $h'(-2) > 0$ or $h'(-2) = 0$ or $h'(-2) < 0$? Show the work that leads to your conclusion.
   d. Determine if k is increasing at $x = -1$. Justify your answer.

Graph of $f(x)$

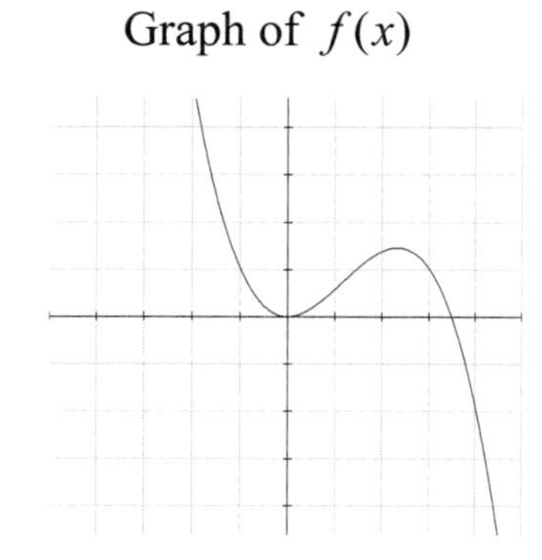

Graph of $g(x)$

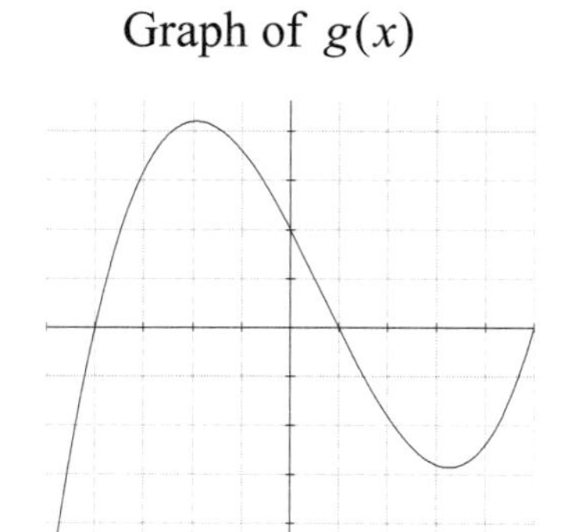

a. $h(-3) = f(g(-3)) = f(3) = 1$	1: answer
b. $h'(-1) = f'(g(-1)) \cdot g'(-1)$ $g'(-1) < 0$ because the graph of $g(x)$ is decreasing $f'(3.5) < 0$ because the graph of $f(x)$ is decreasing $h'(-1) > 0$	$4 \begin{cases} 1: h'(x) \\ 1: g' < 0 \\ 1: f' < 0 \\ 1: \text{answer} \end{cases}$
c. $h'(-2) = f'(g(-2)) \cdot g'(-2) = f'(4) \cdot 0$ $h'(-2) = 0$	1: answer
d. $k'(x) = 4x^3 f'(x^4)$; $k'(-1) = 4(-1)^3 f'((-1)^4)$ k is decreasing at $x = -1$ because $k'(-1) < 0$	$3 \begin{cases} 1: k'(x) \\ 1: k'(-1) < 0 \\ 1: \text{answer} \end{cases}$

Connect2Calculus Videos for Chapter 2

The Calculus Concepts Video's for Chapter 2: *(Calculus BC topics are in italic type)*
Some of the topics on the videos go beyond the scope of Calculus AB/BC, but would be worth watching as an application of calculus.

2.0 **Measurements of Change**
2.1 Tangents and Rates of Change
2.2 Interpreting the Derivative Function
2.3 When the Derivative Does Not Exist
3.0 **Differentiating Functions**
3.1 Basic Differentiation Formulas
3.2 Derivatives of Trigonometric Functions
3.3 Derivatives of Exponential and Logarithmic Functions
4.0 **Modeling with Derivatives**
4.1 Derivatives and Motion: Distance, Velocity, and Acceleration
4.2 Modeling with Exponential Functions (this topic also appears in Chapter 7)
4.3 The Derivative of a Product of Functions: Damped Oscillations
5.0 **Relations and Change in Two and Three Dimensions**
5.1 Implicit Differentiation
5.2 Related Rates in Two Dimensions (this topic also appears in Chapter 3)
5.3 Related Rates in Three Dimensions (not in the Topic Outline for Calculus AB/BC)

CHAPTER 3: APPLICATIONS OF DIFFERENTIATION

Correlations

The section by section correspondence to the Topic Outline for Calculus AB and the Topic Outline for Calculus BC (*Calculus BC topics are in italic type*) is:

AP Topic	Chapter.Section	Pages
I. Functions, Graphs, and Limits **Analysis of graphs** With the aid of technology, graphs of functions are often easy to produce. The emphasis is on the interplay between the geometric and analytic information and on the use of calculus both to predict and to explain the observed local and global behavior of a function.	 3.3 3.4 3.5 3.6	 265-277 277-286 286-296 296-307
I. Functions, Graphs, and Limits **Continuity as a property of functions** • Geometric understanding of graphs of continuous functions (… Extreme Value Theorem)	 3.3	 265-277
II. Derivatives **Derivatives at a point** • Slope of a curve at a point. Examples are emphasized, including points at which there are vertical tangents and points at which there are no tangents • Tangent line to a curve at a point and local linear approximation	 3.3 3.1	 265-277 242-255
II. Derivatives **Derivative as a function** • Relationship between the increasing and decreasing behavior of f and the sign of f'	 3.4	 277-286

AP Topic	Chapter.Section	Pages
II. Derivatives		
Second derivatives		
• Corresponding characteristics of the graphs of f, f', f''	3.5	286-296
• Relationship between the concavity of f and the sign of f''	3.5	286-296
• Points of inflection as places where concavity changes	3.5	286-296
II. Derivatives		
Applications of derivatives		
• Analysis of curves, including the notions of monotonicity and concavity	3.4 3.5 3.6	277-286 286-296 296-307
• Optimization, both absolute (global) and relative (local) extrema	3.3 3.7	265-277 308-320
• Modeling rates of change, including related rates problems	3.8 3.9	321-327 327-338
+ *L'Hopital's Rule, including its use in determining limits .....*	*3.2*	*255-265*
III. Integrals		
Applications of antidifferentiation		
+ *Solving logistics differential equations and using them in modeling*	*3.9*	*327-338*

Textbook Section	AP Topic
3.1 Linear Approximations and Newton's Method	**II. Derivatives** **Derivatives at a point** • Tangent line to a curve at a point and local linear approximation
3.2 Indeterminate Forms and L'Hopital's Rule	**II. Derivatives** **Applications of derivatives** + *L'Hopital's Rule, including its use in determining limits .....*
3.3 Maximum and Minimum Values	**I. Functions, Graphs, and Limits** **Analysis of graphs** With the aid of technology, graphs of functions are often easy to produce. The emphasis is on the interplay between the geometric and analytic information and on the use of calculus both to predict and to explain the observed local and global behavior of a function. **Continuity as a property of functions** • Geometric understanding of graphs of continuous functions (… Extreme Value Theorem) **II. Derivatives** **Derivatives at a point** • Slope of a curve at a point. Examples are emphasized, including points at which there are vertical tangents and points at which there are no tangents **Applications of derivatives** • Optimization, both absolute (global) and relative (local) extrema
3.4 Increasing and Decreasing Functions	**I. Functions, Graphs, and Limits** **Analysis of graphs** With the aid of technology, graphs of functions are often easy to produce. The emphasis is on the interplay between the geometric and analytic information and on the use of calculus both to predict and to explain the observed local and global behavior of a function. **II. Derivatives** **Derivative as a function** • Relationship between the increasing and decreasing behavior of f and the sign of f' **Applications of derivatives** • Analysis of curves, including the notions of monotonicity and concavity

Textbook section	AP topic
3.5 Concavity and the Second Derivative Test	**I. Functions, Graphs, and Limits** **Analysis of graphs** With the aid of technology, graphs of functions are often easy to produce. The emphasis is on the interplay between the geometric and analytic information and on the use of calculus both to predict and to explain the observed local and global behavior of a function. **II. Derivatives** **Second derivatives** • Corresponding characteristics of the graphs of f, f', f'' • Relationship between the concavity of f and the sign of f'' • Points of inflection as places where concavity changes **Applications of derivatives** • Analysis of curves, including the notions of monotonicity and concavity
3.6 Overview of Curve Sketching	**I. Functions, Graphs, and Limits** **Analysis of graphs** With the aid of technology, graphs of functions are often easy to produce. The emphasis is on the interplay between the geometric and analytic information and on the use of calculus both to predict and to explain the observed local and global behavior of a function. **II. Derivatives** **Applications of derivatives** • Analysis of curves, including the notions of monotonicity and concavity
3.7 Optimization	**II. Derivatives** **Applications of derivatives** • Optimization, both absolute (global) and relative (local) extrema
3.8 Related Rates	**II. Derivatives** **Applications of derivatives** • Modeling rates of change, including related rates problems •
3.9 Rates of Change in Economics and the Sciences	**II. Derivatives** **Applications of derivatives** • Modeling rates of change, including related rates problems **III. Integrals** **Applications of antidifferentiation** + *Solving logistics differential equations and using them in modeling*

Vocabulary and Section Notes

Vocabulary used in the Topic Outline for Calculus AB and the Topic Outline for Calculus BC (*Calculus BC topics are in italic type*) include:

Absolute extremum
Concavity
Critical number
Decreasing function
Extreme Value Theorem
First Derivative Test
Global behavior
Increasing function
Indeterminate form
Inflection points
l'Hopital's Rule
Linear approximation
Local extremum
Local linearity
Logistic equation
Optimization
Second Derivative Test
Related rates

Section notes for the Calculus AB Course:

Section 3.1 (Linear Approximation and Newton's Method): Newton's Method is not part of the Topic Outline for Calculus AB.

Section 3.2 (Indeterminate Forms and L'Hopital's Rule): L'Hopital's Rule is not part of the Topic Outline for Calculus AB. However, many Calculus AB teachers choose to include indeterminate forms like $\frac{0}{0}, \frac{\infty}{\infty}$, and $\infty - \infty$ in their discussion of limits because these techniques may simplify limit calculations that occur on the Calculus AB Exam. However, the Topic Outline for Calculus AB specifies that calculation of the value of a limit will only require those methods developed in Chapter 1.

Section 3.9 (Rates of Change in Economics and the Sciences): These are interesting applications of the derivative and students do not need to memorize any of the relationships, but they should be able to solve problems when the pertinent relationship is defined in the problem.

Section notes for the Calculus BC Course:

Section 3.1 (Linear Approximations and Newton's Method): Newton's Method is not part of the Topic Outline for Calculus BC.

Section 3.9 (Rates of Change in Economics and the Sciences): The logistics equation is introduced and the maximum rate of population growth is explored. Pertinent exercises from the end of the chapter are 49 – 53. The "Teacher's Notes: The Logistics Function-(Calculus BC Topic)" in Chapter 7 has more information about the logistics equation and its uses. The multiple-choice and free-response questions in Chapter 7 of the Instructor's Resource Guide will include practice with all aspects of the logistics equation and function. The rest of the applications of the derivative are interesting, and students do not need to memorize any of the relationships, but they should be able to solve problems when the pertinent relationship is defined in the problem.

Student Activity: Reasoning from a Graph

Teacher's Notes

It is important for students to know how to determine the properties of a function and either of its derivatives when they only have the information in a graph of $f(x), f'(x)$, or $f''(x)$. This activity is a matching game designed to give students experience in reasoning from all three perspectives.

Suggestions for using the matching game activity in class:

1. Make several copies of the function cards and have them cut into individual pieces. Keep each card set together (small plastic bags are useful) until ready to use.
2. Be sure to keep one copy of the function cards intact to use as the Master Set.
3. Make each copy of the function cards on a different color of cardstock paper so that cards can be easily sorted into card sets if they become scrambled.
4. This activity can be used after section 3.5, when the students have learned the properties of the first derivative and second derivative.
5. Each matching game should take 45 minutes or less, so this activity would be appropriate for those days when there is less than usual time in class.
6. After students have matched the appropriate cards in a "Matching Game" have them put in writing their reasoning for two or three functions and the appropriate derivative.

Matching games:

1. After scrambling the cards in an individual card set, have students select the "Function" and "First Derivative" cards.
   Variation 1: Using the properties illustrated on the "Function" card, find the matching "First Derivative" card.
   Variation 2: Using the properties illustrated on the "First Derivative" card, find the matching "Function" card.

2. After scrambling the cards in an individual card set, have students select the "Function" and "Second Derivative" cards.
   Variation 1: Using the properties illustrated on the "Function" card, find the matching "Second Derivative" card.
   Variation 2: Using the properties illustrated on the "Second Derivative" card, find the matching "Function" card.

3. After scrambling the cards in an individual card set, have students select the "First Derivative" and "Second Derivative" cards. Using the properties illustrated on the "First Derivative" card, find the matching "Second Derivative" card.

4. After scrambling the cards in an individual card set, have students select the "Function", "First Derivative" and "Second Derivative" cards. Using the properties illustrated on the "First Derivative" card, find the matching "Function" and "Second Derivative" cards.

5. Keeping the "Function" and "First Derivative" cards together, use the "First Derivative" cards to identify the x-values of any relative maxima or relative minima.

6. Keeping the "Function" and "Second Derivative" cards together, use the "Second Derivative" cards to identify the x-values of a points of inflection.

7. After scrambling the cards in an individual card set, have students select the "Function", "Verbal Description" and "Formula" cards. Use the properties on all three cards to find the matching cards.

8. After scrambling the cards in an individual card set, have students combine Matching Game 7 and Matching Game 4 to find the matching cards and complete sets. If the cards are matched properly, they should look like the teacher's Master Set of cards.

These graphs could be used to demonstrate the "Matching Game" for the students:

$$f(x) = \frac{1}{3}x^3 + \frac{1}{2}x^2 - 2x$$

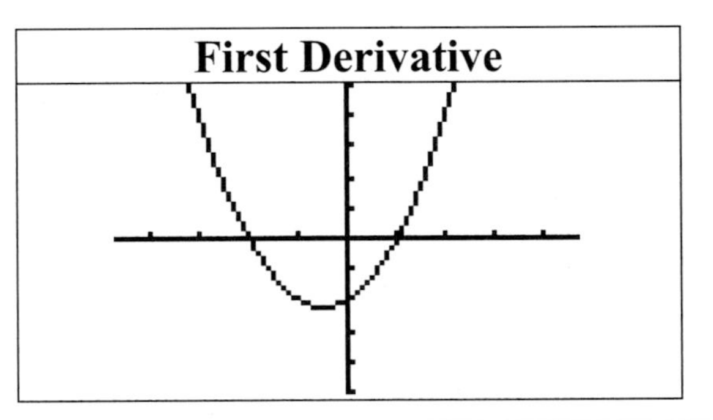

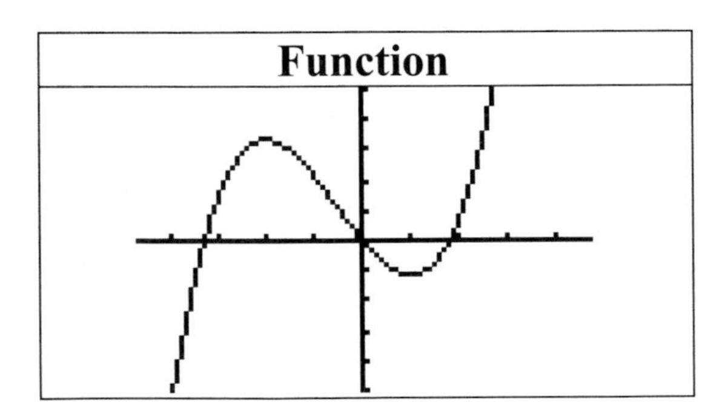

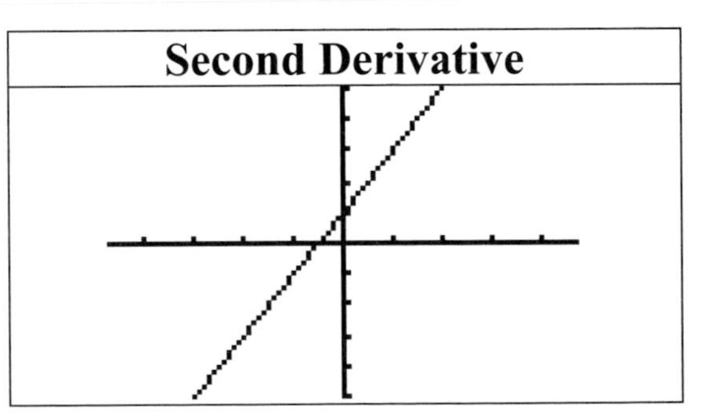

The properties of the "Function" are:

On the interval $-\infty < x < -2$, the values of the function are increasing and the graph of the function is rising.
On the interval $-2 < x < 1$, the values of the function are decreasing and the graph of the function is falling.
On the interval $1 < x < \infty$, the values of the function are increasing and the graph of the function is rising.

Examples of some matching games and expected student reasoning would be:
(The matching games are not in any particular order.)

1. After scrambling the cards in an individual card set, have students select the "Function" and "First Derivative" cards.
   Variation 2: Using the properties illustrated on the "First Derivative" card, find the matching "Function" card.

   On the interval $-\infty < x < -2$, graph of the first derivative lies above the x-axis and the values of the first derivative are positive. Since the values of the first derivative are positive the values of the function are increasing and the graph of the function is rising.

   On the interval $-2 < x < 1$, the graph of the first derivative lies below the x-axis and the values of the first derivative are negative. Since the values of the first derivative are negative the values of the function are decreasing and the graph of the function is falling.

   On the interval $1 < x < \infty$, the graph of the first derivative lies above the x-axis and the values of the first derivative are positive. Since the values of the first derivative are positive the values of the function are increasing and the graph of the function is rising.

5. Keeping the "Function" and "First Derivative" cards together, use the "First Derivative" cards to identify the x-values of any relative maxima or relative minima .

   At $x = -2$, the graph of the derivative crosses the x-axis and the value of the first derivative is zero. This makes $x = -2$ a critical point. Because the values of the first derivative are positive to the left of $x = -2$ and are negative to the right of $x = -2$, $x = -2$ is a relative maximum of the function.

   At $x = 1$, the graph of the derivative crosses the x-axis and the value of the first derivative is zero. This makes $x = 1$ a critical point. Because the values of the first derivative are negative to the left of $x = 1$ and are positive to the right of $x = 1$, $x = 1$ is a relative minimum of the function.

2. After scrambling the cards in an individual card set, have students select the "Function" and "Second Derivative" cards.
Variation 2: Using the properties illustrated on the "Second Derivative" card, find the matching "Function" card.

The graph of the second derivative lies below the x-axis on the interval $-\infty < x < -\frac{1}{2}$ and the values of the second derivative are negative, thus the graph of the function is concave down on the interval $-\infty < x < -\frac{1}{2}$.

The graph of the second derivative lies above the x-axis on the interval $-\frac{1}{2} < x < \infty$ and the values of the second derivative are positive, thus the graph of the function is concave up on the interval $-\frac{1}{2} < x < \infty$.

6. Keeping the "Function" and "Second Derivative" cards together, use the "Second Derivative" cards to identify the x-values of a points of inflection

The graph of the second derivative crosses the x-axis at $x = -\frac{1}{2}$ and the value of the second derivative is zero. This makes $x = -\frac{1}{2}$ a critical point. Because the values of the second derivative are negative to the left of $x = -\frac{1}{2}$ and are positive to the right of $x = -\frac{1}{2}$, $x = -\frac{1}{2}$ is an inflection point.

3. After scrambling the cards in an individual card set, have students select the "First Derivative" and "Second Derivative" cards. Using the properties illustrated on the "First Derivative" card, find the matching "Second Derivative" card

The graph of the first derivative falls on the interval $-\infty < x < -\frac{1}{2}$ and the values of its derivative are negative so the function is concave down on this interval. The graph of the first derivative rises on the interval $-\frac{1}{2} < x < \infty$ and the values of its derivative are positive so the function is concave up on this interval.

The graph of the first derivative has a local minimum at $x = -\frac{1}{2}$ so the function has a point of inflection at $x = -\frac{1}{2}$.

On the following pages you will find 12 card sets to use in this activity.

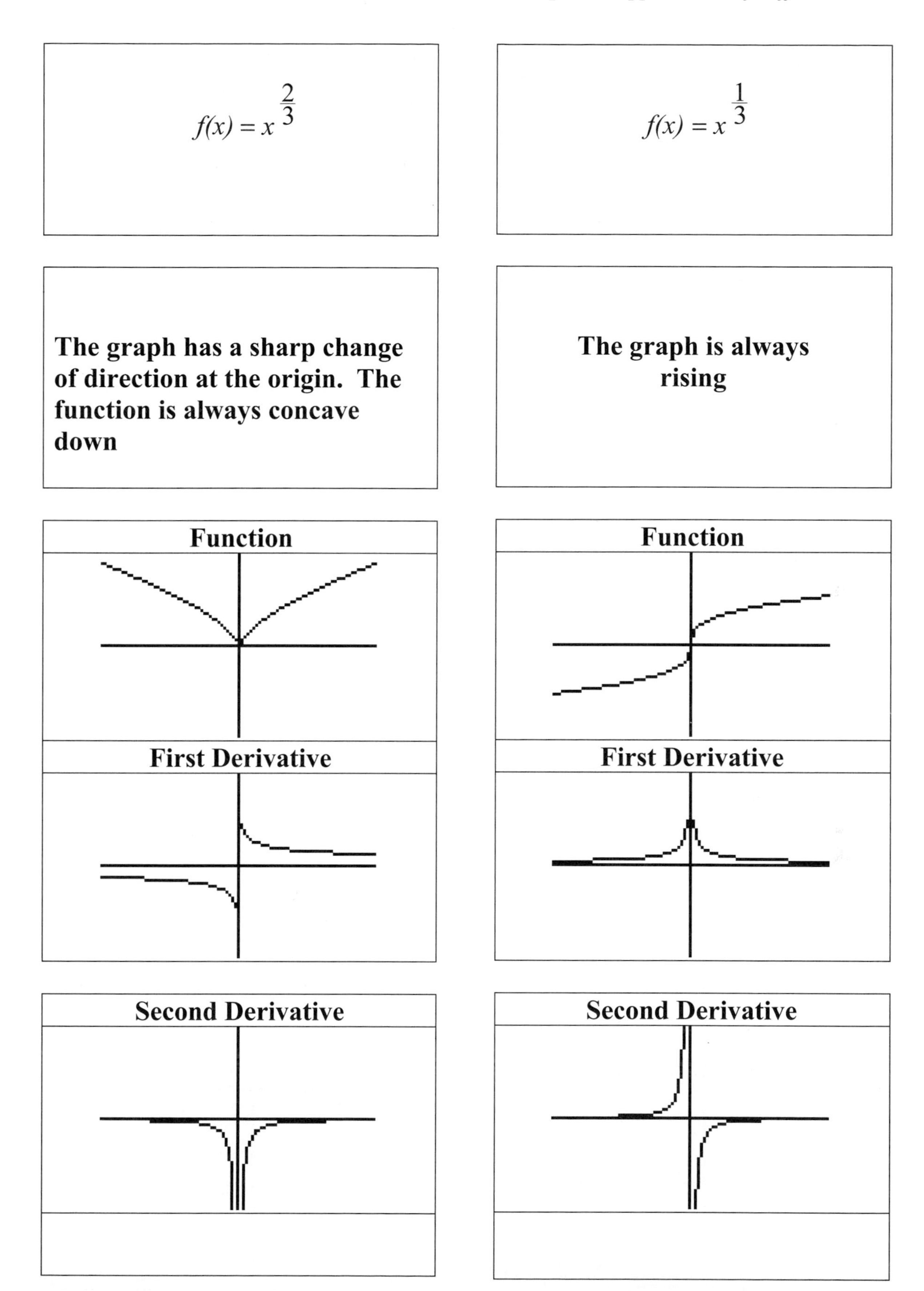
$f(x) = x^{\frac{2}{3}}$
$f(x) = x^{\frac{1}{3}}$
The graph has a sharp change of direction at the origin. The function is always concave down
The graph is always rising
Function
Function
First Derivative
First Derivative
Second Derivative
Second Derivative

$f(x) = \sqrt{4 - x}$

The domain of the function is all real numbers less than or equal to 4

Function

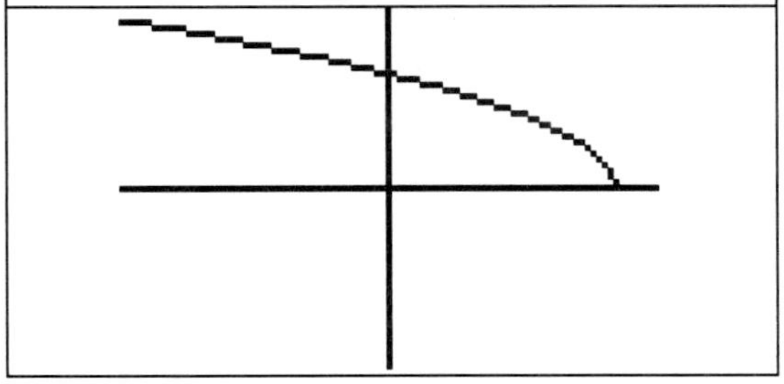

First Derivative

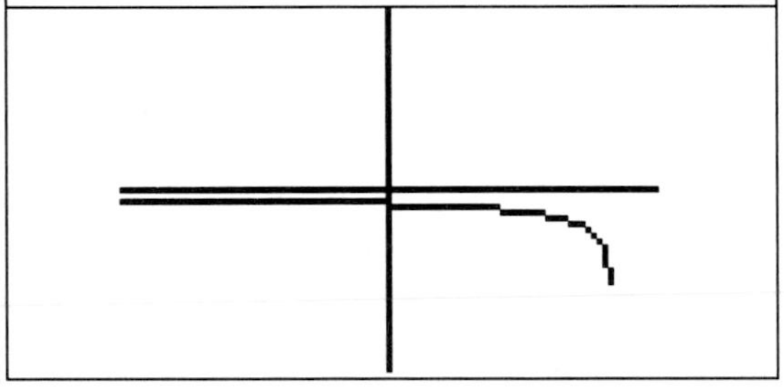

Second Derivative

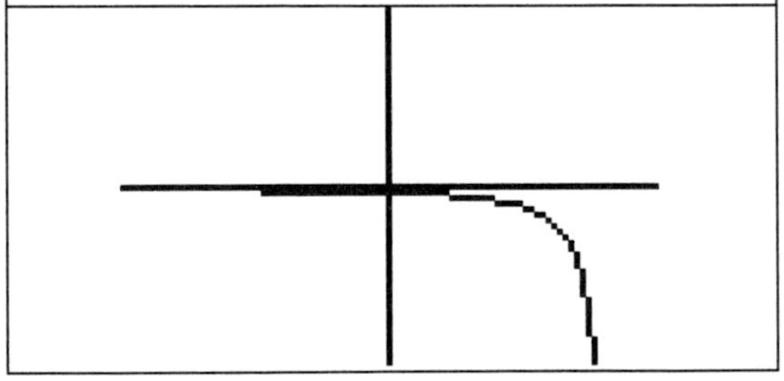

$f(x) = -\sqrt{9 - x^2}$

The range of the function is
$-3 \leq y \leq 0$

Function

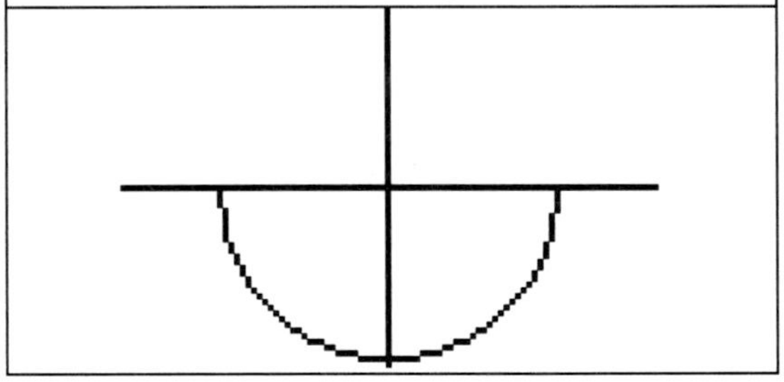

First Derivative

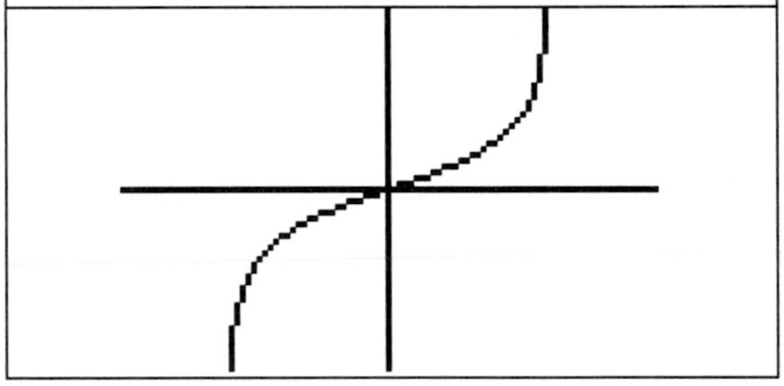

Second Derivative

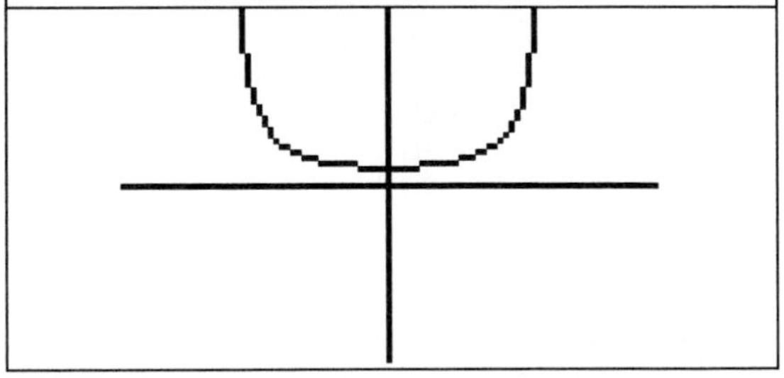

$f(x) = .5(x+4)(x-5)(x-2)$

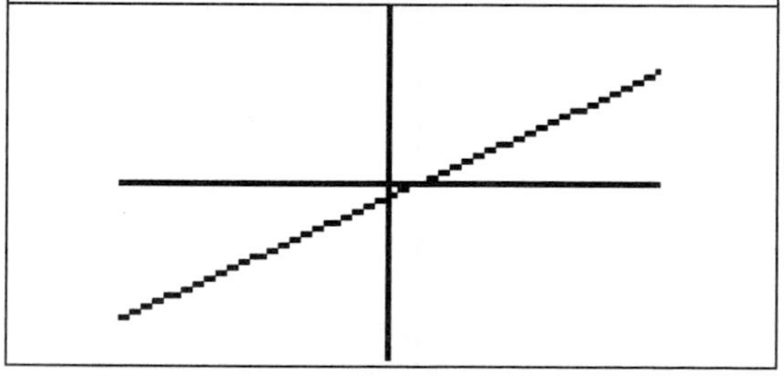

$f(x) = .3(x^2-4)(x+4)(x-6)$

The graph has one negative and two positive zeros.

The graph has two regions where it is concave up and one region where it is concave down

Function

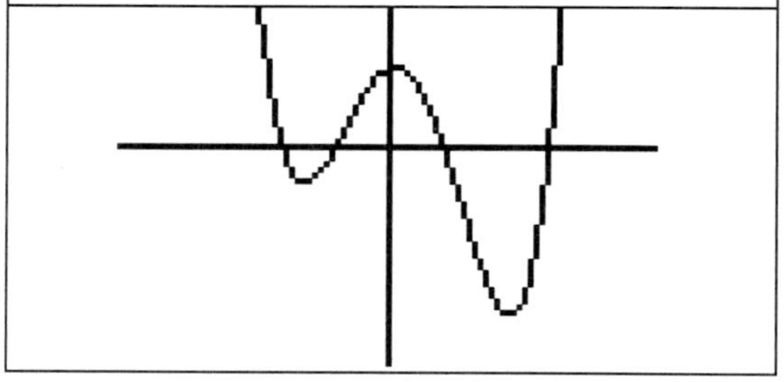

Function

First Derivative

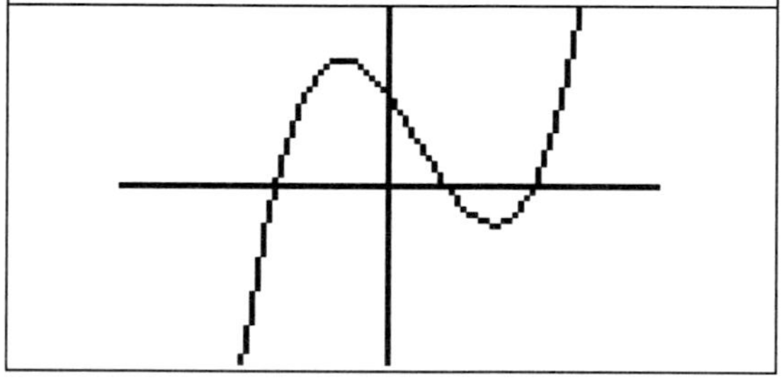

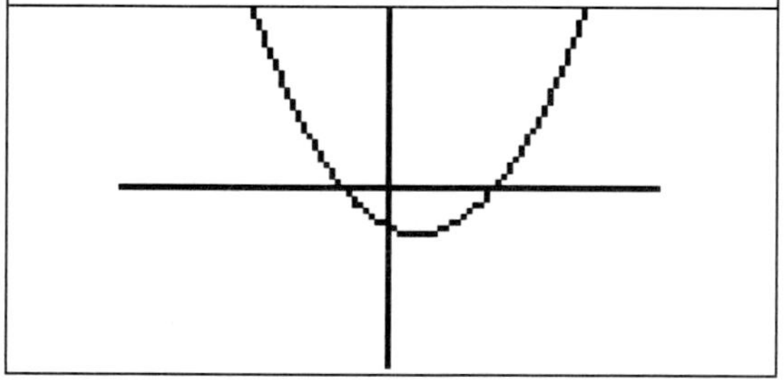

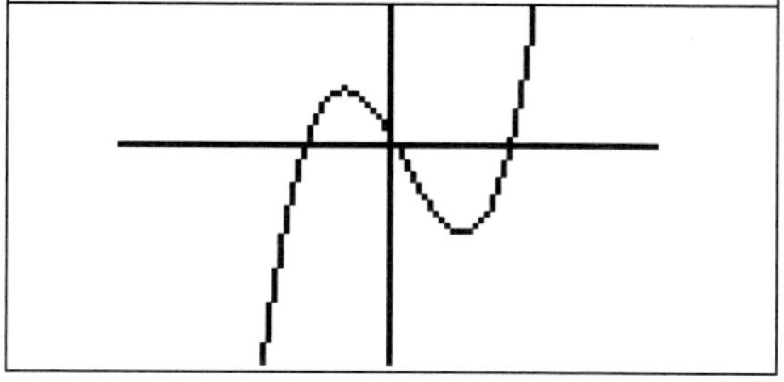

First Derivative

Second Derivative

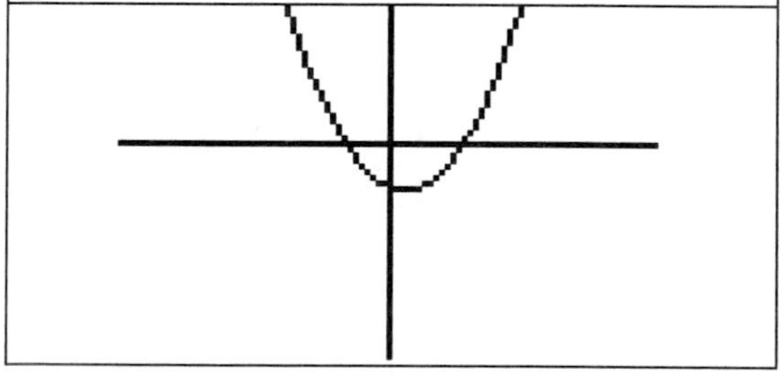

Second Derivative

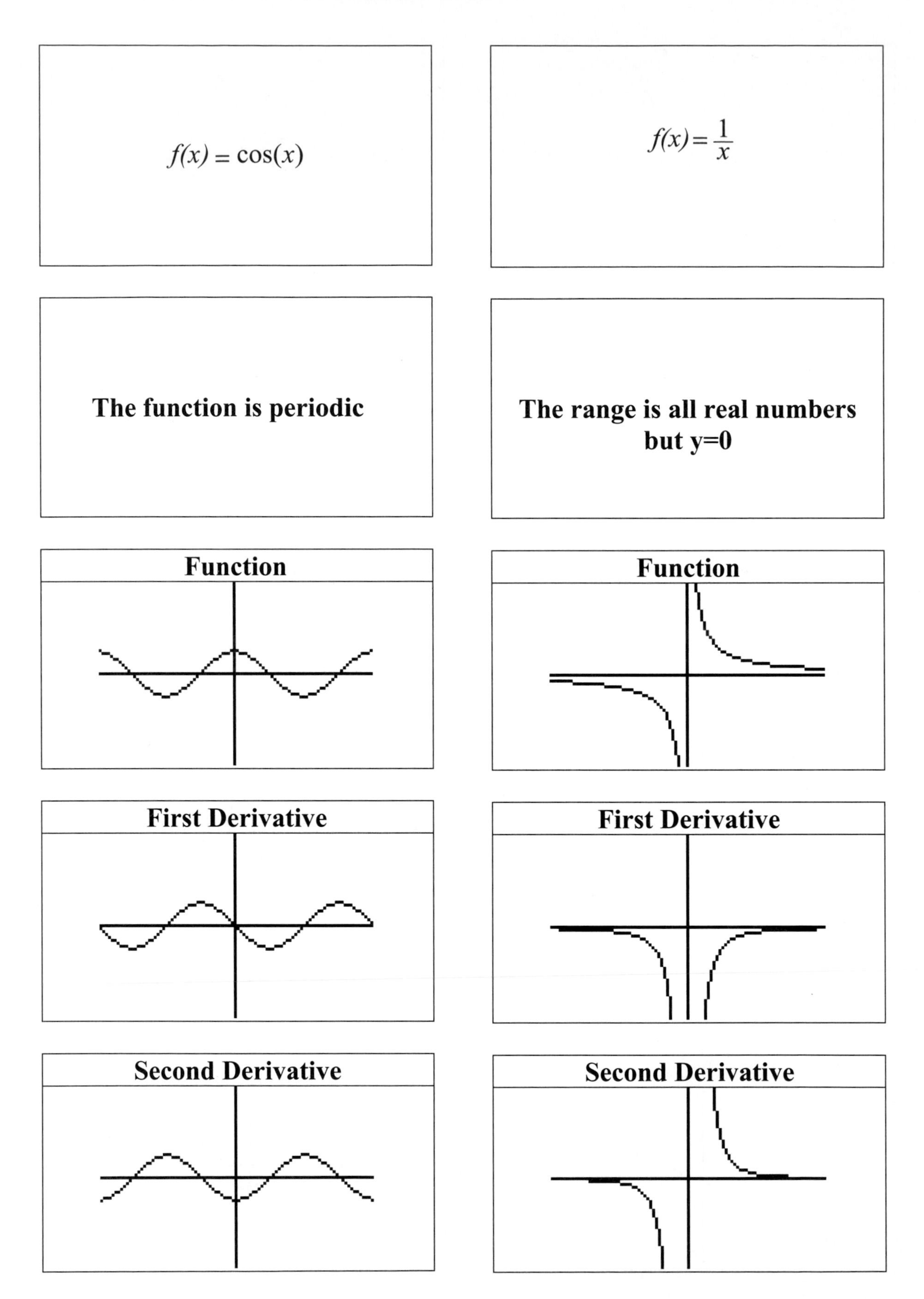
$f(x) = \cos(x)$
$f(x) = \frac{1}{x}$
The function is periodic
The range is all real numbers but y=0
Function
Function
First Derivative
First Derivative
Second Derivative
Second Derivative

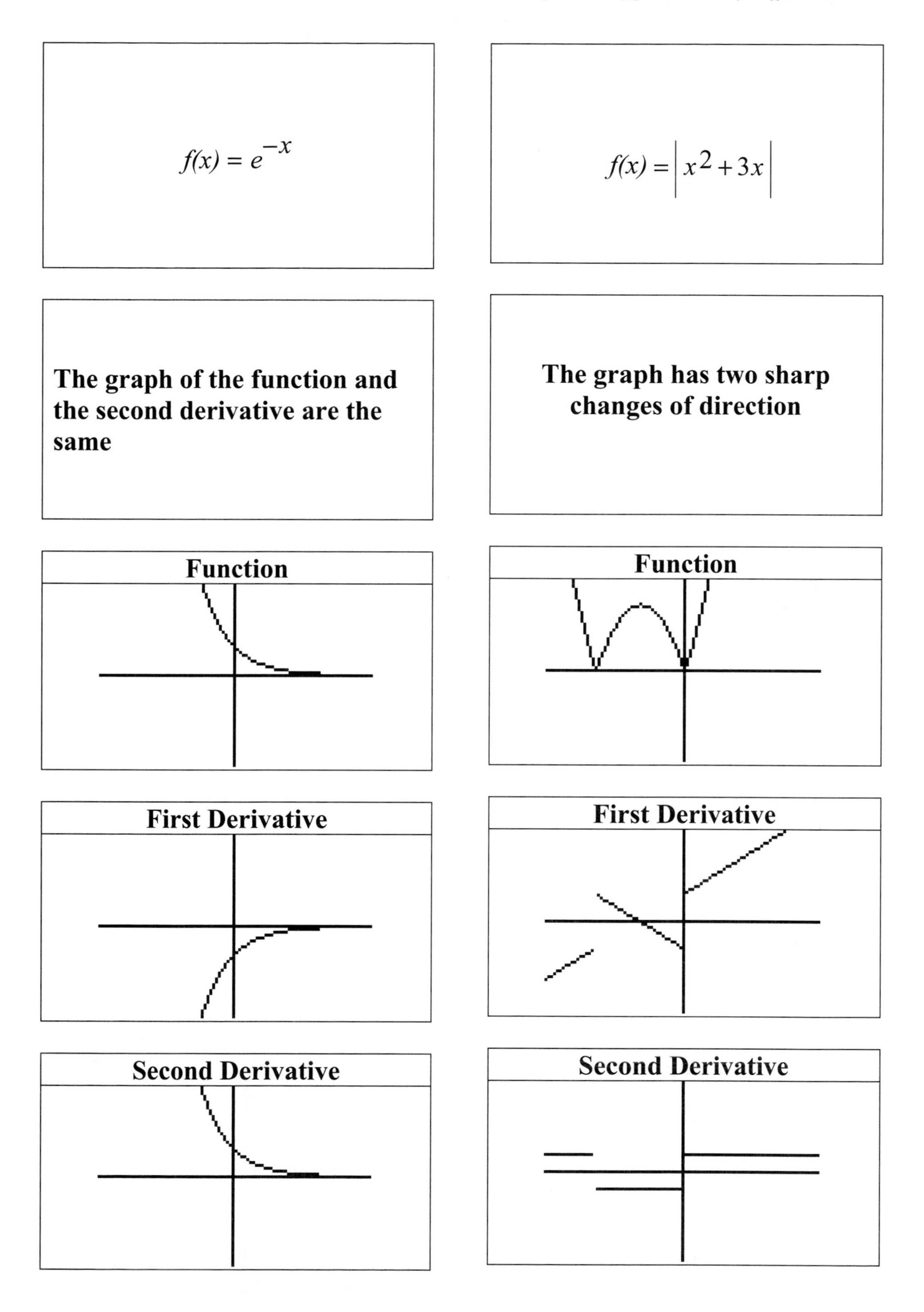

f(x) = e^{-x}
f(x) = |x^2 + 3x|
The graph of the function and the second derivative are the same
The graph has two sharp changes of direction
Function
Function
First Derivative
First Derivative
Second Derivative
Second Derivative

$f(x) = |x|$

$f(x) = \ln(x)$

The graph has a sharp change of direction at the origin.

The domain of the function is $x > 0$

Function

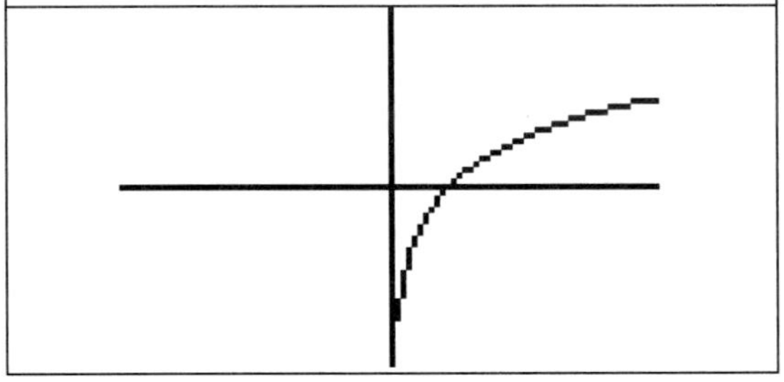

Function

First Derivative

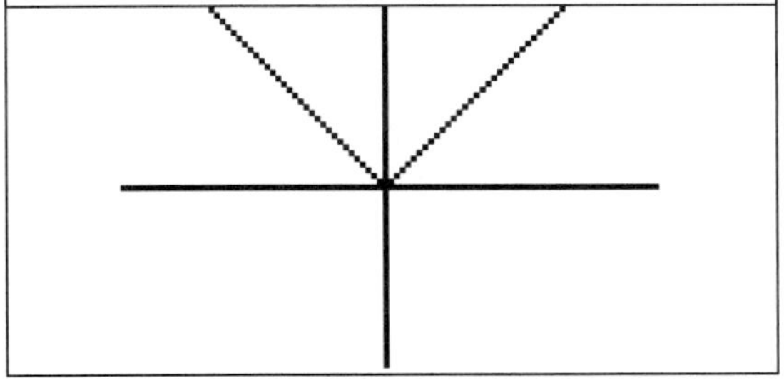

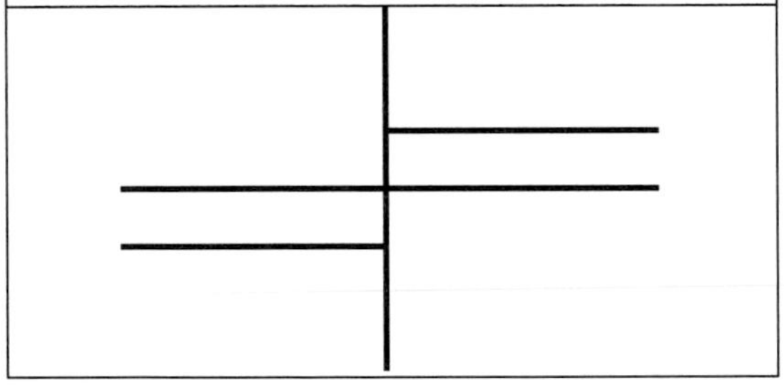

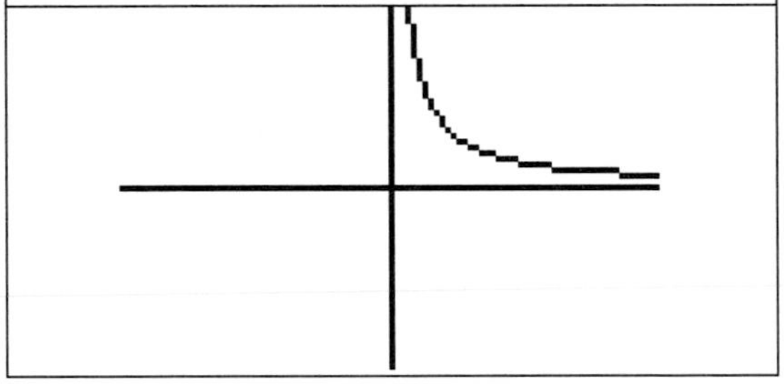

First Derivative

Second Derivative

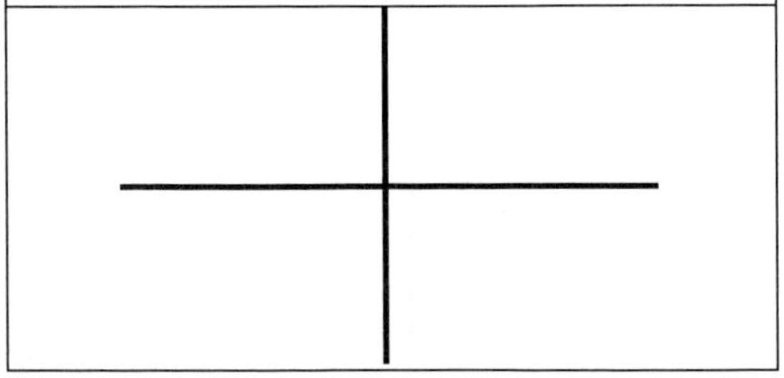

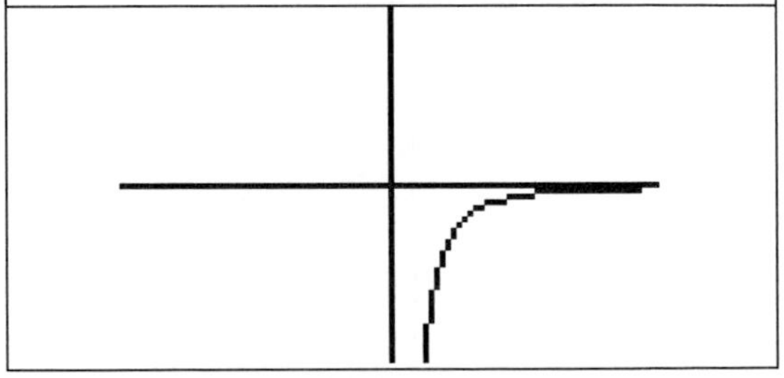

Second Derivative

Teacher's Notes: Demonstrating Particle Motion on a Line

If $x(t) = \frac{1}{2}t^2 - 4t + 5$ gives the position of an object moving along a horizontal line, it is common to ask when the particle is moving to the left and when the particle is moving to the right. Of course, calculus techniques show that when $x'(t) > 0$ the object is moving to the right and when $x'(t) < 0$ the particle is moving to the left and when $x'(t) = 0$ the object is at rest. Most students do not have enough experience with the concept of velocity to answer these questions. However, using the parametric graphing mode found on most calculators, it is possible to demonstrate the relationship between the sign of $x'(t)$ and the direction the object travels.

For purposes of demonstration, let's assume the object is moving along the line $y = 8$. Select parametric **MODE** and simultaneous graphing, then enter these equations (notice the graph style using the "ball") and set the window as follows:

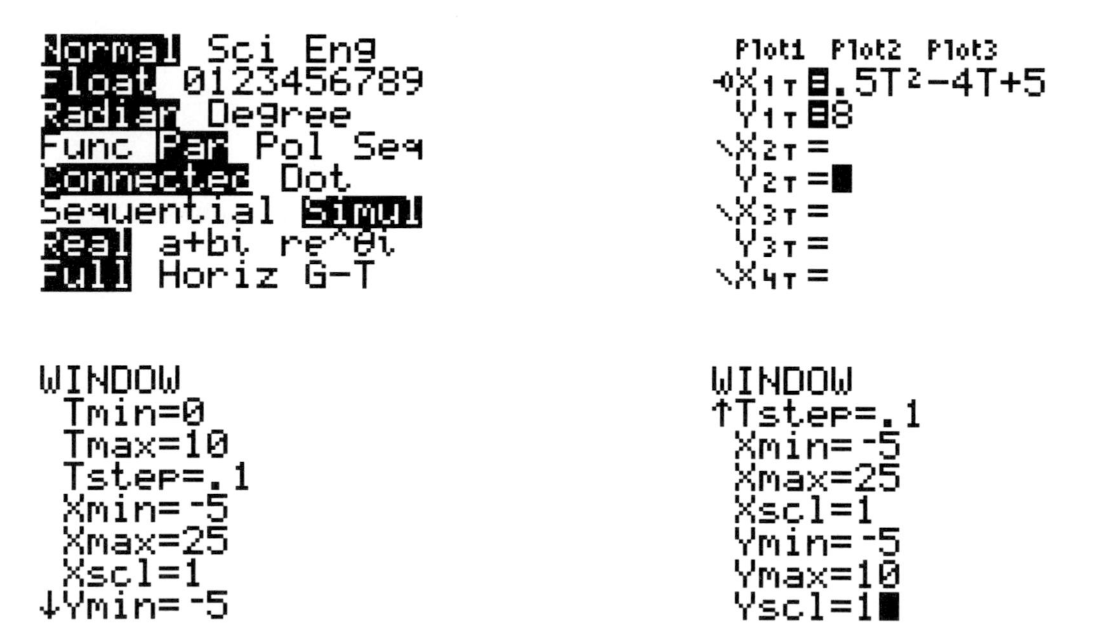

When you press **GRAPH**, you should be able to see a particle start at $x = 5$, move to the left, slow to a stop, and then move to the right. As t increases, it is possible to see the object moving faster and faster.

Questions to ask the students:

1. Where is the object at $t = 0$?
2. The object initially moves to the left and then pauses and begins moving to the right. When does the object pause ($v(t) = 0$)? How do you know?
3. How do you know the object is slowing down or speeding up?
4. Will the object ever move to the left again?

Using the **TRACE** button you can investigate the answers to these questions.

1. At $t = 0$, the object is at $x = 5$ on the horizontal line $y = 8$
2. It appears that at $t = 4$ the object pauses and begins moving to the right. In trace mode, the values of the function show: $x(3.9) = -2.995, x(4) = -3, x(4.1) = -2.995$. Of course, all we know is that somewhere between $t = 3.9$ and $t = 4.1$ the object pauses and then begins moving to the right.
3. If $|x(t_{n+1}) - x(t_n)|$ is larger than $|x(t_n) - x(t_{n-1})|$ the object is speeding up. If $|x(t_{n+1}) - x(t_n)|$ is smaller than $|x(t_n) - x(t_{n-1})|$ the object is slowing down. In **TRACE** mode, compare the magnitude of the jump of the object at three consecutive values of t. If the magnitude is increasing, the object is speeding up and if it is decreasing, the object is slowing down.
4. Change **Tmax** to 20 and **Xmax** to 130, then press graph. After $t = 4$ it appears that the object is still moving to the right. Of course this question cannot be answered using graphical techniques.

What can be learned by including the velocity function?

From **MODE** select **Simul** graphing and in the **Y=** window add the velocity equations and then return to the original window:

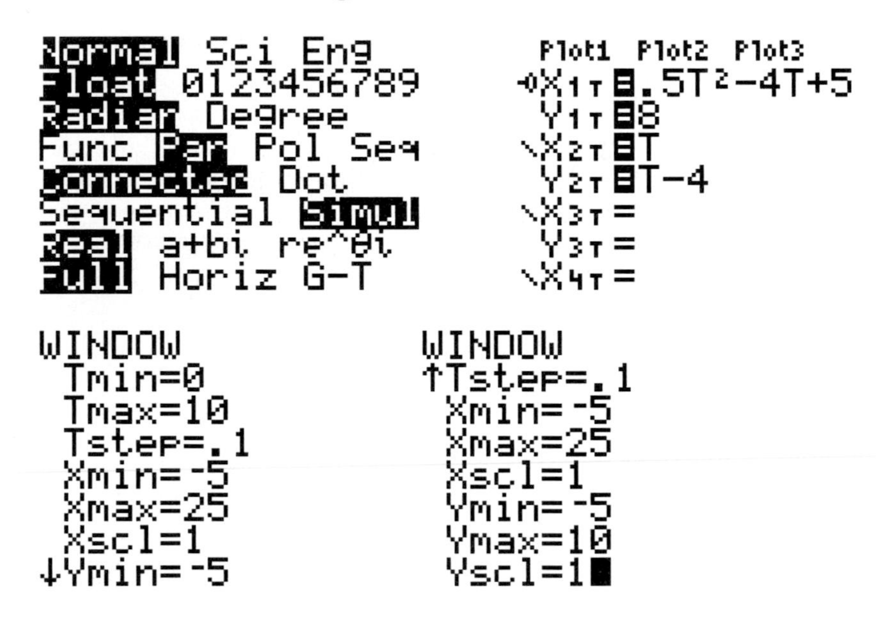

Now when you press graph, two graphs will appear, the path of the object, and the graph of the velocity. While the object is moving to the left, the velocity graph is below the x-axis. When the object pauses (at $t = 4$), the velocity graph is at the x-axis, and when the object is moving to the right the velocity graph is above the x-axis. Here are three snapshots:

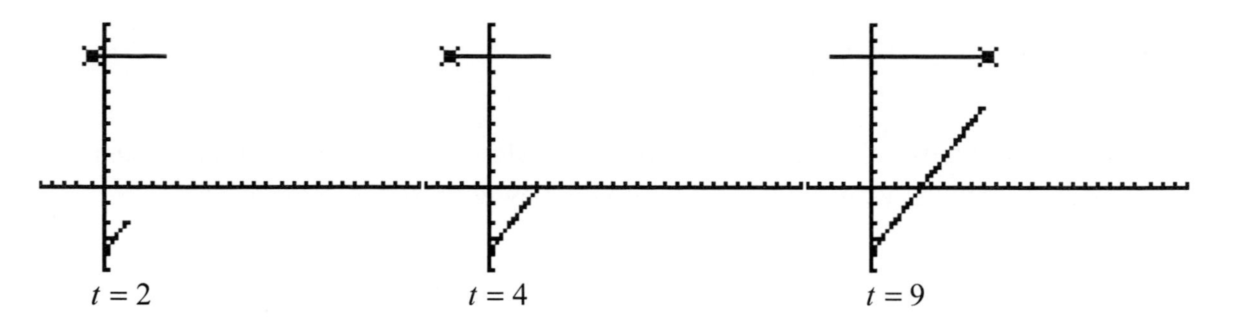

Questions to ask the students:

5. Where is the velocity graph when the object is moving to the left? What are the values of velocity when the object is moving left?
6. Where is the velocity graph when the object pauses? What is the value of the velocity when the object pauses?
7. Where is the velocity graph when the object is moving to the right? What are the values of the velocity when the object is moving right?

Using **TRACE** button you can investigate the answers to these questions:

5. The velocity graph is below the x-axis. The values of the velocity are negative.
6. At $t = 4$ the velocity graph is at the x-axis. At $t = 4$ the value of the velocity is 0.
7. The velocity graph is above the x-axis. The values of the velocity are positive.

This activity is only a demonstration of the properties and relationship of position and velocity functions. To mathematically prove the relationships it would now be necessary to complete a full analysis of the position function:

$x(t) = .5t^2 - 4t + 5$
$x'(t) = v(t) = t - 4$
when $t = 0$, $x(0) = 5$
when $t = 4$, $v(t) = 0$
when $0 < t < 4$, $v(t) < 0$
when $t > 4$, $v(t) > 0$
for $t > 4$ the velocity, $v(t)$, is always greater than 0, so the object never moves to the left again.

This algebraic analysis allows us to determine exactly when the object pauses and whether it ever moves to the left again and establishes the relationship between position and velocity.

This activity is intended for you, the teacher, to use to motivate your students and help them understand the algebraic analysis. Students do not have to become proficient with the calculator analysis.

Extensions:

1. If the object is to move along the x-axis use $y = 0$. However, the x-axis on the screen may interfere with the view of the object, so you may wish to delete the axes **(2nd ZOOM) FORMAT**

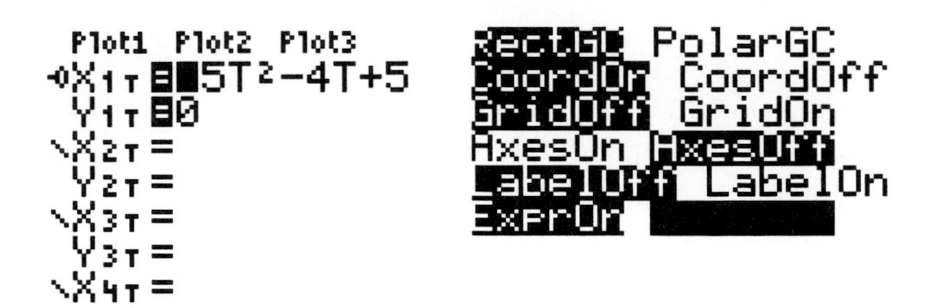

2. If the object is to move in a vertical direction (for example along the line x=2) reverse the x and y values for the position function and adjust the window.

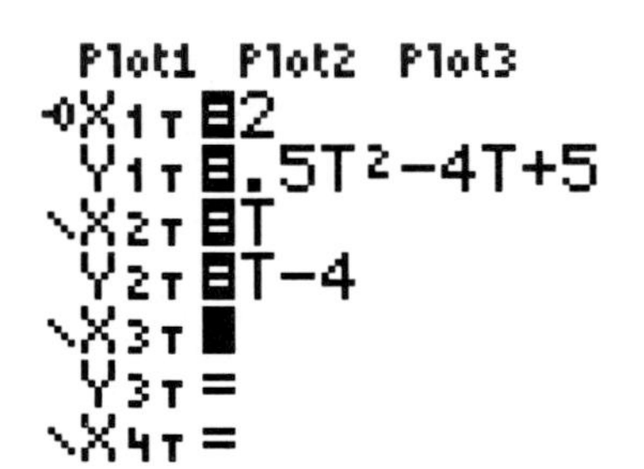

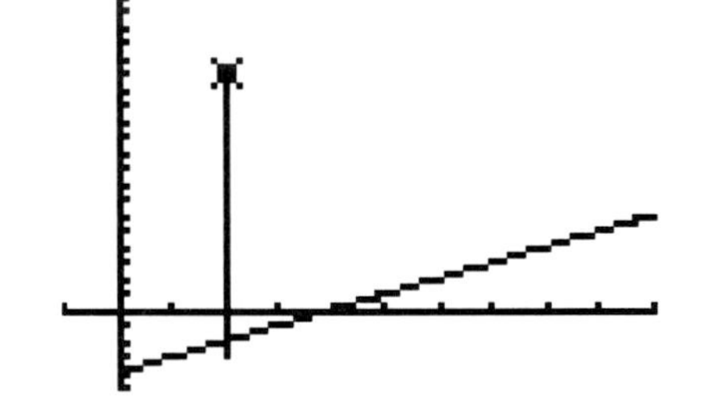

A snap shot showing the vertical path and velocity function at t=10

```
WINDOW
 Tmin=0
 Tmax=10
 Tstep=.1
 Xmin=-1
 Xmax=10
 Xscl=1
↓Ymin=-5
```

```
WINDOW
↑Tstep=.1
 Xmin=-1
 Xmax=10
 Xscl=1
 Ymin=-5
 Ymax=20
 Yscl=1
```

Multiple-Choice Questions–Calculus AB/BC Topics

*1. Let f be the function with derivative given by $f'(x) = \frac{1}{2}e^x \cos(x)$. How many relative extrema does f have on the interval $-2 < x < 6$?

A. 0 B. 1 C. 2 D. 3 E. 4

2. Let f be a function that is differentiable on the open interval $(-2,3)$. If $f(-2) = 4$, $f(3) = -6$, which of the following must be true?

I. for some c, $-2 < c < 3$, $f(c) = 0$
II. for some c, $-2 \le c \le 3$, $f'(c) = -2$
III. for some c, $-2 < c < 3$, $f'(c) = 0$

A. II, III B. I, II C. I, III D. I, II, III E. none

3. What is the maximum area of a rectangle inscribed between the graphs of $y = 4 - x^2$ and $y = x^2 - 8$, with sides parallel to x and y axes?

A. $\sqrt{2}$
B. $2\sqrt{2}$
C. $8\sqrt{2}$
D. $16\sqrt{2}$
E. $32\sqrt{2}$

4. If function f is defined by $f(x) = x^3 - 3x^2 - 9x$, then the minimum value of f on the interval $[-2, 4]$ is

A. 5
B. 0
C. -2
D. -20
E. -27

5. The graph for $f'(x), -5 < x < 5$, is shown below.

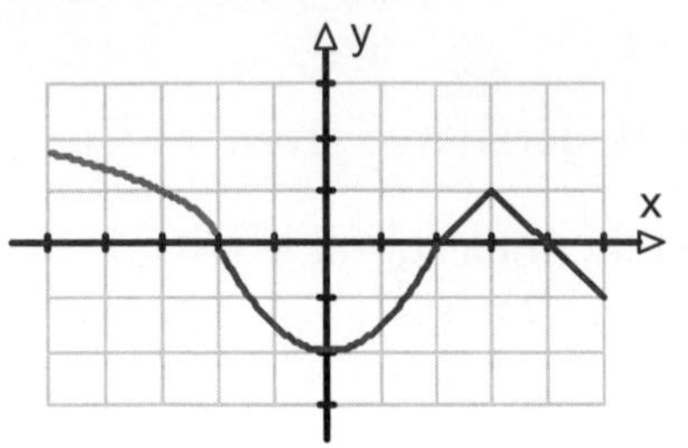

On which intervals is function $f(x)$ both increasing and concave up?

A. $-5 < x < -2$
B. $-2 < x < 2$
C. $2 < x < 3$
D. $2 < x < 5$
E. $0 < x < 3$

6. Let function f be a continuous function on the interval $[-3,1]$ and twice differentiable except at $x = -1$. The table below gives some properties of $f'(x)$ and $f''(x)$.

x	-3	$-3 < x < -2$	-2	$-2 < x < -1$	-1	$-1 < x < 0$	0	$0 < x < 1$	1
$f'(x)$	-10	Negative	0	Negative	d.n.e.	Positive	0	Negative	-2
$f''(x)$	24	Positive	0	Negative	d.n.e	Negative	?	Negative	-2

Which of the following statements are true?

I. f is concave down on $-3 < x < -2$.
II. f has a relative minimum at $x = -1$.
III. $f''(0) < 0$

A. I only
B. II only
C. III only
D. I and II only
E. II and III only

*7. A particle moves along the x-axis so that that is position at time $t, 1 < t < 6$, is given by $x(t) = \sin\left(\frac{1}{2}x\right)\ln(x)$. For what values of t is the particle decreasing its speed?

A. $1 < t < 1.770$

B. $1.770 < t < 3.870$

C. $3.870 < t \leq 4.818$

D. $1.770 < t \leq 4.418$

E. $3.870 < t < 6$

8. The graph for $f''(x), -4 < x < 8$, is shown below. **THIS GRAPH IS CONTINUOUS.**

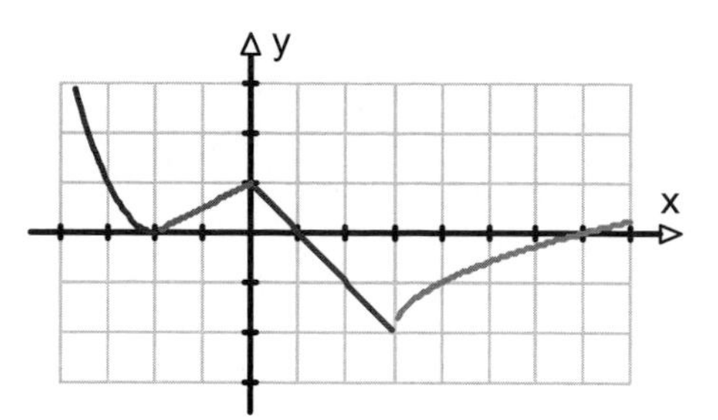

Function *f* has a maximum point at $x = c$ if $f'(c) = 0$ and

A. $c = -3$
B. $c = -2$
C. $c = 0$
D. $c = 2$
E. $c = 7$

9. The perimeter of a rectangle is decreasing at the rate of $2\ ^{cm}/_{sec}$ and the width is increasing at the rate of $3\ ^{cm}/_{sec}$. At what rate is the length of the rectangle changing at the instant when $l = 5$?

A. $2\ ^{cm}/_{sec}$ B. $-2\ ^{cm}/_{sec}$ C. not changing

D. $4\ ^{cm}/_{sec}$ E. $-4\ ^{cm}/_{sec}$

10. $\lim_{x\to 0}\left(\dfrac{x}{\arcsin(x)}\right) =$

A. 1
B. $\frac{\pi}{2}$
C. 0
D. $-\frac{\pi}{2}$
E. -1

11. $\lim_{x\to\infty}(3x-1)^{\frac{2}{x}} =$

A. 0
B. 1
C. e
D. e^2
E. ∞

12. Which of the following statements are true?

I. 4^x grows at a faster rate than 3^x.
II. x^{200} grows at a slower rate than e^{2x}.
III. $\log_2(x)$ grows at the same rate as $\log_{100}(x)$.

A. I only
B. I and II only
C. II and III only
D. I and III only
E. I, II, and III

Free-Response Questions–Calculus AB/BC Topics

1. Let function f be twice differentiable for all real numbers. The table below gives some properties of $f'(x)$ and $f''(x)$ for selected x-values in the closed interval $[-4,4]$.

x	-4	$-4<x<-2$	-2	$-2<x<0$	0	$0<x<2$	2	$2<x<4$	4
$f'(x)$	-13	Negative	-11	Negative	-10	Negative	-11	Negative	-13
$f''(x)$	9	Positive	4	Positive	0	Negative	-4	Negative	-9

a. If $f(2)=20$, write an equation for the line tangent to the graph of f at $x=2$. Use this tangent line to estimate $f(3)$. Is this approximation greater than or less than the actual value of $f(3)$? Give a reason for your answer.

b. Find the value of x on the closed interval $[-4,4]$ at which f attains its absolute maximum. Explain your answer.

c. Find all values of x on the open interval $(-4,4)$ at which the graph of f has an inflection point. Justify your answer.

d. If function f represents the position of a particle on a vertical line and if x represents time, then name a time interval when the particle is increasing its speed. Justify your answer.

2. A particle moves along the x-axis so that at time $t \geq 0$ its position is given by $x(t) = t^3 - 2t^2 + t + 3$.

a. When is the particle at rest?

b. When is the particle moving to the left? Justify your answer.

c. What is the acceleration of the particle at $t = 2$?

d. What is the maximum acceleration attained by the particle on the interval $0 \leq t \leq 4$? Justify your answer.

3. The graph below shows the graph of f', the derivative of a function f. The domain of f is the set of all real numbers such that $-5 \le x \le 8$.

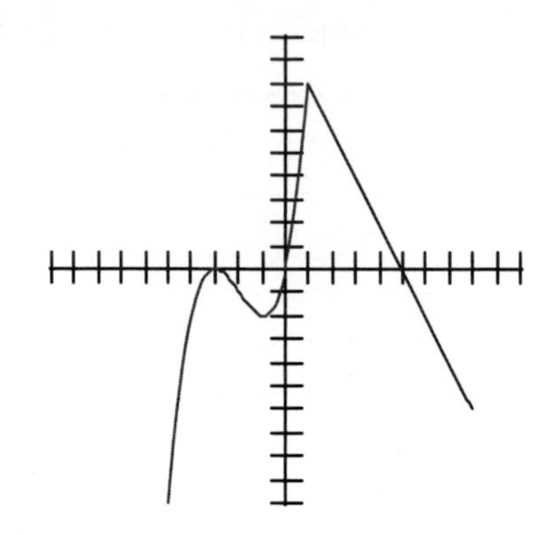

The graph of f'

a. For what values of x does f have a relative extremum? Identify each x as a relative maximum or relative minimum. Justify your answer.

b. Identify the interval of x-values where f is concave up. Justify your answer.

c. If $f(2) = 3$, use the information in the graph to sketch the function on the interval $2 \le x \le 8$. Use the axes provided.

Solutions to Sample Questions

Solutions to Multiple-Choice Questions

*1. D Graph $f'(x)=\frac{1}{2}e^{x}\cos(x)$ in the window $-2\le x\le 6, -3.1\le y\le 3.1$

There are two apparent places where the graph crosses the x-axis, but there is also a zero in the interval $-2<x<-1$. Since $f'(x)$ changes sign at these points, there are 3 relative extrema.

2. B Since f is differentiable on the open interval $(-2,3)$, the Mean Value Theorem applies and II is true. Since $f(-2)=4$ and $f(3)=-6$ the Intermediate Value Theorem applies and I is true. There is no information that makes III true.

3. D $\frac{1}{2}A(x)=x(12-2x^{2}), 0<x<\sqrt{6}$

$\left[\frac{1}{2}A(x)\right]'=12-6x^{2}$

$12-6x^{2}=0$

$x=\sqrt{2}$

Since A' changes from postivive to negative only at

$x=\sqrt{2}$, $x=\sqrt{2}$ is the location of the absolute max.

$A(x)=16\sqrt{2}$

4. E $f'(x)=3x^{2}-6x-9$

$f'(x)=0$

$x=-1$ or $x=3$

$x=-1$ is rel. max.

$f(-2)=-2$

$f(3)=-27$

$f(4)=-20$

min $=-27$

5. C Positive, increasing interval

6. E $f''(x)>0$ on $-3<x<-2$

$f'(x)$ changes from negative to positive at $x=-1$

$f''(0)<0$ because $x=0$ is a relative max

*7. B $x'(t) > 0$ and $x''(t) < 0$

8. D Second Derivative Test
$f'(c) = 0$ and $f''(c) < 0$

9. E.

$$p = 2l + 2w$$
$$\frac{dp}{dt} = 2\frac{dl}{dt} + 2\frac{dw}{dt}$$
$$-2 = 2\frac{dl}{dt} + 2(3)$$
$$\frac{dl}{dt} = -4\ {}^{cm}/_{sec}$$

10. A $\lim_{x\to 0} \frac{1}{\frac{1}{\sqrt{1-x^2}}} = \frac{1}{1}$

11. B. $y = (3x-1)^{\frac{2}{x}}$

$$\lim_{x\to\infty}(\ln y) = \lim_{x\to\infty}\left(\frac{2\ln(3x-1)}{x}\right)$$
$$\lim_{x\to\infty}(\ln y) = \lim_{x\to\infty}\left(\frac{-6}{x^2(3x-1)}\right)$$
$$\lim_{x\to\infty}(\ln y) = 0$$

If $\ln y \to 0$, then $y \to e^0$

12. E.

$$\lim_{x\to\infty}\left(\frac{4^x}{3^x}\right) = \lim_{x\to\infty}\left(\frac{4}{3}\right)^x = \infty$$
$$\lim_{x\to\infty}\left(\frac{x^{200}}{e^{2x}}\right) = \lim_{x\to\infty}\left(\frac{200!}{2^{200}e^{2x}}\right) = 0$$
$$\lim_{x\to\infty}\left(\frac{\log_2(x)}{\log_{100}(x)}\right) = \lim_{x\to\infty}\left(\frac{\ln x}{\ln 2}\cdot\frac{\ln 100}{\ln x}\right) = \frac{\ln 100}{\ln 2}$$

Solutions to Free-Response Questions

1. Let function f be twice differentiable for all real numbers. The table below gives some properties of $f'(x)$ and $f''(x)$ for selected x-values in the closed interval $[-4,4]$.

x	-4	$-4<x<-2$	-2	$-2<x<0$	0	$0<x<2$	2	$2<x<4$	4
$f'(x)$	-13	Negative	-11	Negative	-10	Negative	-11	Negative	-13
$f''(x)$	9	Positive	4	Positive	0	Negative	-4	Negative	-9

a. If $f(2)=20$, write an equation for the line tangent to the graph of f at $x=2$. Use this tangent line to estimate $f(3)$. Is this approximation greater than or less than the actual value of $f(3)$? Give a reason for your answer.

b. Find the value of x on the closed interval $[-4,4]$ at which f attains its absolute maximum. Explain your answer.

c. Find all values of x on the open interval $(-4,4)$ at which the graph of f has an inflection point. Justify your answer.

d. If function f represents the position of a particle on a vertical line and if x represents time, then name a time interval when the particle is increasing its speed. Justify your answer.

(a) $y=-11(x-2)+20$

$f(3)\approx -11(1)+20$

$f(3)\approx 9$

Approximation is greater than actual value. Because f is concave down on $0<x<4$, the tangent line lies above f.

$3\begin{cases}1: f(3)\approx 9\\ 1: \text{approximation greater than}\\ 1: \text{reason}\end{cases}$

(b) Absolute maximum at $x=-4$. Because $f'(x)<0$ on $[-4,4]$, $f(x)$ always decreases.

$2\begin{cases}1: x=-4\\ 1: \text{reason}\end{cases}$

(c) $x=0$ because $f''(x)$ changes signs.

$2\begin{cases}1: x=0\\ 1: \text{reason}\end{cases}$

(d) $0<x<2,\ 2<x<4,$ or $0<x<4$

$f'(x)<0$ and $f''(x)<0$

$2\begin{cases}1: \text{interval}\\ 1: \text{reason}\end{cases}$

2. A particle moves along the x-axis so that at time $t \geq 0$ its position is given by $x(t) = t^3 - 2t^2 + t + 3$.

   a. When is the particle at rest?

   b. When is the particle moving to the left? Justify your answer.

   c. What is the acceleration of the particle at $t = 2$?

   d. What is the maximum acceleration attained by the particle on the interval $0 \leq t \leq 4$? Justify your answer

---

Solution	Scoring
a. $x'(t) = v(t) = 3t^2 - 4t + 1 = 0$ $t = \frac{1}{3}, t = 3$	$2 \begin{cases} 1\text{: } v(t) = 0 \\ 1\text{: answers} \end{cases}$
b. $3t^2 - 4t + 1 < 0$ $\frac{1}{3} < t < 3$	$2 \begin{cases} 1\text{: sets } v(t) < 0 \\ 1\text{: correct interval} \end{cases}$
c. $x''(t) = a(t) = 6t - 4$ $a(2) = 8$	$2 \begin{cases} 1\text{: } a(t) \\ 1\text{: } a(2) \end{cases}$
d. $a'(t) = 6$ There are no critical points The maximum must be at one of the endpoints $a(0) = -4$ $a(4) = 20$ 20 is the maximum acceleration Or, since $a'(t) > 0$, a always increases. Therefore max must be at right endpoint.	$3 \begin{cases} 1\text{: interior analysis} \\ 1\text{: endpoint analysis} \\ 1\text{: answer} \end{cases}$

3. The graph below shows the graph of f', the derivative of a function f. The domain of f is the set of all real numbers such that $-5 \le x \le 8$.

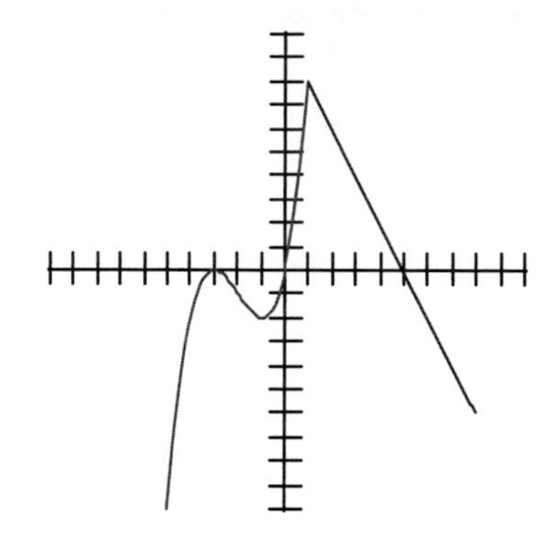

The graph of f'

a. For what values of x does f have a relative extremum? Identify each x as a relative maximum or relative minimum. Justify your answer.

b. Identify the interval of x-values where f is concave up. Justify your answer.

c. If $f(2) = 3$, use the information in the graph to sketch the function on the interval $2 \le x \le 8$. Use the axes provided.

---

a. $x = 0$ is a relative minimum

$f'(x)$ changes from negative to positive

$x = 5$ is a relative maximum

$f'(x)$ changes from positive to negative

$$4\begin{cases}1: x = 0\\ 1: \text{reason}\\ 1: x = 5\\ 1: \text{reason}\end{cases}$$

b. f is concave up $-5 < x < -3$

and $-1 < x < 1$

$f'(x)$ is increasing on those intervals

$$3\begin{cases}2: \text{correct intervals}\\ 1: \text{reason}\end{cases}$$

c.

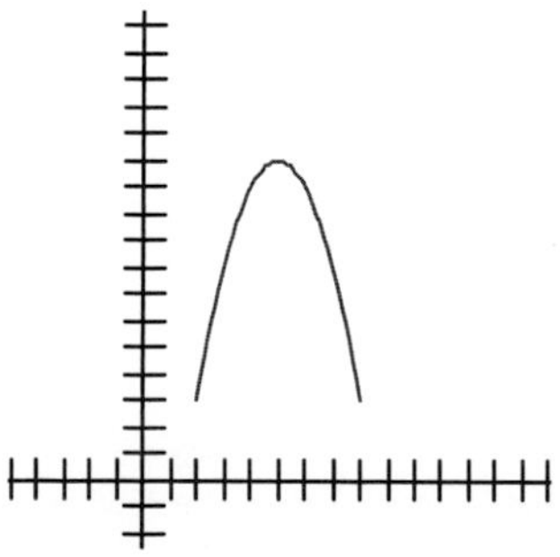

$$2\begin{cases}1: f(2) = f(8) = 3\\ 1: \text{ relative max } 2 < x < 8\end{cases}$$

Connect2Calculus Videos for Chapter 3

The Calculus Concepts Video's for Chapter 3: *(Calculus BC topics are in italic type)*
Some of the topics on the videos go beyond the scope of Calculus AB/BC, but would be worth watching as an application of calculus

5.0	**Relations and Change in Two and Three Dimensions**
5.1	Implicit Differentiation (this topic is from Chapter 2)
5.2	Related Rates in Two Dimensions
5.3	Related Rates in Three Dimensions (not in the Topic Outline for Calculus AB/BC)
6.0	**Theorems About Functions**
6.1	The Intermediate Value Theorem
6.2	Rolle's Theorem
6.3	The Mean Value Theorem
7.0	**Curves, Lines, and Limits: Tools from Calculus**
7.1	Linear Approximation
7.2	*L' Hospital's Rule*
7.3	Newton's Method (not in the Topic Outline for Calculus AB/BC)
8.0	**Tools to Describe Functions**
8.1	The Extreme Value Theorem
8.2	Increasing and Decreasing Functions
8.3	Second Derivatives: Concavity
9.0	**Graphing with the Calculus**
9.1	Reviewing Tools for Graphing
9.2	Using Calculus to Describe a Graph
9.3	Using Graphs and Calculus to Describe Functions
10.0	**Optimization: Using Derivatives**
10.1	Finding Maximum and Minimum Values
10.2	Rates of Change: Chemical Reactions
10.3	Rates of Change and Optimization

CHAPTER 4: INTEGRATION

Correlations

The section by section correspondence to the Topic Outline for Calculus AB and the Topic Outline for Calculus BC (*Calculus BC topics are in italic type*) is:

AP Topic	Chapter.Section	Pages
II. Derivatives **Computation of derivatives** • Knowledge of derivatives of basic functions, including …exponential, logarithmic ….functions	4.8	416-426
III. Integrals **Interpretations and properties of definite integrals**		
• Definite integrals as a limit of Riemann sums	4.4	369-383
• Definite integral of the rate of change of a quantity over an interval interpreted as the change of the quantity over the interval: $\int_a^b f'(x)\,dx = f(b) - f(a)$	4.4, 4.5	369-383, 383-393
• Basic properties of definite integrals (examples include additivity and linearity)	4.4	369-383
III. Integrals **Applications of integrals** Appropriate integrals are used in a variety of applications to model physical, biological, or economics situations. Although only a sampling of applications can be included in any specific course, students should be able to adapt their knowledge and techniques to solve other similar application problems. Whatever applications are chosen, the emphasis is on using the method of setting up an approximating Riemann sum and representing its limit as a definite integral. To provide a common foundation, specific applications should include using the integral of a rate of change to give accumulated change, finding the area of a	4.1, 4.3, 4.4, 4.5	344-354, 362-369, 369-383, 383-393

region… the average value of a function, and the distance traveled by a particle along a line….		

AP Topic	Chapter.Section	Pages
III. Integrals **Fundamental Theorem of Calculus** • Use of the Fundamental Theorem to evaluate definite integrals • Use of the Fundamental Theorem to represent a particular antiderivative, and the analytical and graphical analysis of functions so defined.	4.5 4.5	383-393 383-393
III. Integrals **Techniques of antidifferentiation** • Antiderivatives following directly from derivatives of basic functions • Antiderivatives by substitution of variables (including change of limits for definite integrals)….	4.1 4.6	344-354 393-402
III. Integrals **Applications of antidifferentiation** • Find specific antiderivatives using initial conditions, including applications to motion along a line	4.1	344-354
III. Integrals **Numerical approximations to definite integrals** Use of Riemann sums (using left, right, and midpoint evaluation points) and trapezoidal sums to approximate definite integrals of functions represented algebraically, graphically, and by tables of values	4.3, 4.4, 4.7	362-369, 369-383, 402-416

Textbook Section	AP Topic
4.1 Antiderivatives	**III. Integrals** **Applications of integrals** Appropriate integrals are used in a variety of applications to model physical, biological, or economics situations. Although only a sampling of applications can be included in any specific course, students should be able to adapt their knowledge and techniques to solve other similar application problems. Whatever applications are chosen, the emphasis is on using the method of setting up an approximating Riemann sum and representing its limit as a definite integral. To provide a common foundation, specific applications should include using the integral of a rate of change to give accumulated change, finding the area of a region… the average value of a function, and the distance traveled by a particle along a line…. **Techniques of antidifferentiation** • Antiderivatives following directly from derivatives of basic functions **Applications of antidifferentiation** • Find specific antiderivatives using initial conditions, including applications to motion along a line
4.3 Area	**III. Integrals** **Applications of integrals** Appropriate integrals are used in a variety of applications to model physical, biological, or economics situations. Although only a sampling of applications can be included in any specific course, students should be able to adapt their knowledge and techniques to solve other similar application problems. Whatever applications are chosen, the emphasis is on using the method of setting up an approximating Riemann sum and representing its limit as a definite integral. To provide a common foundation, specific applications should include using the integral of a rate of change to give accumulated change, finding the area of a region… the average value of a function, and the distance traveled by a particle along a line…. **Numerical approximations to definite integrals** Use of Riemann sums (using left, right, and midpoint evaluation points) and trapezoidal sums to approximate definite integrals of functions represented algebraically, graphically, and by tables of values

<table>
<tr><th>Textbook Section</th><th colspan="2">AP Topic</th></tr>
<tr><td>4.4 The Definite Integral</td><td>III.</td><td>Integrals

Interpretations and properties of definite integrals<ul><li>Definite integrals as a limit of Riemann sums</li><li>Definite integral of the rate of change of a quantity over an interval interpreted as the change of the quantity over the interval:
$$\int_a^b f'(x)\,dx = f(b) - f(a)$$</li><li>Basic properties of definite integrals (examples include additivity and linearity)</li></ul>Applications of integrals Appropriate integrals are used in a variety of applications to model physical, biological, or economics situations. Although only a sampling of applications can be included in any specific course, students should be able to adapt their knowledge and techniques to solve other similar application problems. Whatever applications are chosen, the emphasis is on using the method of setting up an approximating Riemann sum and representing its limit as a definite integral. To provide a common foundation, specific applications should include using the integral of a rate of change to give accumulated change, finding the area of a region… the average value of a function, and the distance traveled by a particle along a line….

Numerical approximations to definite integrals Use of Riemann sums (using left, right, and midpoint evaluation points) and trapezoidal sums to approximate definite integrals of functions represented algebraically, graphically, and by tables of values</td></tr>
<tr><td>4.5 The Fundamental Theorem of Calculus</td><td>III.</td><td>Integrals

Interpretations and properties of definite integrals<ul><li>Definite integral of the rate of change of a quantity over an interval interpreted as the change of the quantity over the interval:
$$\int_a^b f'(x)\,dx = f(b) - f(a)$$</li></ul>Applications of integrals Appropriate integrals are used in a variety of applications to model physical, biological, or economics situations. Although only a sampling of applications can be included in any specific course, students should be able to adapt their knowledge and techniques to solve other similar application problems. Whatever applications are chosen, the emphasis is on using the method of setting up an approximating Riemann sum and representing its limit as a definite integral. To provide a common foundation, specific applications should include using the integral of a rate of change to give accumulated change, finding the area of a region… the average value of a function, and the distance traveled by a particle along a line….</td></tr>
</table>

	Fundamental Theorem of Calculus • Use of the Fundamental Theorem to evaluate definite integrals • Use of the Fundamental Theorem to represent a particular antiderivative, and the analytical and graphical analysis of functions so defined.
4.6 Integration by Substitution	**III. Integrals** **Techniques of antidifferentiation** • Antiderivatives by substitution of variables (including change of limits for definite integrals)….
4.7 Numerical Integration	**III. Integrals** **Numerical approximations to definite integrals** Use of Riemann sums (using left, right, and midpoint evaluation points) and trapezoidal sums to approximate definite integrals of functions represented algebraically, graphically, and by tables of values
4.8 The Natural Logarithm as an Integral	**II. Derivatives** **Computation of derivatives** • Knowledge of derivatives of basic functions, including …exponential, logarithmic ….functions

Vocabulary and Section Notes

Vocabulary used in the Topic Outline for Calculus AB and the Topic Outline for Calculus BC (*Calculus BC topics are in italic type*) include:

Antiderivatives
Area
Area function
Average value of a function
Constant of integration
Definite integral
Differential equation
Function defined as an integral
Fundamental Theorem of Calculus
Indefinite integral
Integrand
Integration by substitution
Integral Mean Value Theorem
Left-hand endpoint
Lower-limit of integration
Midpoint Rule
Natural logarithm
Regular partition
Riemann sum
Right-hand endpoint
Signed area
Simpson's Rule (Optional)
Total area
Trapezoidal Rule
Upper-limit of integration
Variable of integration

Section notes for the Calculus AB Course:

Section 4.1, 4.4, 4.5: The antiderivative relationships of position, velocity, and acceleration are developed throughout this chapter. Please read "Teacher's Notes: Position, Velocity, and Acceleration" for more information and details.

Section 4.2 (Sums and Sigma Notation): This is a review of precalculus topics. Sigma notation is used in the development of the Riemann Sum and Infinite Series. Mathematical Induction is not part of the Topic Outline for Calculus AB, and is only used for a few exercises (33, 34, and 40).

Section 4.7 (Numerical Integration): Simpson's Rule is not part of the Topic Outline for Calculus AB but many teachers chose to include it in their courses (Optional topic). Error Bounds for Numerical Integration is not part of the Topic Outline for Calculus AB.

Section notes for the Calculus BC Course:

Section 4.1, 4.4, 4.5: The antiderivative relationships of position, velocity, and acceleration are developed throughout this chapter. Please read "Teacher's Notes: Position, Velocity, and Acceleration" for more information and details.

Section 4.2 (Sums and Sigma Notation): This is a review of precalculus topics. Sigma notation is used in the development of the Riemann Sum and Infinite Series. Mathematical Induction is not part of the Topic Outline for Calculus BC, and is only used for a few exercises (33, 34, and 40).

Section 4.7 (Numerical Integration): Simpson's Rule is not part of the Topic Outline for Calculus BC but many teachers chose to include it in their courses (Optional topic). Error Bounds for Numerical Integration is not part of the Topic Outline for Calculus BC.

Student Activity: Another 20 Minute Ride

Teacher's Notes:

This activity is a follow-up to the 20 Minute Ride. It is designed to give students a practical application for Riemann sums. Recent questions on the Free-Response portion of the AP Exam have used the definite integral as an accumulator (see 2004 AB1 or 2006 AB2). It is no longer sufficient for students to view a definite integral as the area under a curve. Now, they must be able to see a rate of change over time yielding an amount.

As the students work out the approximations using the trapezoids or sub-intervals, have them show the work by hand. To score points on the Free-Response portion of the AP Exam, students are required to show the setup that lead to their answers. They can leave the answer in unsimplified format. Students cannot use any calculator programs that compute Riemann sums or trapezoidal approximations. In fact, in recent years, questions dealing with this topic have used unequal intervals to test students' understanding of this topic (see 2003 AB3). Most calculator programs cannot use intervals of unequal width.

You might need to help students figure the appropriate unit. The product of each rectangle represents time (width) by speed (height) which gives total distance traveled. The unit is $\frac{\text{miles}}{\text{hour}} \times \text{time(minutes)} \times \frac{1 \text{ hour}}{60 \text{ minutes}} = \text{miles}$.

Student Worksheet

As a passenger in a car, take a 20 minute ride with a responsible adult. At the end of each minute, record your speed (to the nearest mile/hour). Spend no more than half your time on the freeway and observe all traffic laws.

Time	0	1	2	3	4	5	6
Distance							
Time	7	8	9	10	11	12	13
Distance							
Time	14	15	16	17	18	19	20
Distance							

Make a connected scatter plot of your results on the grid below. Let t (time) be the horizontal axis and v (velocity) be the vertical axis. Let each horizontal unit represent 1 min and each vertical unit represent 5 miles per hour.

FOLLOW-UP FOR ANOTHER TWENTY MINUTE RIDE

1. What does the area under the graph represent? Be specific. Use dimensional analysis to support your response.

2. Use four trapezoids of equal width to approximate the area under the graph.

3. Use a mid-point Riemann sum with five subintervals of equal width to approximate the distance traveled.

4. Use a left Riemann sum with five subintervals of equal width to approximate the distance traveled.

5. Use a right Riemann sum with five subintervals of equal width to approximate the distance traveled.

6. What was the average speed over the 20 minutes?

7. Over what intervals did the velocity increase?

8. Over what intervals was the acceleration negative?

9. Over what intervals did the velocity decrease?

Student Activity: What's an Accumulator?

Teacher's Notes:

The Riemann Sum and its relationship to the definite integral are used to develop the concept of area between a curve and the x-axis. This concept can be extended to use the definite integral as an accumulator, that is, the definite integral can be used to calculate a total value over an interval.

Consider this:

The rate of fuel consumption, in lbs/second, for a booster rocket motor, during a space shuttle launch is given by a differentiable function R of time t. The graph of $R(t)$ for the first 60 seconds after launch is

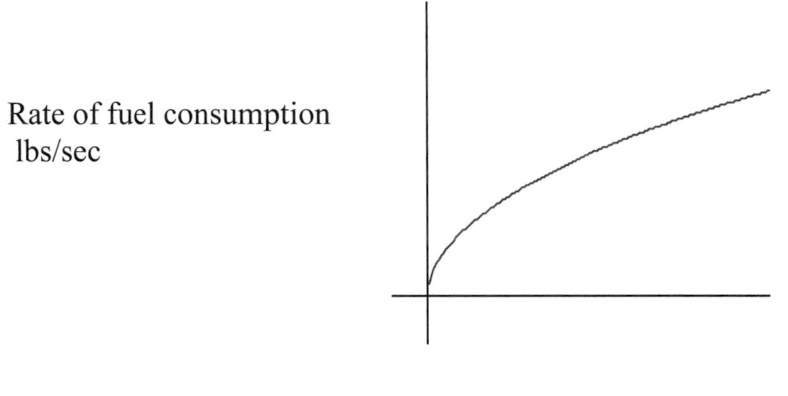

Time (secs)
$0 \le t \le 60$

If any time sub-interval $[a,b]$ of $[0,60]$ is divided into n equal pieces, then the width of each subinterval is $\Delta t = \frac{b-a}{n} \cdot {}^{\text{sec}}\!/_{\text{subinterval}}$. If t_i is any time in a subinterval then $R(t_i)\Delta t$ (the area of a rectangle where $b = \Delta t$ and $h = R(t_i)$) calculates ${}^{\text{lbs}}\!/_{\text{sec}} \cdot {}^{\text{sec}}\!/_{\text{subinterval}}$ or ${}^{\text{lbs of fuel consumed}}\!/_{\text{subinterval}}$ during the subinterval that includes t_i and $\lim_{n\to\infty}\sum_{i=1}^{\infty} R(t_i)\Delta t = \int_a^b R(t)\,dt$ would be the total pounds of fuel consumed between time a and time b. The definite integral $\int_0^{60} R(t)\,dt$ would represent the total pounds of fuel consumed by the booster motor during the first 60 seconds after launch.

This application of the Riemann Sum/definite integral can be generalized to allow the use of the definite integral (when $R(t_i)\Delta t$ makes sense) in many more ways than just the area between a curve and the x-axis.

For example:

Copper is being extracted from a mine at the rate, in tons of copper per day, given by $C'(x) = 10e^{-0.03t}$. If C is measured in tons of copper and t in days since the opening of the mine, how much copper is mined in the first 30 days?

Since the units for $C'(t)dt$ are $\frac{\text{tons of copper}}{\text{day}} \cdot \text{day} = \text{tons of copper}$, then $\int_0^{30} C'(t)dt$ represents the total amount of copper (tons) taken from the mine during the first 30 days.

$\int_0^{30} C'(t)dt = 197.810$ tons of copper during the first 30 days.

Another example:

A pizza, heated to a temperature of 325 degrees Fahrenheit $({}^0F)$, is taken out of an oven and placed in a $70^0 F$ room at time $t = 0$ minutes. The temperature of the pizza is changing at a rate of $T'(t) = -100e^{-0.4t}$ degrees Fahrenheit per minute. To the nearest degree, what is the temperature of the pizza at time $t = 10$ minutes?

The units for $T'(t)dt$ are $\frac{{}^\circ\text{Farenheit}}{\text{minute}} \cdot \text{minute} = {}^\circ\text{Farenheit}$ and $\int_0^{10} -100e^{-0.4t}dt$ represents the total change in the temperature of the pizza during the first 10 minutes. This can be extended to finding the temperature of the pizza after 10 minutes by using the Fundamental Theorem of Calculus. Although it is possible to find the antiderivative of the rate of change, it is more efficient to find the value of $T(10) = T(0) + \int_0^{10} -100e^{-0.4t)}dt$ using a calculator. The answer is $79.579^0 F$.

Free-response question 5, at the end of this chapter, asks students to calculate an accumulated change in two different ways. In part (c) students are asked to approximate the value of $\int_4^9 s(t)dt$ using a right-hand Riemann sum and then explain what the definite integral represents. In part (e) students are asked to use a function to find the value of $\int_4^9 S(t)dt$.

There are two Multiple-Choice questions on the 2003 AP Calculus exam (AB84 and BC80) and one on the 1998 exam (AB9/BC9) that ask students to apply this concept.

Past free-response questions have used a variety of methods to represent the rate function. Sometimes the rate function is given as a formula (1996, 2002, and 2005) and so the students need to evaluate $\int_a^b R(t)dt$. In other years (1999, 2006) only a table of values of $R(t)$ is given. The students are asked to approximate $\int_a^b R(t)dt$ using any of the approximation (left-hand, right-hand, mid-point and trapezoidal) methods that are part of the Topic Outline for Calculus AB and the Topic Outline for Calculus BC.

The definite integral as an accumulator has become an important topic on the AP Calculus exam and there is usually at least one question that asks students to apply this concept when solving the problem.

Student Worksheet

a) Sketch a graph that might represent the given relationship, including possible values for t and y on their axes
b) Pick an interval of values on the t-axis and draw a rectangle on the graph that encloses the area between the graph and the t-axis
c) Write a Riemann Sum for the given relationship (include units).
d) If the Riemann Sum is reasonable, write a definite integral to represent the relationship. Use correct units to explain its meaning
e) For any relationship where the Riemann Sum in unreasonable, suggest a change of units that could create a meaningful Riemann Sum and then repeat steps a – e.

(1). t: time (days); y: daily television set sales (sets/day): S(t)

(2). t: time (hours); y: velocity (miles/hour): V(t)

(3). t: time (years); y: high school graduates (thousands): G(t)

(4). t: time (years); y: birth rate (births/year) (thousands): B(t)

(5). t: time (days); y: price of cup of coffee ($/cup): P(t)

(6). t: time (min); y: rate of change of temperature (degrees F/min): T(t)

Some partial solutions:

(1*c*) $\lim_{n\to\infty}\sum_{i=1}^{n} S(t_i)\Delta t\left(\text{sets}/_{\text{day}}\right)(\text{day})$;

(1*d*) $\int_a^b S(t)dt$ total number of sets sold on the interval $[a,b]$

(2c) $\lim_{n\to\infty}\sum_{i=1}^{n} V(t_i)\Delta t\ \left(\text{miles}/_{\text{hour}}\right)(\text{hour})$

(2d) $\int_a^b V(t)dt$ total miles traveled on the time interval $[a,b]$

(3e). x: (years); y: graduation rate (graduates/year). New expressions:

(3c) $\lim_{n\to\infty}\sum_{i=1}^{n} G(t_i)\Delta t\ \left(\text{graduates}/_{\text{year}}\right)(\text{year})$

(3d) $\int_a^b G(t)dt$ total graduates on the interval $[a,b]$

(4*c*) $\lim_{n\to\infty}\sum_{i=1}^{n} B(t_i)\Delta t\left(\text{births}/_{\text{year}}\right)(\text{year})$;

(4*d*) $\int_a^b B(t)dt$ total number of births on the interval $[a,b]$

(5e). x: time (days); y: money spent for coffee each day ($/day). New expressions:

(5c) $\lim_{n\to\infty}\sum_{i=1}^{n} P(t_i)\Delta t\ \left(\text{cost}/_{\text{cup}}\right)(\text{cups})$

(5d) $\int_a^b P(t)dt$ total amount of money spent for coffee on the interval $[a,b]$

(6c) $\lim_{n\to\infty}\sum_{i=1}^{n} T(t_i)\Delta t\left(\text{degrees}/_{\text{min}}\right)(\text{min})$

(6d) $\int_a^b T(t)dt$ total change of temperature (degrees) on the interval $[a,b]$

Teacher's Notes: Position, Velocity, and Acceleration

Teacher's Notes:

The relationship of the position, velocity and acceleration of an object when it is moving along a horizontal or vertical line form the basis for several multiple-choice or free-response questions on the AP Calculus Exams. A quick review of the multiple-choice questions on the 2003 Released AP Calculus Exam shows that there are four questions on the Calculus AB Exam and two questions on the Calculus BC Exam that explore the relationship of these three functions. Since 1995, every exam, except 1996, has included a free-response question involving these topics. The methods of presentation include functional formulas, the graph of one of the functions or a table of data for one of the functions. Some of the questions students are asked to answer are related to such topics as displacement over an interval of time, the total distance traveled on an interval of time, the maximum velocity attained on an interval of time, the relationship of speed, velocity and acceleration and, given an initial position and the velocity function, the position after an interval of time has elapsed. If students hope to be successful on the AP Calculus Exam, it is imperative that they be proficient with the various inter-relationships of these functions.

Calculus (3rd edition) explores the relationships of the position, velocity and acceleration of an object when it is moving along a horizontal or vertical line throughout the text. The development of the first relationship, between position and velocity, begins in 2.1 on page 150. Related exercises include problems like 31-36. Exercises in 33 and 34 in section 2.2 use tables of values to estimate the value of the velocity for specific values of t. Section 2.3 introduces acceleration and shows how to use the position function to find the velocity and acceleration functions. Exercises 25-28 and 29-32 ask the student to interpret the meaning of the sign of the velocity or acceleration. Sections 2.5, 2.6, and 2.7 also have exercises that ask students to find the velocity or acceleration functions and answer questions about them.

Development of the antiderivative relationships of position, velocity and acceleration begins in 4.1, page 351. Students use the traditional method of solution, which is to find an antiderivative of the velocity function, evaluate to find the value of the constant of integration and then find the position function, to solve exercises 47-52. Exercises 57-60 ask students to use tables of values to approximate the distance traveled and the acceleration of an object.

Overall change in position (displacement) and total distance traveled are discussed in 4.4, page 374, (Exercises 19 and 20). Since the student hasn't learned the Fundamental Theorem of Calculus, numerical approximations are used to calculate the value of the definite integral. The expression $\int_0^T v(t)\,dt$ is used to represent the displacement of any object, but students are not asked to find the displacement in the exercises.

In section 4.5, page 388 and 389, the expression $\int_0^T v(t)\,dt$ and the Fundamental Theorem of Calculus are used to calculate the distance fallen by an object and in the exercises, students are asked to find the position function, given velocity or acceleration functions and pertinent initial values. The solutions demonstrate traditional methods of finding the position function. Again, although displacement or distance traveled by an object is discussed in an example (Example 5.10), students are not asked to apply this concept in any exercises.

There are several instances where questions on the free-response portion of AP Calculus Exams (1997 AB1, 1998 AB3, 1999 AB1, 2000 AB2/BC2, 2002 AB3, 2003 AB2 and 2005 AB5) ask students to find either the total distance traveled by an object over an interval of time or to determine the displacement of the object over an interval of time. The expression $\int_0^T v(t)\,dt$ can be used to calculate the displacement from time $t = 0$ until $t = T$, but a more general expression would be to use $\int_a^b v(t)\,dt$ to find the displacement over the interval of time $[a, b]$. If students have access to their calculator, this value can be determined regardless of the format of the velocity function. Total distance traveled can be calculated by finding the value of the expression $\int_0^T |v(t)|\,dt$ or the more general expression $\int_a^b |v(t)|\,dt$.

To help students master these topics, the multiple-choice and free-response questions for Chapter 2, Chapter 3 and Chapter 4 all include questions about the relationship of position, velocity and acceleration.

Teacher's Notes: The End-Value Problem

Teacher's Notes:

Some questions on the AP Calculus Exam ask students to find the position of an object at a specified time t, given an initial position and velocity. In many cases, the velocity is in a form that does not allow the students to find an antiderivative, evaluate to find the value of the constant of integration and then find the position of the object at the given value of t. In these cases, it is necessary to find the relationship of position and velocity through the Fundamental Theorem of Calculus.

Typical problems usually include a given velocity function $v(t)$, with initial position given by $s(a)$, and students are asked to find the position of the object at time b. The Fundamental Theorem of Calculus says that

$$\int_a^b v(t)dt = s(b) - s(a) \text{ and so}$$

$$s(b) = s(a) + \int_a^b v(t)dt$$

This application can be generalized to include

$$v(b) = v(a) + \int_a^b a(t)dt \quad \text{or even} \quad f(b) = f(a) + \int_a^b f'(x)dx$$

One way to ask a question, using this concept might be:

A particle moves along the x-axis so that at any time $t > 0$, its acceleration is given by $a(t) = 2^{\ln(t)}$. If the velocity of the particle is 3 at time $t = 1$, find the velocity of the particle at time $t = 2$.

A. 0.462 B. 1.319 C. 2.555 D. 2.886 E. 4.319

The traditional solution would have students find the antiderivative $v(t)$, use $v(1) = 3$ to determine the value of the constant of integration, and then evaluate $v(t)$ at $t = 2$. Although this is an appropriate method of solution, it is impossible to find the antiderivative of $a(t) = 2^{\ln(t)}$ using the techniques of Calculus AB or Calculus BC.

However, if the student were to use a calculator it would be easy to determine the value of the expression: $v(2) = v(1) + \int_1^2 2^{\ln(t)}\, dt = 4.419208$ which is choice E.

Students are often asked to apply this technique to several seemingly different applications. In some of them traditional solution techniques can be used, but in others, the expression $s(b) = s(a) + \int_a^b v(t)\,dt$ or the more general statement $f(b) = f(a) + \int_a^b f'(x)dx$ (which demonstrates the relationship for any function and its derivative) is necessary to the solution of the problem. Consider this problem:

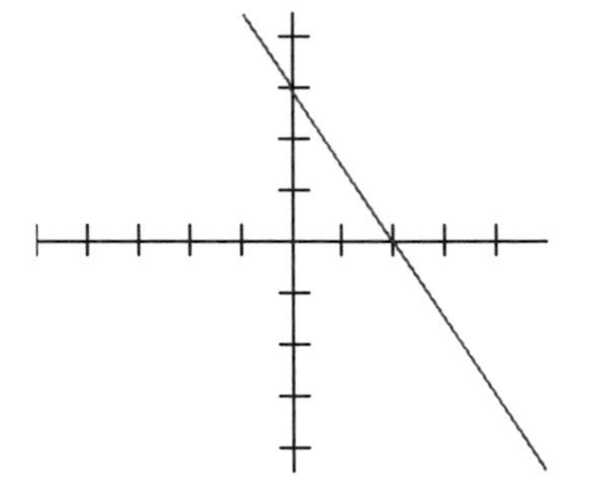

The graph of f', the derivative of f is the line shown in the figure above. If $f(0) = -2$, find $f(2)$.

The solution to this problem would be $f(2) = f(0) + \int_0^2 f'(x)dx = -2 + \int_0^2 f'(x)dx$ and the value of $\int_0^2 f'(x)dx$ can be determined by finding the area of the triangular region in the first quadrant bounded by the graph of $f'(x)$ and the axes.

$$f(2) = -2 + \int_0^2 f'(x)dx = -2 + \left(\frac{1}{2}\right)(3)(2) = -2 + 3 = 1$$

Another way to ask this question might include a table of data values like

t (sec)	0	2	4	6
a(t) (ft/sec^2)	4	7	5	6

The data for the acceleration $a(t)$ of a car from 0 to 6 seconds are given in the table above. If the velocity at $t = 0$ is 9 feet per second, find the approximate value of the velocity at $t = 6$, computed using a right-hand Riemann sum with three subintervals of equal length.

The solution can be represented by the expression $v(6) = v(0) + \int_0^6 a(t)dt = 9 + \int_0^6 a(t)dt$. Since there is no formula for the acceleration, the integral must be approximated with the right-hand Riemann sum. $v(6) = 9 + \int_0^6 a(t)dt = 9 + (2)(7) + (2)(5) + (2)(6) = 45$ ft/sec.

Another application of the Fundamental Theorem of Calculus might be:

The graph of a function f' is shown below. If $f(-1) = 2$ find $f(-3)$ and $f(2)$.

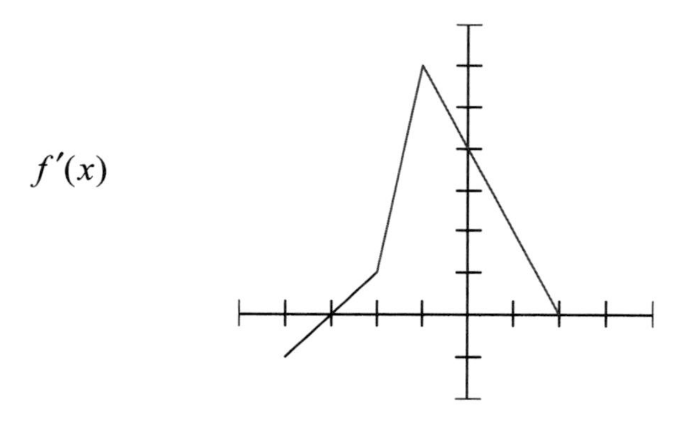

Since no explicit function for $f'(x)$ is given, it is easier to use the Fundamental Theorem of Calculus to find the requested values.

$$f(-3) = f(-1) + \int_{-1}^{-3} f'(x)\,dx\,.$$

This expression can be rewritten as

$f(-3) = f(-1) - \int_{-3}^{-1} f'(x)\,dx$ and it can be evaluated by finding the area of the triangular region from $x = -3$ to $x = -2$ and the trapezoidal region from $x = -2$ to $x = -1$.

$$f(-3) = 2 - \frac{1}{2}(1)(1) - \frac{1}{2}(1)(1+6) = -2$$

Similarly, $f(2) = f(-1) + \int_{-1}^{2} f'(x)\,dx = 2 + \frac{1}{2}(6)(3) = 11$

The 2003 Calculus AB Multiple-Choice Exam includes other examples of these types of problems (22 and 82). The 2003 Calculus BC Multiple-Choice Exam asks for similar procedures in problems 82 and 87. Free-response questions from the years 1999 AB1, 2002 AB3, 2003 AB2, 2004 AB3, 2005 AB5, and 2006 AB4/BC4 also used this technique.

Multiple-Choice Questions–Calculus AB/BC Topics

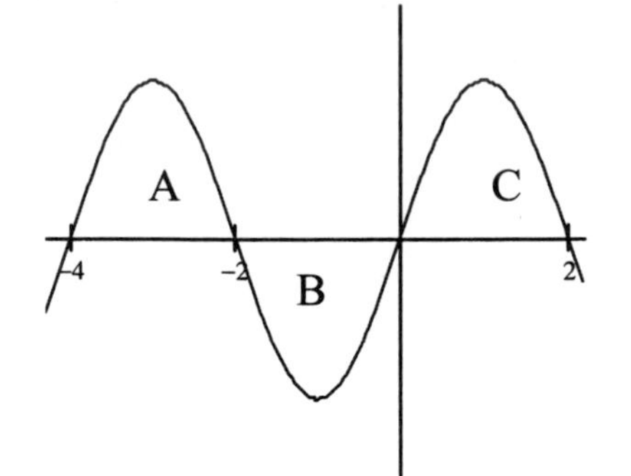

1. The regions A, B, and C in the figure above are bounded by the graph of the function f and the x-axis. If the area of each region is 3, what is the value of

$$\int_{-4}^{2} (f(x)+1)\,dx$$

A. 3 B. 4 C. 7 D. 9 E. 10

2. $$\frac{d}{dx}\left(\int_{3}^{x^3} e^{2t}\,dt\right)$$

A. e^{2x^3} B. e^{x^3} C. $\frac{1}{2}e^{2x^3} - \frac{1}{2}e^{3}$ D. $e^{2x^3} \cdot 3x^2$

E. $e^{x^3} \cdot 3x^2$

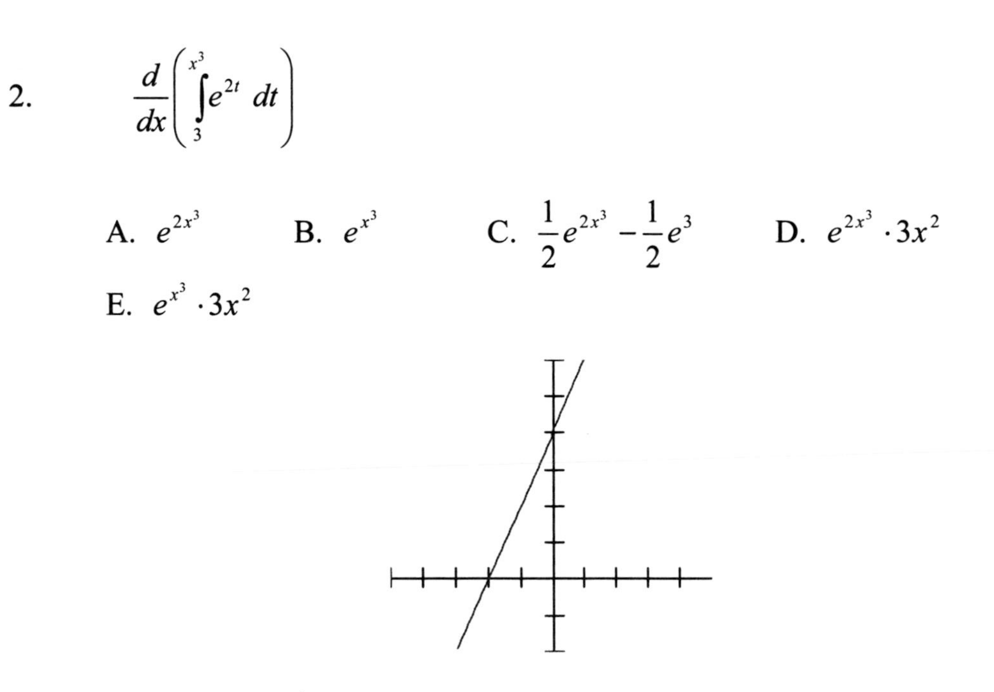

3. The graph of f', the derivative of f is the line shown in the figure above. If $f(0) = -2$, then $f(-2) =$

A. -10 B. -6 C. 0 D. 4 E. 6

*4. Let g be the function given by $g(x) = \int_0^x \cos(t^3)\, dt$ for $1 \le x \le 2$. On which of the following intervals is $g(x)$ decreasing?

A. $1.162 < x < 1.677$ B. $1 < x < 1.464$ C. $1.845 < x < 2$

D. $1.465 < x < 1.845$ E. $1 < x < 1.845$

*5. The velocity, in ft/sec, of a particle moving along the x-axis is given by the function $v(t) = e^t - t^2 e^t$. What is the average velocity of the particle from $t = 0$ to $t = 2$?

A. -3.195 B. -6.389 C. -23.167 D. -22.167 E. -52.723

6. The graph of a piecewise function f, $-4 \le t \le 4$, consists of two line segments and a semicircle as shown below.

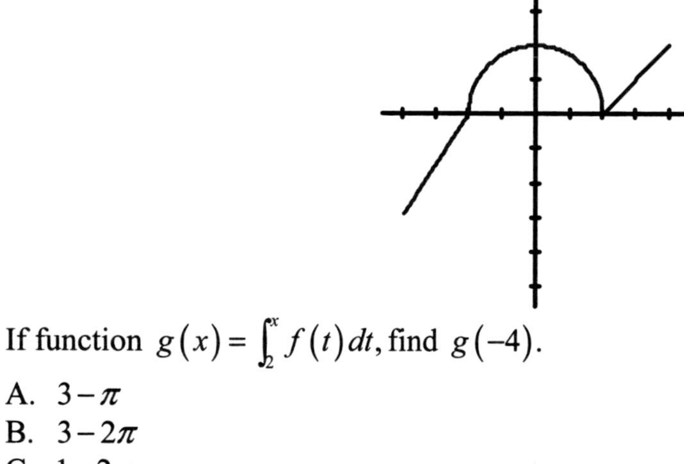

If function $g(x) = \int_2^x f(t)\,dt$, find $g(-4)$.

A. $3-\pi$
B. $3-2\pi$
C. $1-2\pi$
D. $2\pi-3$
E. $\pi-3$

7. A factory is currently producing $10\sqrt[3]{2t+1}$ machines per hour. If a day starts at $t = 0$, how many machines are produced in an 8-hour day?
A. 10
B. 16
C. 26
D. 121
E. 160

8. The function f is continuous on the closed interval $[-2,10]$ and has values given in the table below.

x	-2	0	3	4	7	9	10
$f(x)$	3	6	-1	2	8	4	-3

Using the subintervals $[-2,3],[3,7]$, and $[7,10]$, find the midpoint Riemann sum for $\int_{-2}^{10} f(x)\,dx$.

A. 18
B. 35
C. 50
D. 55
E. 95

*9. Let $g(x)$ be an antiderivative of $\frac{e^x}{x^2}$. If $g(3) = 0$, then $g(6) =$

A. 8.488 B. 8.975 C. 10.206

D. 11.206 E. 15.513

10. What is the value of $\int_{-1}^{5} f'(2t)\,dt$? ?

A. $2f(10) - 2f(-2)$
B. $\frac{1}{2}f(5) - \frac{1}{2}f(-1)$
C. $\frac{1}{2}f(10) - \frac{1}{2}f(-2)$
D. $f(10) - f(-2)$
E. $2f(5) - 2f(-1)$

*11. A particle moves on a horizontal line with velocity $v(t) = e^{-x}\cos(3x)$ feet per second. What is the total distance the particle moves in the first second?
A. 0.151
B. 0.208
C. 0.364
D. 0.403
E. 1.377

Free-Response Questions–Calculus AB/BC Topics

*1. A particle moves along the y-axis so that its velocity at any time $t \geq 0$ is given by $v(t) = -2t\cos(t)$. At time $t = 0$, the particle is at position $y(t) = 2$.

a. For what values of t, $0 \leq t \leq \frac{3\pi}{2}$, is the particle moving downward?

b. For what values of t, $0 \leq t \leq \frac{3\pi}{2}$, is the particle moving upward?

c. Find the acceleration of the particle at time $t = 5$. Is the velocity of the particle increasing or decreasing at $t = 5$? Why or why not?

d. Find the position $y(t)$ of the particle at time $t = 5$.

2. For $-4 \leq t \leq 2$ the graph of a function f is shown below. Let $g(x) = \int_0^{\frac{1}{2}x} f(t)\, dt$.

The graph of $f(t)$

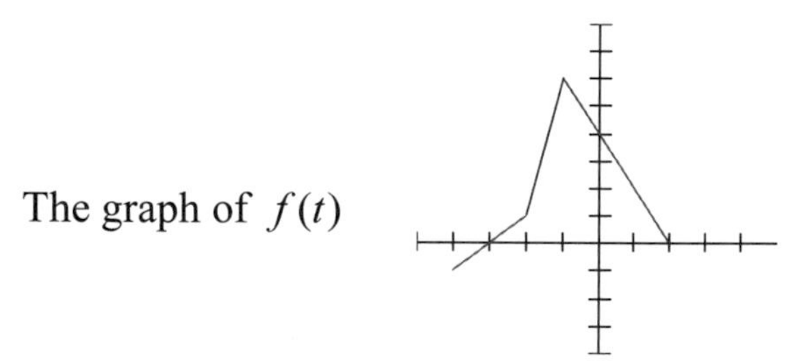

a. What is the domain of $g(x)$?

b. Compute, or state that it does not exist, $g(-2), g'(-2), g''(-2)$.

c. Find all values of x where $g(x)$ has a relative minimum. Justify your answer.

d. Find all values of x in the open interval $(-8, 4)$ at which the graph of g has a point of inflection.

3. The graph of $y = f(x)$, shown below, consists of three line segments and a semicircle.

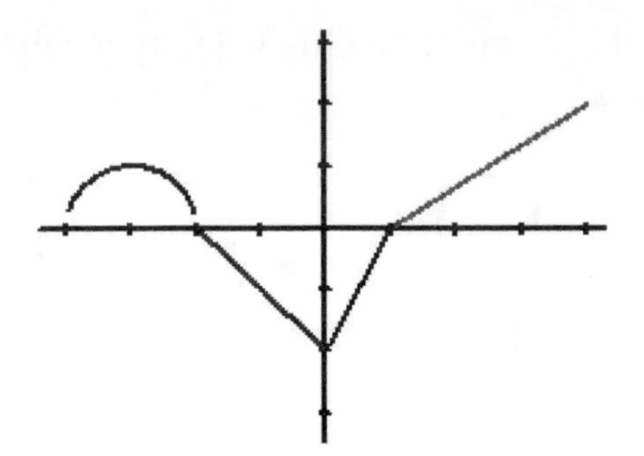

a. Find the average rate of change for function f over the interval $[-4, 4]$.

b. Find the average value of function f over the interval $[-4, 4]$.

Let function g be defined by $g(x) = \int_{-2}^{x} f(t)\,dt$ for all x in the closed interval $[-4, 4]$.

c. Which is larger $g(-4)$ or $g(-2)$? Explain why.

d. Write an equation for the line tangent to the graph of $y = g(x)$ at $x = 1$.

4. A car is traveling on a straight road with velocity 50 ft/sec at time $t = 0$. For $0 \le t \le 20$, the car's acceleration $a(t)$, in $ft/\sec^2$, is the piecewise linear function defined by the graph below.

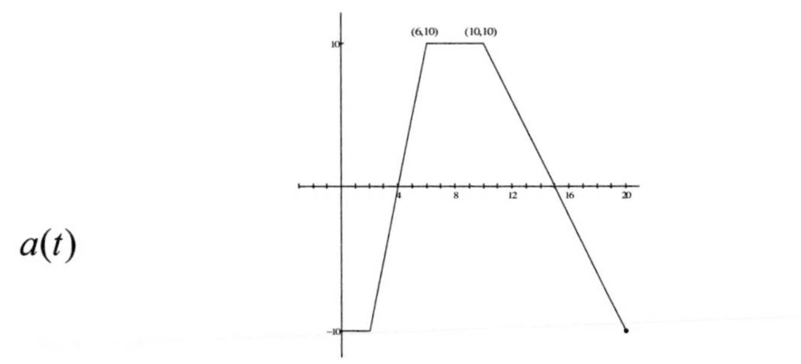

a. Is the velocity of the car increasing at $t = 2$ seconds? Why or why not?

b. Is the speed of the car increasing or decreasing at time $t = 2$? Give a reason for your answer.

c. At what time in the interval $0 < t \le 20$ is the velocity of the car 50 ft/sec?

d. On the time interval $0 \le t \le 20$, what is the car's absolute maximum velocity, in ft/sec? At what time does it occur? Why?

*5. The sales $s(t)$, in billions of dollars per year, of sporting goods for the years 1984 through 1989 are given in the table, where $t = 4$ corresponds to 1984

a. Use the data from the table to find an approximation to $s'(7)$. Show computations that lead to your answer. Using correct units, explain the meaning of $s'(7)$.

t time since 1980	s(t) Sales
4	26.4
5	27.4
6	30.6
7	33.9
8	42.1
9	45.2

b. Approximate the value of $\int_4^9 s(t)\,dt$ using a right Riemann sum with the five subintervals indicated by the data in the table. Using correct units, explain the meaning of $\int_4^9 s(t)\,dt$.

c. Explain the meaning of $\frac{1}{5}\int_4^9 s(t)\,dt$ in terms of sales of sporting goods. Indicate units of measure in your answer.

The sales per year from 1984 through 1989 can be approximated by $S(t) = 15.73(1.12)^t$.

d. Use $S(t)$ to approximate $S'(7)$.

e. Use $S(t)$ to approximate $\int_4^9 S(t)dt$.

Solutions to Sample Questions

Solutions to Multiple-Choice Questions

1. D $\int_{-4}^{2}(f(x)+1)\,dx = \int_{-4}^{2} f(x)\,dx + \int_{-4}^{2} dx = 3+-3+3+6=9$

2. D $e^{2(x^3)} \cdot 3x^2$

3. B $\int_{-2}^{0} f'(x)\,dx = f(0)-f(-2)$

$f(-2) = f(0) - \int_{-2}^{0} f'(x)\,dx = -2-\frac{1}{2}(2)(4) = -6$

*4. A $g'(x) = \cos(x^3)$

$\cos(x^3) < 0$ when $1.162 < x < 1.677$

*5. A $\frac{1}{2-0}\int_{0}^{2} e^t - t^2e^2\,dt = -3.195$

6. B $\int_{2}^{-4} f(t)\,dt = -\int_{-4}^{2} f(t)\,dt$

$-\left[\frac{1}{2}(2)(-3)+\frac{1}{2}\pi\cdot 2^2\right]$

$-[-3+2\pi]$

7. E $\int_{0}^{8} 10\sqrt[3]{2t+1}\,dt$

8. C $6(5)+2(4)+4(3)$

*9. E $g(6) = g(3) + \int_3^6 \frac{e^x}{x^2} = 15.51297..$

10. C $\int_{-1}^{5} f'(2t)dt = \int_{-2}^{10} \frac{1}{2} f'(u)du = \frac{1}{2}(f(10) - f(-2))$

*11. D $\int_0^1 \left| e^{-x} \cos(3x) \right| dx$

Solutions to Free-Response Questions

*1. A particle moves along the y-axis so that its velocity at any time $t \geq 0$ is given by $v(t) = -2t\cos(t)$. At time $t = 0$, the particle is at position $y(t) = 2$.

a. For what values of t, $0 \leq t \leq \frac{3\pi}{2}$, is the particle moving downward?

b. For what values of t, $0 \leq t \leq \frac{3\pi}{2}$, is the particle moving upward?

c. Find the acceleration of the particle at time $t = 5$. Is the velocity of the particle increasing or decreasing at $t = 5$? Why or why not?

d. Find the position $y(t)$ of the particle at time $t = 5$.

Solution	Points
a. $-2t\cos(t) < 0$ $0 < t < \frac{\pi}{2}$ $0 < t < 1.571$	2 $\begin{cases} 1: v(t) < 0 \\ 1: \text{answer} \end{cases}$
b. $-2t\cos(t) > 0$ $\frac{\pi}{2} < t < \frac{3\pi}{2}$ $1.571 < t < 4.712$	2 $\begin{cases} 1: v(t) > 0 \\ 1: \text{answer} \end{cases}$
c. $a(t) = v'(5) = -10.157$ $v(5) = -2.837$ The velocity is decreasing because $a(5) < 0$ and $v(5) < 0$	3 $\begin{cases} 1: a(5) \\ 1: v(5) \\ 1: \text{velocity decreasing with reason} \end{cases}$
d. $y(5) = y(0) + \int_0^5 v(t)\,dt$ $y(5) = 13.022$	2 $\begin{cases} 1: \text{integral} \\ 1: \text{answer} \end{cases}$

2. For $-4 \le t \le 2$ the graph of a function f is shown below. Let $g(x) = \int_0^{\frac{1}{2}x} f(t)\,dt$.

The graph of $f(t)$

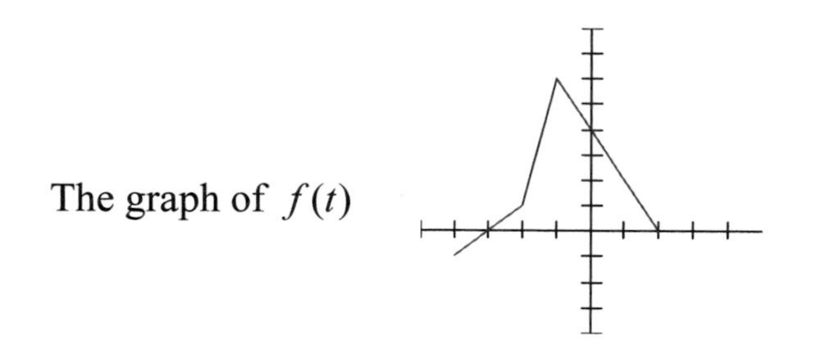

a. What is the domain of $g(x)$?
b. Compute, or state that it does not exist, $g(-2), g'(-2), g''(-2)$
c. Find all values of x where $g(x)$ has a relative minimum. Justify your answer.
d. Find all values of x in the open interval $(-8,4)$ at which the graph of g has a point of inflection.

---

a. $-4 \le \frac{1}{2}x \le 2$ $-8 \le x \le 4$	1: answer
b. $g(-2) = \int_0^{\frac{1}{2}(-2)} f(t)\,dt = -\int_{-1}^{0} f(t)\,dt =$ $-\frac{1}{2}1(6+4) = -5$ $g'(x) = f(\frac{1}{2}x)\cdot\frac{1}{2}$ $g'(-2) = f(-1)\cdot\frac{1}{2} = (6)\cdot\frac{1}{2} = 3$ $g''(x) = f'(\frac{1}{2}x)\cdot\frac{1}{4}$ $g''(-2) = f'(-1)\cdot\frac{1}{4}$ Does not exist	5 $\begin{cases} 1: & g(-2) \\ 1: & g'(x) \\ 1: & g'(-2) \\ 1: & g''(x) \\ 1: & \text{answer} \end{cases}$
c. g has a relative minimum at $\frac{1}{2}x = -3; x = -6$ This is the only x value where $g'(x)$ changes from negative to positive	2 $\begin{cases} 1: & x = -6 \\ 1: & \text{justification} \end{cases}$
d. $x = -2$	1: answer

3. The graph of $y = f(x)$, shown below, consists of three line segments and a semicircle.

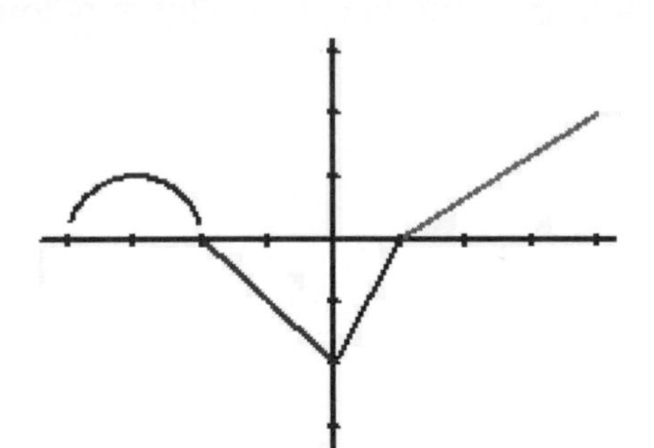

a. Find the average rate of change for function f over the interval $[-4, 4]$.

b. Find the average value of function f over the interval $[-4, 4]$.

Let function g be defined by $g(x) = \int_{-2}^{x} f(t)\,dt$ for all x in the closed interval $[-4, 4]$.

c. Which is larger $g(-4)$ or $g(-2)$? Explain why.

d. Write an equation for the line tangent to the graph of $y = g(x)$ at $x = 1$.

(a) $\dfrac{f(4) - f(-4)}{8} = \dfrac{2-0}{8} = \dfrac{1}{4}$

1: answer

(b) $\frac{1}{8}\int_{-4}^{4} f(t) = \frac{1}{8}\left[\frac{1}{2}\pi \cdot 1^2 + \frac{1}{2}(3)(-2) + \frac{1}{2}(3)(2)\right]$

$\frac{1}{8}\left(\frac{1}{2}\pi\right)$

$\frac{1}{16}\pi$

$3\begin{cases} 1:\ \frac{1}{8}\int_{-4}^{4} f(t)\,dt \\ 1:\ \int_{-2}^{1} f(t)\,dt = -\int_{1}^{4} f(t)\,dt \\ 1:\ \text{answer} \end{cases}$

(c) $g(-2)$ because $g(-4) < 0$ and $g(-2) = 0$.

1: answer with explanation

(d) $g(1) = \frac{1}{2}(3)(-2) = -3$

$g'(x) = f(x)$

$g'(1) = 0$

$y = 0(x-1) - 3$

$y = -3$

$4\begin{cases} 1:\ g(1) \\ 1:\ g'(x) = f(x) \\ 1:\ g'(1) \\ 1:\ \text{answer} \end{cases}$

4. A car is traveling on a straight road with velocity 50 ft/sec at time $t = 0$. For $0 \le t \le 20$, the car's acceleration $a(t)$, in $ft/\sec^2$, is the piecewise linear function defined by the graph below.

$a(t)$

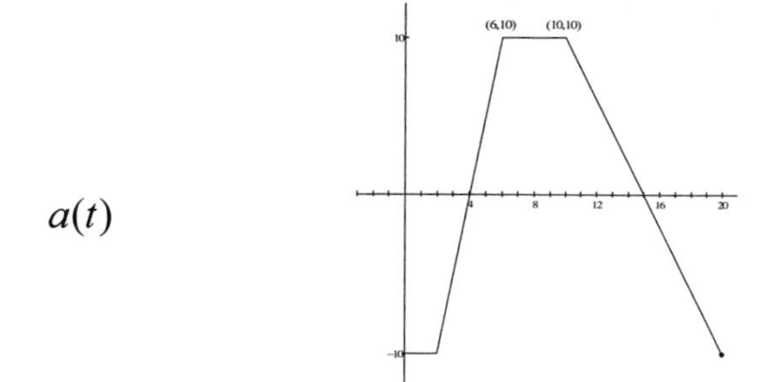

a. Is the velocity of the car increasing at $t = 2$ seconds? Why or why not?

b. Is the speed of the car increasing or decreasing at time $t = 2$? Give a reason for your answer.

c. At what time in the interval $0 < t \le 20$ is the velocity of the car 50 ft/sec?

d. On the time interval $0 \le t \le 20$, what is the car's absolute maximum velocity, in ft/sec? At what time does it occur? Why?

---

a. Since $v'(2) = a(2) = -10$, the velocity is decreasing at $t = 2$

$2 \begin{cases} 1: \text{ answer} \\ 1: \text{ reason} \end{cases}$

b. $v(2) = v(0) + \int_0^2 a(t)dt = 50 + -20 = 30$ ft/sec

Speed is decreasing since $a(2) < 0$ and $v(2) > 0$

$2 \begin{cases} 1: \text{ decreasing} \\ 1: \text{ reason} \end{cases}$

c. at time $t = 8$

$v(8) = v(0) + \int_0^8 a(t)dt = 50 + 0 = 50$

$2 \begin{cases} 1: \ t = 8 \\ 1: \text{ reason} \end{cases}$

d. The absolute maximum velocity is 95 ft/sec at $t = 15$

$v'(t)$ decreases on the interval $0 < t < 4$,

$v'(t)$ increases on the interval $4 < t < 15$ and

$v'(t)$ decreases on the interval $15 < t < 20$

the candidates are $v(0) = 50$ ft/sec

and $v(15) = v(0) + \int_0^{15} a(t)dt = 50 + 45 = 95$ ft/sec

$3 \begin{cases} 1: \ t = 15 \\ 1: \text{ absolute maximum velocity} \\ 1: \text{ identifies } t = 0 \text{ and } t = 15 \text{ as candidates or indicates that v decreases, increases and then decreases} \end{cases}$

*5. The sales $s(t)$, in billions of dollars per year, of sporting goods for the years 1984 through 1989 are given in the table, where $t = 4$ corresponds to 1984

a. Use the data from the table to find an approximation to $s'(7)$. Show computations that lead to your answer. Using correct units, explain the meaning of $s'(7)$.

t time since 1980	s(t) Sales
4	26.4
5	27.4
6	30.6
7	33.9
8	42.1
9	45.2

b. Approximate the value of $\int_4^9 s(t)\,dt$ using a right Riemann sum with the five subintervals indicated by the data in the table. Using correct units, explain the meaning of $\int_4^9 s(t)\,dt$.

c. Explain the meaning of $\frac{1}{5}\int_4^9 s(t)\,dt$ in terms of sales of sporting goods. Indicate units of measure in your answer.

The sales per year from 1984 through 1989 can be approximated by $S(t) = 15.73(1.12)^t$.

d. Use $S(t)$ to approximate $S'(7)$.

e. Use $S(t)$ to approximate $\int_4^9 S(t)dt$.

*5. Solutions:

Solution	Points
a. $s'(7) \approx \frac{s(8)-s(6)}{8-6} = \frac{42.1-30.6}{2} = 5.75$ or $s'(7) \approx \frac{s(8)-s(7)}{8-7} = \frac{42.1-33.9}{1} = 8.2$ or $s'(7) \approx \frac{s(7)-s(6)}{7-6} = \frac{33.9-30.6}{1} = 3.3$ In 1990 Sales per year are increasing at the rate of (student answer here) billion dollars/year^2	2 $\begin{cases} 1: \text{ difference quotient} \\ 1: \text{ explanation} \end{cases}$
b. $\int_4^9 s(t)dt \approx (27.4+30.6+33.9+42.1+45.2) =$ 179.2 Total sales for the years 1984-1989 were 179.2 billion dollars	3 $\begin{cases} 1: s(5)+s(6)+s(7)+s(8)+s(9) \\ 1: \text{ answer} \\ 1: \text{ explanation} \end{cases}$
c. $\frac{1}{5}\int_4^9 s(t)dt$ is the average sales per year in billions of dollars per year for 1984-1989	1: explanation
d. $S'(7) = 3.941$	1: answer
e. $\int_4^9 S(t)dt = 166.499$	1: answer
(units) correct units in part a, b, c	1: units

Connect2Calculus Videos for Chapter 4

The Calculus Concepts Video's for Chapter 4: *(Calculus BC topics are in italic type)*
Some of the topics on the videos go beyond the scope of Calculus AB/BC, but would be worth watching as an application of calculus.

11.0 Introducing Integration: Finding Areas
11.1 Integration: Foundations and Notation
11.2 Integration as a Limit of Sums
11.3 The Area Problem
12.0 Integration: Connections to the Derivative
12.1 From Riemann Sums to the Definite Integral
12.2 Fundamental Theorem of Calculus I: Using Antiderivatives
12.3 Fundamental Theorem of Calculus II: Unifying Calculus

CHAPTER 5: APPLICATIONS OF THE DEFINITE INTEGRAL

Correlations

The section by section correspondence to the Topic Outline for Calculus AB and the Topic Outline for Calculus BC (*Calculus BC topics are in italic type*) is:

AP Topic	Chapter.Section	Pages
III. Integrals **Interpretations and properties of definite integrals** • Definite integral of the rate of change of a quantity over an interval interpreted as the change of the quantity over the interval: $\int_a^b f'(x)\,dx = f(b) - f(a)$	5.1	432-441
III. Integrals **Applications of integrals** Appropriate integrals are used in a variety of applications to model physical, biological, or economics situations. Although only a sampling of applications can be included in any specific course, students should be able to adapt their knowledge and techniques to solve other similar application problems. Whatever applications are chosen, the emphasis is on using the method of setting up an approximating Riemann sum and representing its limit as a definite integral. To provide a common foundation, specific applications should include using the integral of a rate of change to give accumulated change, finding the area of a region, the volume of a solid with known cross sections, ... *and the length of a curve*	5.1, 5.2, 5.3, 5.6, 5.7, *5.4*	432-441, 441-456, 456-464, 484-496, 496-505, *464-472*
III. Integrals **Applications of antidifferentiation** • Finding specific antiderivatives using initial conditions, including applications to motion along a line	5.5	472-484

Textbook Section	AP Topic
5.1 Area Between Curves	**III. Integrals** **Interpretations and properties of definite integrals** • Definite integral of the rate of change of a quantity over an interval interpreted as the change of the quantity over the interval: $\int_a^b f'(x)\,dx = f(b) - f(a)$ **Applications of integrals** Appropriate integrals are used in a variety of applications to model physical, biological, or economics situations. Although only a sampling of applications can be included in any specific course, students should be able to adapt their knowledge and techniques to solve other similar application problems. Whatever applications are chosen, the emphasis is on using the method of setting up an approximating Riemann sum and representing its limit as a definite integral. To provide a common foundation, specific applications should include using the integral of a rate of change to give accumulated change, finding the area of a region, the volume of a solid with known cross sections, ... *and the length of a curve*
5.2 Volume: Slicing, Disks, and Washers	**III. Integrals** **Applications of integrals** Appropriate integrals are used in a variety of applications to model physical, biological, or economics situations. Although only a sampling of applications can be included in any specific course, students should be able to adapt their knowledge and techniques to solve other similar application problems. Whatever applications are chosen, the emphasis is on using the method of setting up an approximating Riemann sum and representing its limit as a definite integral. To provide a common foundation, specific applications should include using the integral of a rate of change to give accumulated change, finding the area of a region, the volume of a solid with known cross sections, ... *and the length of a curve*
5.3 Volumes by Cylindrical Shells	**III. Integrals** **Applications of integrals** Appropriate integrals are used in a variety of applications to model physical, biological, or economics situations. Although only a sampling of applications can be included in any specific course, students should be able to adapt their knowledge and techniques to solve other similar application problems. Whatever applications are chosen, the emphasis is on using the method of setting up an approximating Riemann sum and representing its limit as a definite integral. To provide a common foundation, specific applications should include using the integral of a rate of change to give accumulated change, finding the area of a region, the volume of a solid with known cross sections, ... *and the length of a curve*

Textbook Section		AP Topic
5.4 Arc Length and Surface Area	**III.**	**Integrals** **Applications of integrals** Appropriate integrals are used in a variety of applications to model physical, biological, or economics situations. Although only a sampling of applications can be included in any specific course, students should be able to adapt their knowledge and techniques to solve other similar application problems. Whatever applications are chosen, the emphasis is on using the method of setting up an approximating Riemann sum and representing its limit as a definite integral. To provide a common foundation, specific applications should include using the integral of a rate of change to give accumulated change, finding the area of a region, the volume of a solid with known cross sections, ... *and the length of a curve*
5.5 Projectile Motion	**III.**	**Integrals** **Applications of antidifferentiation** • Finding specific antiderivatives using initial conditions, including applications to motion along a line
5.6 Applications of Integration to Physics and Engineering	**III.**	**Integrals** **Applications of integrals** Appropriate integrals are used in a variety of applications to model physical, biological, or economics situations. Although only a sampling of applications can be included in any specific course, students should be able to adapt their knowledge and techniques to solve other similar application problems. Whatever applications are chosen, the emphasis is on using the method of setting up an approximating Riemann sum and representing its limit as a definite integral. To provide a common foundation, specific applications should include using the integral of a rate of change to give accumulated change, finding the area of a region, the volume of a solid with known cross sections, ... *and the length of a curve*
5.7 Probability	**III.**	**Integrals** **Applications of integrals** Appropriate integrals are used in a variety of applications to model physical, biological, or economics situations. Although only a sampling of applications can be included in any specific course, students should be able to adapt their knowledge and techniques to solve other similar application problems. Whatever applications are chosen, the emphasis is on using the method of setting up an approximating Riemann sum and representing its limit as a definite integral. To provide a common foundation, specific applications should include using the integral of a rate of change to give accumulated change, finding the area of a region, the volume of a solid with known cross sections, ... *and the length of a curve*

Vocabulary and Section Notes

Vocabulary used in the Topic Outline for Calculus AB and the Topic Outline for Calculus BC (*Calculus BC topics are in italic type*) include:

Arc length
Volume by disks
Volume by shells (Optional)
Volume by slicing
Volume by washers
Volumes by known cross-sections

Section notes for the Calculus AB Course:

Section 5.3 (Volumes by Cylindrical Shells): The cylindrical shell method is not specifically mentioned in the Topic Outline for Calculus AB, but it can be used to set up definite integrals to determine the volume of some solids. (Optional)

Section 5.4 (Arc Length and Surface Area): These topics are not part of the Topic Outline for Calculus AB.

Section 5.5 (Projectile Motion): Motion of a particle along a horizontal or vertical line is part of the Topic Outline for Calculus AB. Motion of a projectile in two dimensions is not.

Section 5.6 (Applications of Integration to Physics and Engineering): These are interesting applications of integration in physics and engineering. Students do not need to memorize any of the relationships, but they should be able to solve problems when the pertinent relationship is defined in the problem.

Section 5.7 (Probability): This is another interesting application of integration. Students do not need to memorize any of the relationships, but they should be able to solve the problems when the pertinent relationship is defined in the problem.

Section notes for the Calculus BC Course:

Section 5.3 (Volumes by Cylindrical Shells): The cylindrical shell method is not specifically mentioned in the Topic Outline for Calculus BC, but it can be used to set up definite integrals to determine the volume of some solids. (Optional)

Section 5.4 (Arc Length and Surface Area): Surface Area is not included in the Topic Outline for Calculus BC.

Section 5.5 (Projectile Motion): Motion of a particle along a horizontal or vertical line is part of the Topic Outline for Calculus BC. Motion of a projectile in two dimensions is in parametric form (which is in the Topic Outline for Calculus BC), but students do not have to memorize the formulas for the horizontal and vertical components of the velocity.

Section 5.6 (Applications of Integration to Physics and Engineering): These are interesting applications of integration in physics and engineering. Students do not need to memorize any of the relationships, but they should be able to solve problems when the pertinent relationship is defined in the problem.

Section 5.7 (Probability): This is another interesting application of integration. Students do not need to memorize any of the relationships, but they should be able to solve the problems when the pertinent relationship is defined in the problem.

Student Activity: Models of Solids with Known Cross-Sections

Teacher Notes:

This project is designed to help students in three areas. First, they can actually visualize what a solid with a known cross section looks like. Second, they can see how describing one slice of a region can be used to find the total volume using a definite integral. Finally, students can see how to approximate a definite integral using a Riemann Sum.

This project can be assigned after you have covered Section 5.2. If you have time to work on it during the year, it will help students better understand similar problems on the AP Calculus Exam. Otherwise, it can be done after the AP Calculus Exam.

This project easily fits a two-week time line.

Day 1: Explain the project. Show some physical models. Suggest typical base functions and cross-section shapes.

Day 3-4. Have students discuss with you individually what base functions and cross-sectional shapes they are considering. Offer suggestions to make the project more reasonable. For example, if a student chooses $y = x^3$ from 0 to 6 inches, he will probably not be aware that the end of the model will be 216 inches tall. $y = \sin x$ is also difficult to construct since no slice will be taller than 1 inch. A base function like $y = 5\sin x$ would be easier to build.

Day 7-8. Students show you the spreadsheet calculations for the dimensions of each lamination. This means that students have to choose the material used to build the model. Materials can be purchased at craft stores or hobby shops. Corrugated cardboard can be used since it is only $3/16$" thick.

A note of caution: Some students use Styrofoam to build their model. They often want to decorate the model with spray paint. Unfortunately, spray paint is a solvent for Styrofoam, which will dissolve their model.

Day 14. Students present their models to the class

Student Directions:

Make a physical model of a solid with a known cross section on a base with a standard function. The following guidelines apply:

1) The base function can be any non-linear function except a parabola, square root, or absolute value. Combinations are allowed.

2) The cross section can be any shape except a rectangle.

3) The materials can be no thicker than 0.25". Your model must be at least 6 inches long. There must be at least 24 laminations.

Your presentation must have the following information

1) A description of the functions used.
2) An explanation of what the cross section looks like.
3) The computed volume for each slice.
4) The total volume of the slices in your model using a spread sheet.
5) The theoretical volume as defined by a definite integral. If your problem is not integrable, you may use the Numerical Integration feature of your calculator.

Points will awarded for

20 points: difficulty of the function and cross section used.
20 points: neatness and appeal of your model.
10 points: presentation of the information and calculations.

Those projects showing extra effort and performance can earn extra-credit points.

Multiple-Choice Questions–Calculus AB/BC Topics

* 1. The area of the regions bounded by the graphs of $y = x^3 - x - 3$ and $y = 2.5x - 3.75$ is

A. 2.801
B. 3
C. 6.367
D. 6.573
E. 6.876

2. Which of the following integral expressions represents the volume of the solid formed by revolving $y = \frac{1}{3}x^2$ and $y = 2x$ about the y-axis?

A. $\pi \int_0^{12} \left(3y - \frac{1}{4}y^2\right) dy$
B. $\pi \int_0^{6} \left(3y - \frac{1}{4}y^2\right) dy$
C. $\pi \int_0^{12} \left(\sqrt{3y} - \frac{1}{2}y\right)^2 dy$
D. $\pi \int_0^{12} \left(\frac{1}{4}y^2 - 3y\right) dy$
E. $\pi \int_0^{12} \left(\frac{1}{2}y - \sqrt{3y}\right)^2 dy$

* 3. The region enclosed by the graphs $y = 2x\cos x - 3\cos x - 2$ and $y = x^2 - 8x + 9$ is revolved about the line $y = -10$. The volume of the solid generated is

A. 71
B. 328
C. 1412
D. 1415
E. 1444

* 4. The region bounded by the graphs of $y = x^2 - 3x + 2$ and $y = 2 - x$ forms the base of a solid. For this solid, each cross section perpendicular to the x-axis is a semicircle. What is the volume of this solid?

A. $\frac{4}{15}\pi$
B. $\frac{2}{5}\pi$
C. $\frac{8}{15}\pi$
D. $\frac{2}{3}\pi$
E. $\frac{4}{3}\pi$

* 5. The region enclosed by the graphs $y = 2$ and $y = e^{x^2}$ is revolved about the line $y = 2$. The volume of the solid generated is

A. 1.534
B. 3.069
C. 3.722
D. 11.824
E. 73.347

6. The region enclosed by the graphs $y = -x^2 + 2x$ and $y = -\sqrt{x}$ is revolved about the line $y = 3$. Which of the following integrals represents the volume of the generated solid?

A. $\pi \int_0^{2.6180} \left[\left(3 - \sqrt{x}\right)^2 - \left(3 - x^2 + 2x\right)^2 \right] dx$

B. $\pi \int_0^{2.6180} \left[\left(3 + x^2 - 2x\right)^2 - \left(3 + \sqrt{x}\right)^2 \right] dx$

C. $\pi \int_0^{2.6180} \left[\left(3 + \sqrt{x}\right) - \left(3 + x^2 - 2x\right) \right]^2 dx$

D. $\pi \int_0^{2.6180} \left[\left(3 + x^2 - 2x\right) - \left(3 + \sqrt{x}\right) \right]^2 dx$

E. $\pi \int_0^{2.6180} \left[\left(3 + \sqrt{x}\right)^2 - \left(3 + x^2 - 2x\right)^2 \right] dx$

7. Which of the following expressions gives the length of the curve $x = \ln(y)$ from $y = 1$ to $y = 2$?

A. $\int_1^2 \sqrt{1+e^y}\, dy$

B. $\int_1^2 \sqrt{1+e^{2y}}\, dy$

C. $\int_1^2 \sqrt{1+\frac{1}{y^2}}\, dy$

D. $\int_1^2 \sqrt{1+\frac{1}{y}}\, dy$

E. $\int_1^2 \sqrt{1+(y\ln(y)-y)^2}\, dy$

Free-Response Questions–Calculus AB/BC Topics

* 1. Let R be the shaded region in the fourth quadrant enclosed by the graphs $f(x) = x^2 - 4x + 1$ and $g(x) = -2\tan^{-1}(x)$, as shown in the figure below.

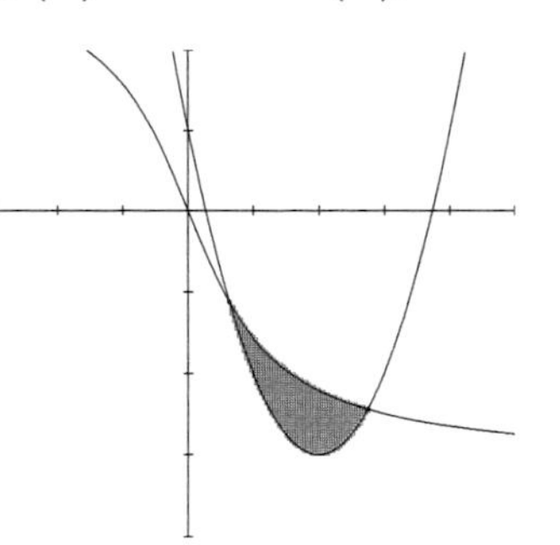

a. Find the area of region R.
b. Find the volume of the solid generated when region R is revolved about the line $y = 1$.
c. Region S, bounded above by g and below by f, is the base of a solid. For this solid, each cross section perpendicular to x-axis is rectangle with the base of the rectangle in the xy-plane. If the height of each rectangle is twice the base, find the volume of this solid.

* 2. Let R be the shaded region bounded by the graphs of $y = 3^x - 3$ and $y = 4x - 2$, as shown in the figure below.

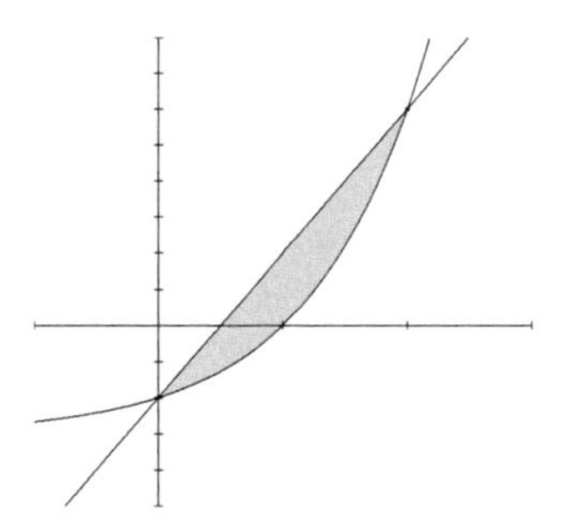

a. Find the area of region R.
b. Find the volume of the solid generated when R is revolved about the line $y = -4$.
c. Write, but do not evaluate, an integral expression that can be used to find the volume of the solid generated when R is revolved about the y-axis.
d. The region R is the base of a solid. For this solid, each cross section perpendicular to x-axis is a square with one of the sides in the xy-plane. Find the volume of this figure.

3. Let R be the region bounded by the y-axis, the graph $y = e^{2x}$, and the line $x = \ln(3)$.
   a. Find the area of region R.
   b. The line $x = h$ divides the region R into two regions of equal area. Find the value of h.
   c. Find the volume of the solid generated when region R is revolved about the x-axis.
   d. The line $x = k$ divides region R into two regions such that when these two regions are revolved about the x-axis, they generate solids with equal volumes. Set up, but to solve, an integral equation that can be used to find the value of k.

Solutions to Sample Questions

<u>Solutions to Multiple-Choice Questions</u>

*1. C $\int_{-1.96995}^{1.75274} \left| \left(x^3 - x - 3\right)^2 - \left(2.5x - 3.75\right)^2 \right| dx$

2. A $\pi \int_0^{12} \left(\left(\sqrt{3y}\right)^2 - \left(\frac{1}{2}y\right)^2 \right) dy$

*3. D $\pi \int_{1.79299}^{7.31371} \left(\left(2x\cos(x) - 3\cos(x) + 8\right)^2 - \left(x^2 - 8x + 19\right)^2 \right) dx$

*4. A $\pi \int_0^2 \left[\frac{1}{2}\left((2-x) - \left(x^2 - 3x + 2\right) \right) \right]^2 dx$

*5. B $\pi \int_{-0.83255}^{0.83255} \left(2 - e^{x^2}\right)^2 dx$

6. E

7. C

Solutions to Free-Response Questions

*1. Let R be the shaded region in the fourth quadrant enclosed by the graphs $f(x) = x^2 - 4x + 1$ and $g(x) = -2\tan^{-1}(x)$, as shown in the figure below.

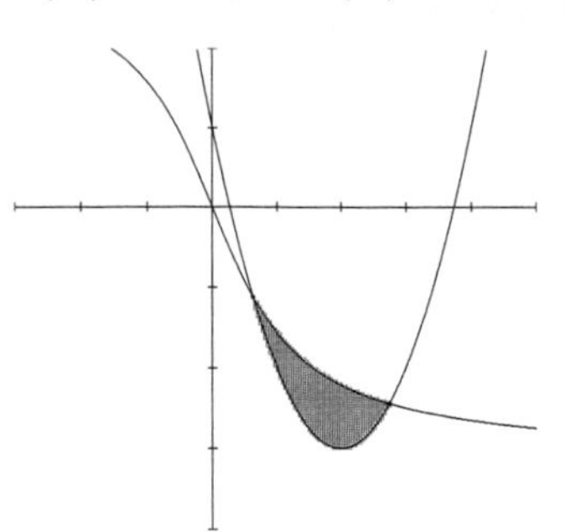

a. Find the area of region R.
b. Find the volume of the solid generated when region R is revolved about the line $y = 1$.
c. Region S, bounded above by g and below by f, is the base of a solid. For this solid, each cross section perpendicular to x-axis is rectangle with the base of the rectangle in the xy-plane. If the height of each rectangle is twice the base, find the volume of this solid.

Solution	Scoring
	1: Correct limits integral in (a), (b), or (c)
(a) $\int_{0.63097}^{2.74621} (g(x) - f(x))\,dx = 1.162$ or 1.163	2 { 1: integrand; 1: answer
(b) $\pi\int_{0.63097}^{2.74621} \left(\left(1 - f(x)^2\right) - \left(1 - g(x)\right)^2\right) dx = 24.594$ or 24.595	3 { 1: constant; 1: integrand; 1: answer
(c) $\int_{0.63097}^{2.74621} 2\left(g(x) - f(x)\right)^2\,dx = 1.544$	3 { 2: integrand, $\langle -1 \rangle$ incorrect but has $g(x) - f(x)$ as a factor; 1: answer

*2. Let R be the shaded region bounded by the graphs of $y = 3^x - 3$ and $y = 4x - 2$, as shown in the figure below.

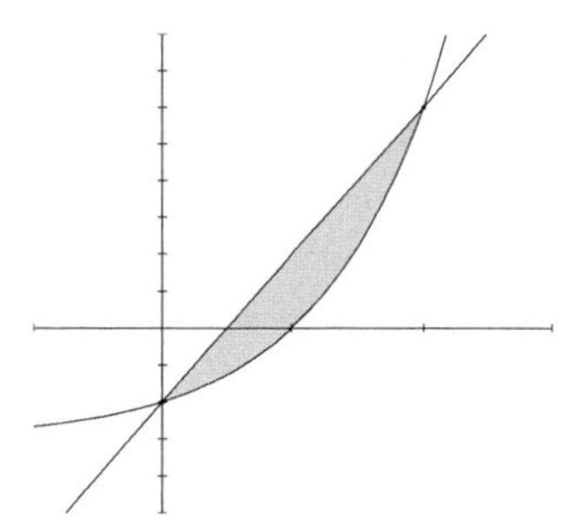

a. Find the area of region R.
b. Find the volume of the solid generated when R is revolved about the line $y = -4$.
c. Write, but do not evaluate, an integral expression that can be used to find the volume of the solid generated when R is revolved about the y-axis.
d. The region R is the base of a solid. For this solid, each cross section perpendicular to x-axis is a square with one of the sides in the xy-plane. Find the volume of this figure.

	1: Correct limits in integral in (a), (b), or (d)
(a) $\int_0^2 \left((4x-2)-(3^x-3)\right)dx = 2.718$	$2\begin{cases}1\text{: integrand}\\1\text{: answer}\end{cases}$
(b) $\pi\int_0^2 \left((4x+2)^2-(3^x+1)^2\right)dx = 93.284$	$2\begin{cases}1\text{: integrand and constant}\\1\text{: answer}\end{cases}$
(c) $\pi\int_{-2}^{6}\left[\left(\dfrac{\ln(y+3)}{\ln(3)}\right)^2-\left(\dfrac{y+2}{4}\right)^2\right]dy$	$2\begin{cases}1\text{: limits and constant}\\1\text{: integrand}\end{cases}$
(d) $\int_0^2 \left(4x-3^x+1\right)^2 dx = 4.464$	$2\begin{cases}1\text{: integrand}\\1\text{: answer}\end{cases}$

3. Let R be the first quadrant region bounded by the graph $y = e^{2x}$ and the line $x = \ln(3)$.
   a. Find the area of region R.
   b. The line $x = h$ divides the region R into two regions of equal area. Find the value of h.
   c. Find the volume of the solid generated when region R is revolved about the x-axis.
   d. The line $x = k$ divides region R into two regions such that when these two regions are revolved about the x-axis, they generate solids with equal volumes. Set up, but to not solve, an integral equation that can be used to find the value of k.

(a)

$$\int_0^{\ln(3)} e^{2x}\,dx = \tfrac{1}{2}e^{2x}\Big|_0^{\ln(3)}$$
$$= \tfrac{1}{2}\left(e^{2\ln(3)} - e^0\right)$$
$$= \tfrac{1}{2}(9-1)$$
$$= 4$$

$2\begin{cases}1: \text{integral}\\1: \text{answer}\end{cases}$

(b)

$$\int_0^h e^{2x}\,dx = 2$$
$$\tfrac{1}{2}e^{2x}\Big|_0^h = 2$$
$$e^{2x}\Big|_0^h = 4$$
$$e^{2h} - 1 = 4$$
$$h = \tfrac{1}{2}\ln(5)$$

$3\begin{cases}1: \text{integral}\\1: \text{sets integral } = 2\\1: \text{answer}\end{cases}$

(c)

$$\pi\int_0^{\ln(3)} \left(e^{2x}\right)^2 dx = \pi\int_0^{\ln(3)} e^{4x}\,dx$$
$$\tfrac{\pi}{4}e^{4x}\Big|_0^{\ln(3)} = \tfrac{\pi}{4}\left(e^{\ln 81} - e^0\right)$$
$$= \tfrac{\pi}{4}(81-1)$$
$$= 20\pi$$

$3\begin{cases}1: \text{limits and constant}\\1: \text{integrand}\\1: \text{answer}\end{cases}$

(d)

$$\pi\int_0^k \left(e^{2x}\right)^2 dx = 10\pi$$

1: answer

Connect2Calculus Videos for Chapter 5

The Calculus Concepts Video's for Chapter 5: *(Calculus BC topics are in italic type)*
Some of the topics on the videos go beyond the scope of Calculus AB/BC, but would be worth watching as an application of calculus

13.0 Physical Measurements: Going Beyond Traditional Geometries
13.1 Area for an Irregular Planar Region
13.2 Volume of an Irregular Space
13.3 *Arc Length* and Surface Area (not in the Topic Outline for Calculus AB/BC)

CHAPTER 6: INTEGRATION TECHNIQUES

Correlations

The section by section correspondence to the Topic Outline for Calculus AB and the Topic Outline for Calculus BC (*Calculus BC topics are in italic type*) is:

AP Topic	Chapter.Section	Pages
II. Derivatives		
Applications of derivatives		
+ *L'Hopital's Rule, including its use in ...convergence of improper integrals ...*	*6.6*	*546-561*
III. Integrals		
Techniques of antidifferentiation		
• Antiderivatives following directly from derivatives of basic functions	6.1, 6.3	510-514, 521-530
+ *Antiderivatives by substitution of variables (including change of limits for definite integrals), parts, and simple partial fractions (nonrepeating linear factors only)*	6.1, *6.2,* 6.3, *6.4*	510-514, *514-521,* 521-530, *530-538*
+ *Improper integrals (as limits of definite integrals)*	*6.6*	*546-561*

Textbook Section	AP Topic
6.1 Review of Formulas and Techniques	**III. Integrals** **Techniques of antidifferentiation** • Antiderivatives following directly from derivatives of basic functions + *Antiderivatives by substitution of variables (including change of limits for definite integrals), parts, and simple partial fractions (nonrepeating linear factors only)* + *Improper integrals (as limits of definite integrals)*
6.2 Integration by Parts	**III. Integrals** **Techniques of antidifferentiation** • Antiderivatives following directly from derivatives of basic functions + *Antiderivatives by substitution of variables (including change of limits for definite integrals), parts, and simple partial fractions (nonrepeating linear factors only)* + *Improper integrals (as limits of definite integrals)*
6.3 Trigonometric Techniques of Integration	**III. Integrals** **Techniques of antidifferentiation** • Antiderivatives following directly from derivatives of basic functions + *Antiderivatives by substitution of variables (including change of limits for definite integrals), parts, and simple partial fractions (nonrepeating linear factors only)* + *Improper integrals (as limits of definite integrals)*

Textbook Section	AP Topic
6.4 Integration of Rational Functions Using Partial Fractions	**III. Integrals** **Techniques of antidifferentiation** • Antiderivatives following directly from derivatives of basic functions + *Antiderivatives by substitution of variables (including change of limits for definite integrals), parts, and simple partial fractions (nonrepeating linear factors only)* + *Improper integrals (as limits of definite integrals)*
6.6 Improper Integrals	**II. Derivatives** **Applications of derivatives** + *L'Hopital's Rule, including its use in ...convergence of improper integrals ...* **III. Integrals** **Techniques of antidifferentiation** • Antiderivatives following directly from derivatives of basic functions + *Antiderivatives by substitution of variables (including change of limits for definite integrals), parts, and simple partial fractions (nonrepeating linear factors only)* + *Improper integrals (as limits of definite integrals)*

Vocabulary and Section Notes

Vocabulary used in the Topic Outline for Calculus AB and the Topic Outline for Calculus BC (*Calculus BC topics are in italic type*) include:
(There is no new vocabulary for the AB Course in Chapter 6)

Comparison Test
Improper integral
Integral converges
Integral diverges
Integration by parts
Partial fraction decomposition

Section notes for the Calculus AB Course:

Section 6.1 (Review of Formulas and Techniques) and selected exercises from Section 6.3 (Trigonometric Techniques of Integration) are the only topics in this chapter that are included in the Topic Outline for Calculus AB. All of the techniques reviewed in Section 6.1 were first introduced in Section 4.1. In Section 6.3 only those exercises that use substitution are necessary (and they are a review of techniques first introduced in section 4.6). Suggested exercises for 6.3 would include 1, 3, 5, 7, 9, 10, 12, 14, and 31.

Section notes for the Calculus BC Course

Section 6.3 (Trigonometric Techniques of Integration): Integrals that involve powers of trigonometric functions that cannot be resolved using simple substitution techniques (section 4.6) are not part of the Topic Outline for Calculus BC. Trigonometric Substitution is not part of the Topic Outline for Calculus BC.

Section 6.4 (Integration of Rational Functions Using Partial Fractions): The Topic Outline for Calculus BC only requires non-repeating linear factors.

Section 6.5 (Integration Tables and Computer Algebra Systems): These are not part of the Topic Outline for Calculus BC.

Teacher's Notes: Tabular Integration by Parts

Teacher's Notes:

Some Integration by Parts problems can be solved using a method found in many textbooks called "Tabular Integration". Informally, the method is also referred to as "Tic-Tac-Toe", from a scene in the movie "Stand and Deliver". In the movie, a student is trying to work an Integration by Parts problem on the board, and after having difficulty finding the solution, asks Mr. Escalante for help. After quickly writing the solution on the board, Escalante says, "Tic-Tac-Toe. Simple."

The Tabular Method can only be applied if these two conditions are met:

1. Repeated derivatives of the function labeled u can be calculated until a value of 0 occurs

2. An equal number of antiderivatives of the function labeled dv can be easily calculated

The process involves arranging the derivatives and antiderivatives in two vertical columns and taking the derivative of the column labeled u until the derivative equals 0 and finding the antiderivative of the dv column an equal number of times. To form the final answer, link the product of the entries in the columns with alternating signs on a downward diagonal

For example: To find $\int x\cos(x)\,dx$ arrange two columns

u	dv
x	$\cos(x)$
1	$-\sin(x)$
0	$-\cos(x)$

u		dv
x	↘	$\cos(x)$
1	↘	$-\sin(x)$
0		$-\cos(x)$

$$\int x\cos(x)\,dx = +(x\cdot -\sin(x)) - (1(-\cos(x)) + C = -x\sin(x) + \cos(x) + C$$

This is the same answer obtained using a traditional Integration by Parts process:
$\int x\cos(x)\,dx$

Let $\begin{array}{c} u = x \\ du = dx \end{array}$ $\quad\begin{array}{c} dv = \cos(x)dx \\ v = -\sin(x) \end{array}$ and

$$\int x\cos(x)\,dx = -x\cdot\sin(x) - \int \sin(x)\,dx = -x\cdot\sin(x) + \cos(x) + C$$

The Tabular Method becomes advantageous when it would be necessary to use the Integration by Parts process more than once as in $\int -x^3e^x\,dx$.

The Tabular Method can produce the solution in just a few short steps:

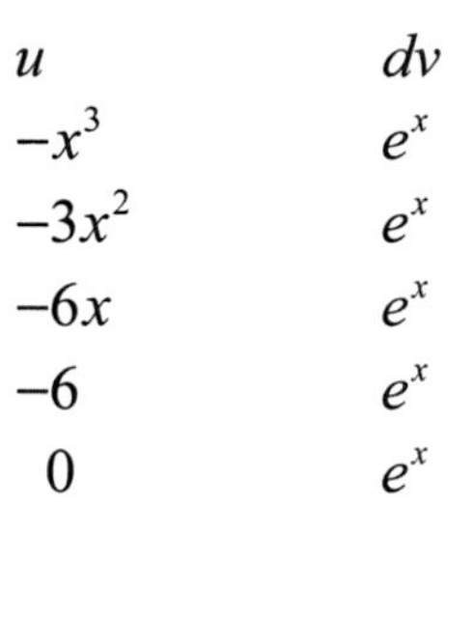

u	dv
$-x^3$	e^x
$-3x^2$	e^x
$-6x$	e^x
-6	e^x
0	e^x

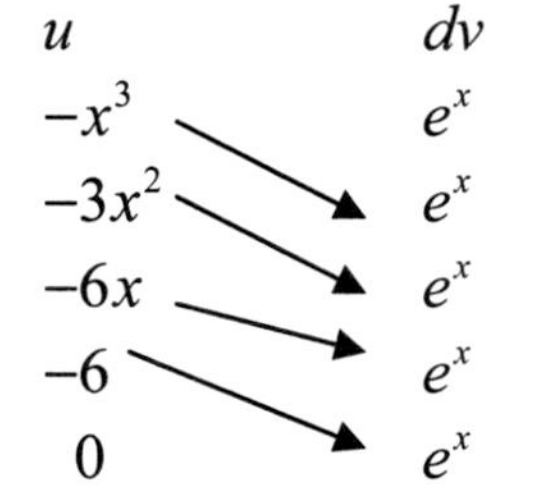

u	dv
$-x^3$	e^x
$-3x^2$	e^x
$-6x$	e^x
-6	e^x
0	e^x

$$\int -x^3e^x\,dx = +(-x^3\cdot e^x) - (-3x^2\cdot e^x) + (-6x\cdot e^x) - (-6e^x) + C$$
$$= -x^3e^x + 3x^2e^x - 6xe^x + 6e^x + C$$

Note: In reality, the two sets of columns are usually combined into one step by inserting the necessary linkage arrows after the derivatives and antiderivatives have been calculated.

Multiple-Choice Questions–Calculus BC Topics

1. $\int x^2 e^{2x}\, dx =$

   A. $2x^2e^{2x} + 2xe^{2x}$
   B. $\frac{1}{3}x^3e^{2x} + \frac{1}{2}x^2e^{2x} + C$
   C. $x^2e^{2x} - 2xe^{2x} + 2e^{2x} + C$
   D. $\frac{1}{2}x^2e^{2x} + \frac{1}{2}xe^{2x} + \frac{1}{4}e^{2x} + C$
   E. $\frac{1}{2}x^2e^{2x} - \frac{1}{2}xe^{2x} + \frac{1}{4}e^{2x} + C$

2. $\int x^3 \ln x\, dx =$

   A. $2x \ln x + x^2$
   B. $\frac{1}{4}x^4 \ln x - \frac{3}{4}x^2 + C$
   C. $\frac{1}{4}x^4 \ln x - \frac{1}{16}x^4 + C$
   D. $\frac{1}{4}x^4 \ln x - \frac{1}{20}x^5 + C$
   E. $\frac{1}{4}x^4 \left(x \ln x - x\right) + C$

3. $\int \frac{3}{2x^2 - 5x + 2}\, dx =$

   A. $\ln|2x-1| - \ln|x-2| + C$
   B. $\ln|x-2| - \ln|2x-1| + C$
   C. $2\ln|2x-1| - \ln|x-2| + C$
   D. $\ln|x-2| + 2\ln|2x-1| + C$
   E. $\ln|x-2| - 2\ln|2x-1| + C$

4. Which of the following three improper integrals converge?

   I. $\int_{-\infty}^{\infty} \frac{1}{1+x^2}\, dx$

   II. $\int_0^1 \frac{1}{x^3}\, dx$

   III. $\int_1^{\infty} \frac{1}{\sqrt[3]{x}}\, dx$

   A. I only
   B. I and II only
   C. I and III only
   D. II and III only
   E. I, II, and III

5. $\int_1^\infty \frac{x}{\left(1+x^2\right)^4}\,dx =$
   A. $-\frac{1}{48}$
   B. $-\frac{1}{6}$
   C. $\frac{1}{48}$
   D. $\frac{1}{6}$
   E. divergent

6. $\int_0^\infty \frac{\sin\left(e^{-x}\right)}{e^x}\,dx =$
   A. $\sin(1)$
   B. $\pi-\sin(1)$
   C. $\cos(1)-1$
   D. $1-\cos(1)$
   E. $\frac{1}{2}$

7. Find the area of the region bounded above by the curve $y=\frac{1}{x\ln^3(x)}$, below by the x-axis, and on the left by the line $x=e$.
   A. $\frac{1}{4}$
   B. $\frac{1}{2}$
   C. 2
   D. e
   E. 4

Free-Response Questions–Calculus BC Topics

1. Let $f(x) = xe^{-x}$, $x \geq 0$.

   a. Find the maximum value of f on the closed interval $[0,3]$.

   b. Evaluate $\lim_{x \to \infty} f(x)$.

   c. Evaluate $\int_0^\infty f(x)\,dx$.

   d. Find the volume, if it exists, of the solid generated when the region bounded by function f and the x-axis is revolved about the x-axis.

Solutions to Sample Questions

Solutions to Multiple-Choice Questions

1. E

$$\begin{array}{ll} x^2 & e^{2x} \\ -2x & \tfrac{1}{2}e^{2x} \\ 2 & \tfrac{1}{4}e^{2x} \\ -0 & \tfrac{1}{8}e^{2x} \end{array}$$

$$x^2 \cdot \tfrac{1}{2}e^{2x} - 2x \cdot \tfrac{1}{4}e^{2x} + 2 \cdot \tfrac{1}{8}e^{2x} + C$$

2. C

$$u = \ln(x) \quad v' = x^3$$

$$u' = \tfrac{1}{x} \quad v = \tfrac{1}{4}x^4$$

$$\tfrac{1}{4}x^4 \ln(x) - \int \tfrac{1}{x} \cdot \tfrac{1}{4}x^4 \, dx$$

$$\tfrac{1}{4}x^4 \ln(x) - \tfrac{1}{4} \int x^3 \, dx$$

3. B

$$\int \frac{3}{(x-2)(2x-1)} dx$$

$$\frac{A}{x-2} + \frac{B}{2x-1} = \frac{3}{(x-2)(2x-1)}$$

$$A(2x-1) + B(x-2) = 3$$

$$x = \tfrac{1}{2} \Rightarrow -\tfrac{3}{2}B = 3, B = -2$$

$$x = 2 \Rightarrow 3A = 3, A = 1$$

$$\int \left[\frac{1}{x-2} - \frac{2}{2x-1}\right] dx$$

4. A

5. C

$$u = 1 + x^2$$

$$du = 2x \, dx$$

$$\tfrac{1}{2}\int_1^\infty \frac{1}{(1+x^2)^4} \cdot 2x \, dx$$

$$\tfrac{1}{2}\int_2^\infty \frac{1}{u^4} du$$

$$\tfrac{1}{2}\lim_{x\to\infty}\left(\frac{-1}{3u^3}\right)\Bigg|_2^b$$

$$\tfrac{1}{2}\left(0 + \tfrac{1}{24}\right)$$

6. D $u = e^{-x}$

$du = -e^{-x}dx$

$-\int_0^\infty \sin\left(e^{-x}\right) \cdot \frac{-1}{e^x} dx$

$-\int_1^0 \sin u \, du$

$\int_0^1 \sin u \, du$

$-\cos u \Big|_0^1$

7. B $\int_e^\infty \frac{1}{x \ln^3(x)} dx$

$u = \ln(x)$

$du = \frac{1}{x} dx$

$\int_1^\infty \frac{1}{u^3} du$

$\lim_{b \to \infty} \frac{-1}{2u^2} \Big|_1^\infty$

$0 + \frac{1}{2}$

Solutions to Free-Response Questions

1. Let $f(x) = xe^{-x}$, $x \geq 0$.

   a. Find the maximum value of f on the closed interval $[0,3]$.

   b. Evaluate $\lim\limits_{x\to\infty} f(x)$.

   c. Evaluate $\int_0^\infty f(x)\,dx$.

   d. Find the volume, if it exists, of the solid generated when the region bounded by function f and the x-axis is revolved about the x-axis.

(a)

$f'(x) = e^{-x} - xe^{-x} = e^{-x}(1-x)$

$f'(x) = 0$

$x = 1$

$f(0) = 0$

$f(1) = e^{-1}$

$f(3) = 3e^{-3}$

Maximum value is e^{-1}.

$4\begin{cases} 1: & f'(x) \\ 1: & \text{solves } f'(x) = 0 \\ 1: & \text{considers } f(0), f(1), f(3) \\ 1: & \text{answer} \end{cases}$

(b)

$\lim\limits_{x\to\infty} xe^{-x} = \lim\limits_{x\to\infty}\left(\dfrac{x}{e^x}\right) = \lim\limits_{x\to\infty}\left(\dfrac{1}{e^x}\right) = 0$

1: answer

(c)

$\int_0^\infty xe^{-x}\,dx$

$\lim\limits_{b\to\infty}\left(-xe^{-x} - e^{-x}\right)\Big|_0^b$

$\lim\limits_{b\to\infty}\dfrac{-x-1}{e^x}\Bigg|_0^b$

1

$2\begin{cases} 1: & \text{limit} \\ 1: & \text{answer} \end{cases}$

(d)

$\pi\int_0^\infty \left(xe^{-x}\right)^2 dx$

$\pi \lim\limits_{b\to\infty}\dfrac{-\frac{1}{2}x^2 - \frac{1}{2}x - \frac{1}{4}}{e^{2x}}\Bigg|_0^b$

$\pi\left(0 + \frac{1}{4}\right)$

$\frac{1}{4}\pi$

$3\begin{cases} 1: & \text{integral} \\ 1: & \text{limit} \\ 1: & \text{answer} \end{cases}$

Connect2Calculus Videos for Chapter 6

The Calculus Concepts Video's for Chapter 6 include:

There are no videos specifically for Chapter 6

CHAPTER 7: FIRST-ORDER DIFFERENTIAL EQUATIONS

Correlations

The section by section correspondence to the Topic Outline for Calculus AB and the Topic Outline for Calculus BC (*Calculus BC topics are in italic type*) is:

AP Topic	Chapter.Section	Pages
II. Derivatives **Derivative as a function** • Equations involving derivatives. Verbal descriptions are translated into equations involving derivatives and vice versa	7.1	566-577
II. Derivatives **Applications of derivatives** + *Numerical solution of differential equations using Euler's method* • Geometric interpretation of differential equations via slope fields and the relationship between slope fields and solution curves for differential equations	*7.3* 7.3	*587-599* 587-599
III. Integrals **Applications of antidifferentiation** • Solving separable differential equations and using them in modeling (in particular, studying the equation $y' = ky$ and exponential growth) + *Solving logistic differential equations and using them in modeling*	7.1, 7.2 *7.2*	566-577, 577-587 *577-587*

<table>
<tr><th>Textbook Section</th><th>AP Topic</th></tr>
<tr><td>7.1 Modeling with Differential Equations</td><td>II. Derivatives

Derivative as a function
• Equations involving derivatives. Verbal descriptions are translated into equations involving derivatives and vice versa

III. Integrals

Applications of antidifferentiation
• Solving separable differential equations and using them in modeling (in particular, studying the equation $y' = ky$ and exponential growth)</td></tr>
<tr><td>7.2 Separable Differential Equations</td><td>III. Integrals

Applications of antidifferentiation
• Solving separable differential equations and using them in modeling (in particular, studying the equation $y' = ky$ and exponential growth)

+ Solving logistic differential equations and using them in modeling</td></tr>
<tr><td>7.3 Direction Fields and Euler's Method</td><td>II. Derivatives

Applications of derivatives
+ Numerical solution of differential equations using Euler's method

• Geometric interpretation of differential equations via slope fields and the relationship between slope fields and solution curves for differential equations</td></tr>
</table>

Vocabulary and Section Notes

Vocabulary used in the Topic Outline for Calculus AB and the Topic Outline for Calculus BC (*Calculus BC topics are in italic type*) include:

Continuous compounding
Differential equation
Direction field (slopefield)
Exponential growth and decay
Euler's method
General solution or family of solutions
Half-life
IVP (initial value problem)
k – the growth constant
Logistic growth
Newton's Law of Cooling
Separable equation
Separation of variables

Section notes for the Calculus AB Course:

Section 7.2 (Separable Differential Equations): Logistic Growth is not part of the Topic Outline for Calculus AB.

Section 7.3 (Direction Fields and Euler's Method): Euler's Method and Equilibrium Solutions are not part of the Topic Outline for Calculus AB.

Section 7.4 (Systems of First-Order Differential Equations): This topic is not part of the Topic Outline for Calculus AB.

Section notes for the Calculus BC Course:

Section 7.2 (Separable Differential Equations): The logistics equation is used to develop a general formula for the size of the population. Please read the "Teacher's Notes: The Logistics Function" for more information about this topic.

Section 7.3 (Direction Fields and Euler's Method): The major subtopic: Equilibrium Solutions is not part of the Topic Outline for Calculus BC.

Section 7.4 (Systems of First-Order Differential Equations): This topic is not part of the Topic Outline for Calculus BC.

Student Activity: Investigating Slope Fields

Teacher's Notes:

Slope fields are an excellent way to visualize a family of solutions to a differential equation. If the differential equation can be solved algebraically the slope field provides a way to verify the algebraic solution matches the graphical solution.

Students should be able to do the following with slope fields:

1. Sketch a slope field for a given differential equation.
2. Given a slope field, sketch a solution curve through a given point.
3. Match a slope field to a differential equation.
4. Match a slope field to a solution of a differential equation.

To sketch a slope field, students should know how to graph a line given a point and a slope.

For a given differential equation use a piece of gridded graph paper to plot short segments that represent the slope of the function if it passes through that point.

1. Pick a point on the grid and calculate the slope of the function at that point by substituting the x and y coordinates (as needed) into the differential equation.
2. At that point on the grid, draw a short line segment with the calculated slope.
3. Repeat steps one and two until all points on the grid have a line segment plotted.

If the differential equation is only in terms of x, i.e. $\frac{dy}{dx} = 2x$, students should notice that all points with the same x-coordinate have the same slope. This means that all the short line segments in a vertical column will have the same slope. If the differential equation is only in terms of y, i.e. $\frac{dy}{dx} = 2y$, students should notice that all points with the same y-coordinate have the same slope. This means that all the short segments in a horizontal row will have the same slope. If the differential equation is in terms of both x and y there will probably be no simple pattern visible. Knowledge of these patterns can help students match a slope field to a differential equation. If the differential equation is in terms of x and y, it is helpful to find points with slopes of 0, 1 or -1 and use them to help identify the differential equation.

Slope fields have been a topic on the Calculus BC Exam since 1998 and on the Calculus AB Exam since 2004. Multiple-Choice questions involving slope fields can be found on the 1998 Calculus BC exam (question 24) and the 2003 Calculus BC exam (question 14). Free-Response questions include 1998 BC4, 2000 BC6, 2002 BC5, 2004 AB6, 2005 AB6, and 2006 AB5.

Student Worksheet

Draw a slope field for each differential equation

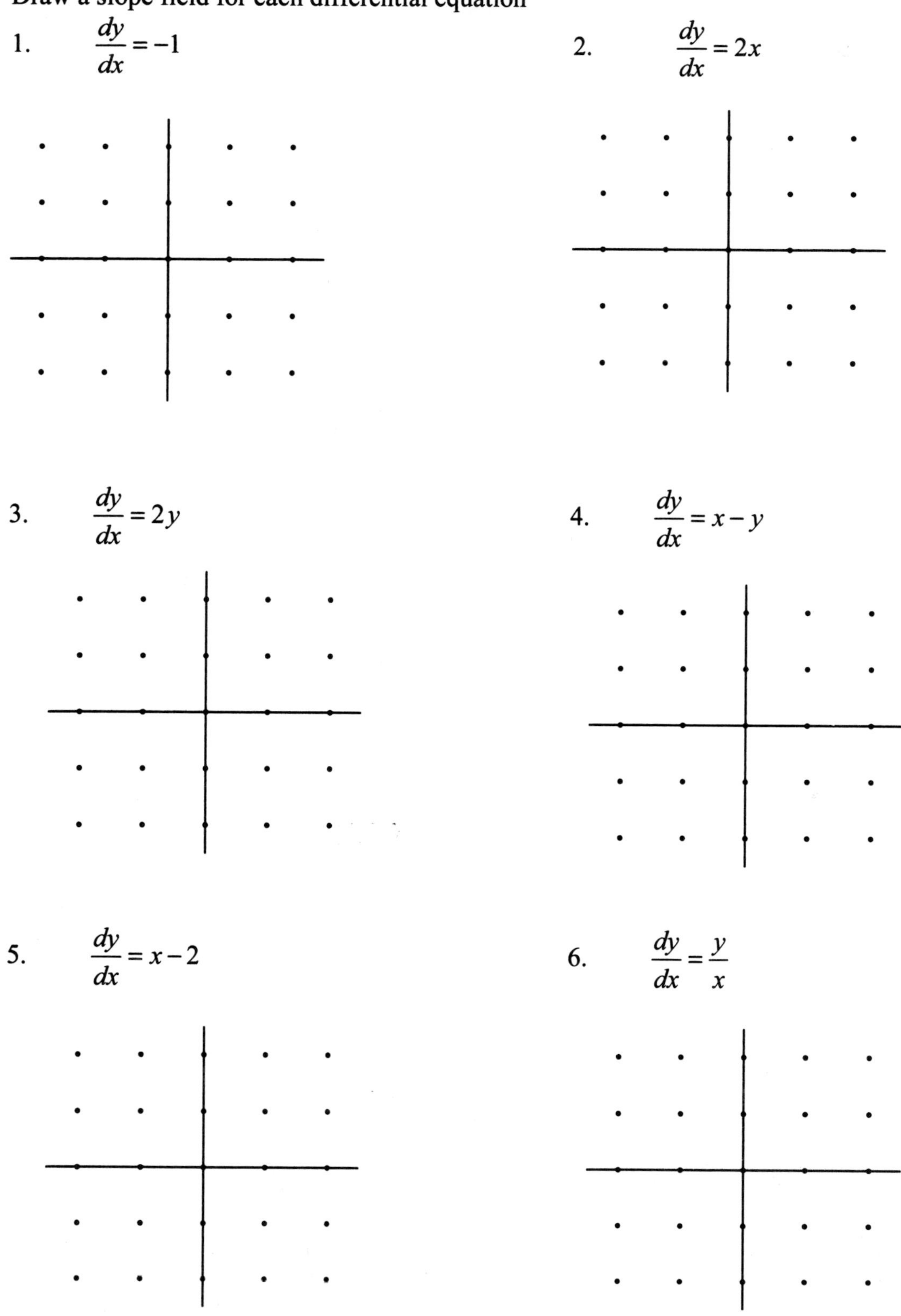

1. $\frac{dy}{dx} = -1$
2. $\frac{dy}{dx} = 2x$
3. $\frac{dy}{dx} = 2y$
4. $\frac{dy}{dx} = x - y$
5. $\frac{dy}{dx} = x - 2$
6. $\frac{dy}{dx} = \frac{y}{x}$

Match each slope field with the equation that the slope field could represent

(a)

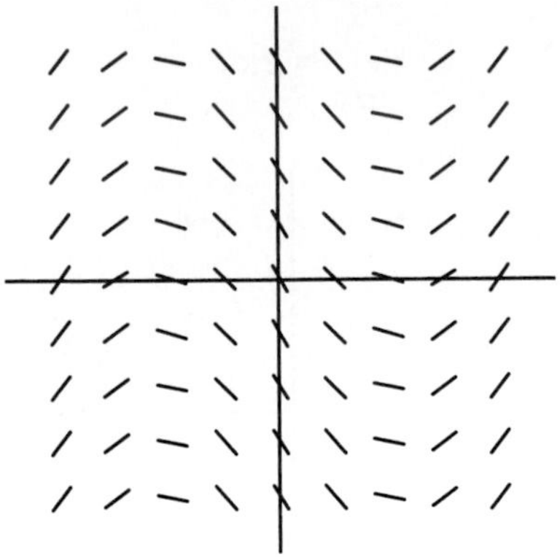

(b)

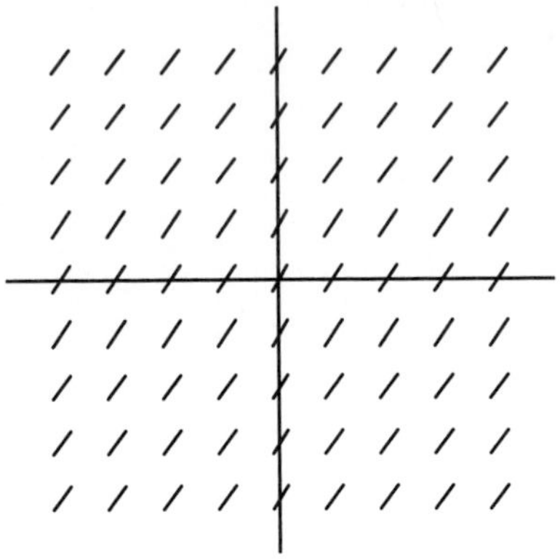

(c)

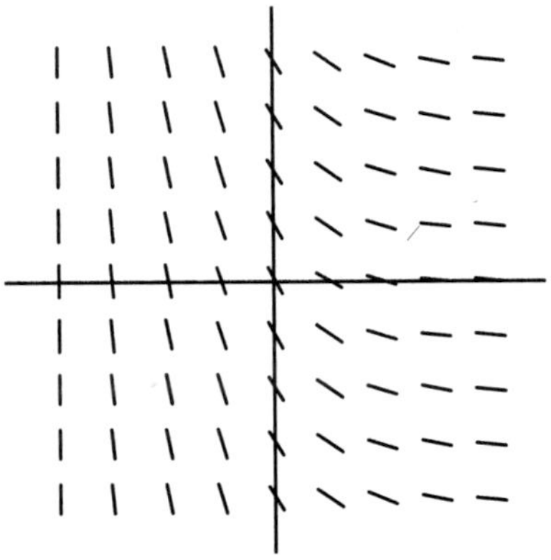

(d)

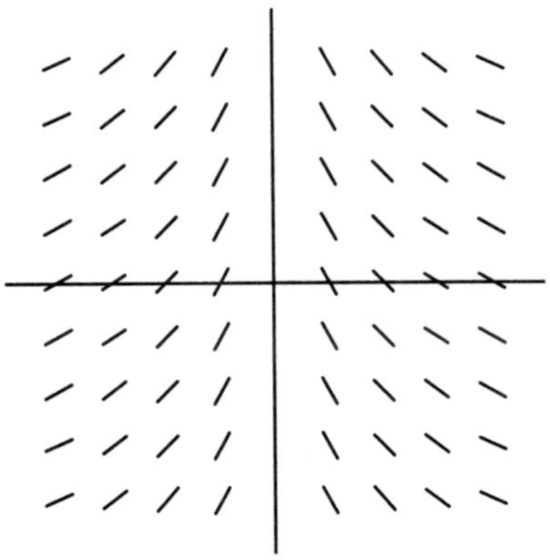

(e)

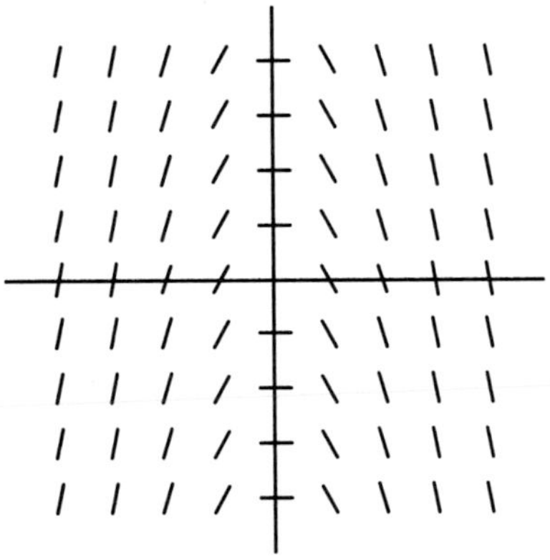

(f)

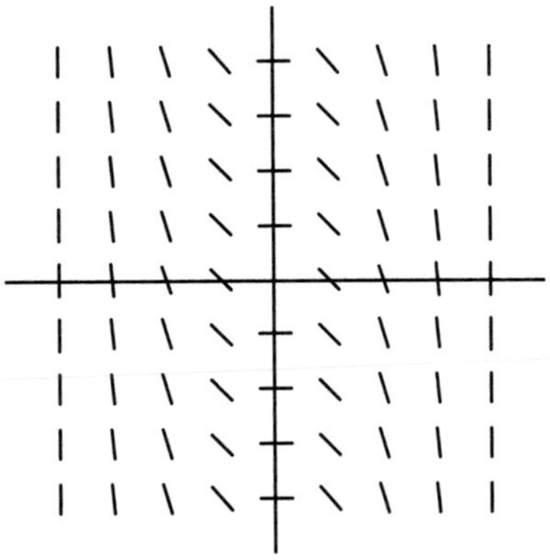

7. $y = x$

8. $y = \frac{1}{x}$

9. $y = -\sin(x)$

10. $y = -x^2$

11. $y = e^{-x}$

12. $y = -.5x \wedge 3$

Match the slope fields with their differential equations:

(A)

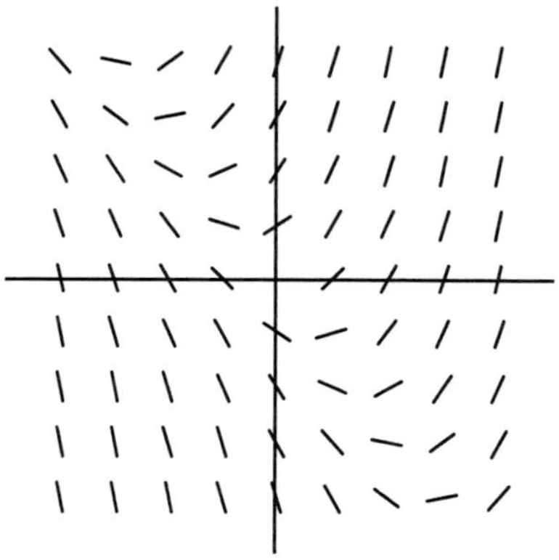

(B)

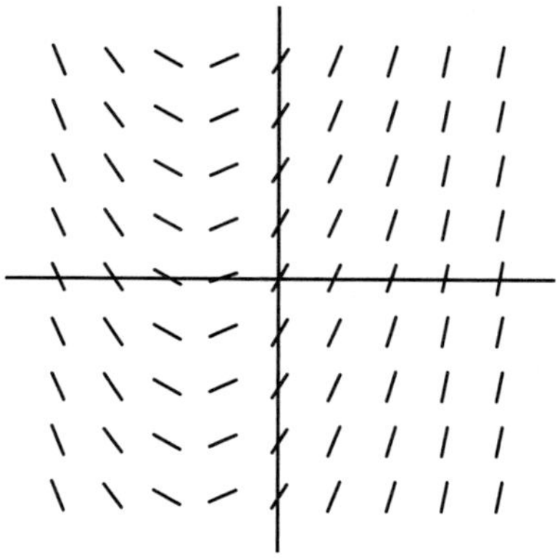

(C)

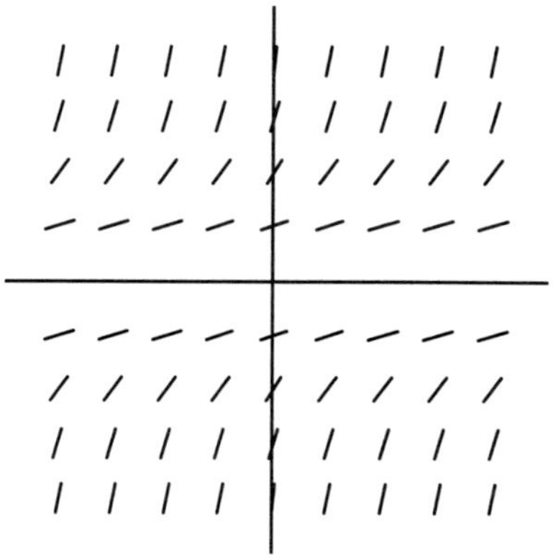

(D)

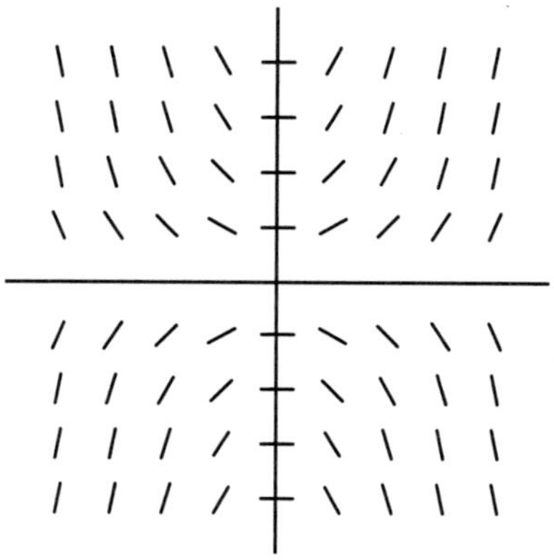

13. $\dfrac{dy}{dx} = x + 1$

14. $\dfrac{dy}{dx} = y^2$

15. $\dfrac{dy}{dx} = x + y$

16. $\dfrac{dy}{dx} = xy$

17. The slope field for the differential equation $\dfrac{dy}{dx} = y - x$ is shown in the figure below.

(a) Sketch the solution curve through the point $(2,0)$.

(b) Sketch the solution curve through the point $(-3,0)$.

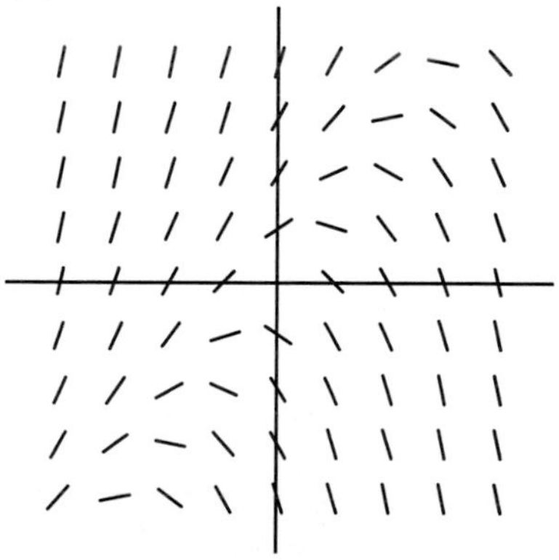

Solutions:

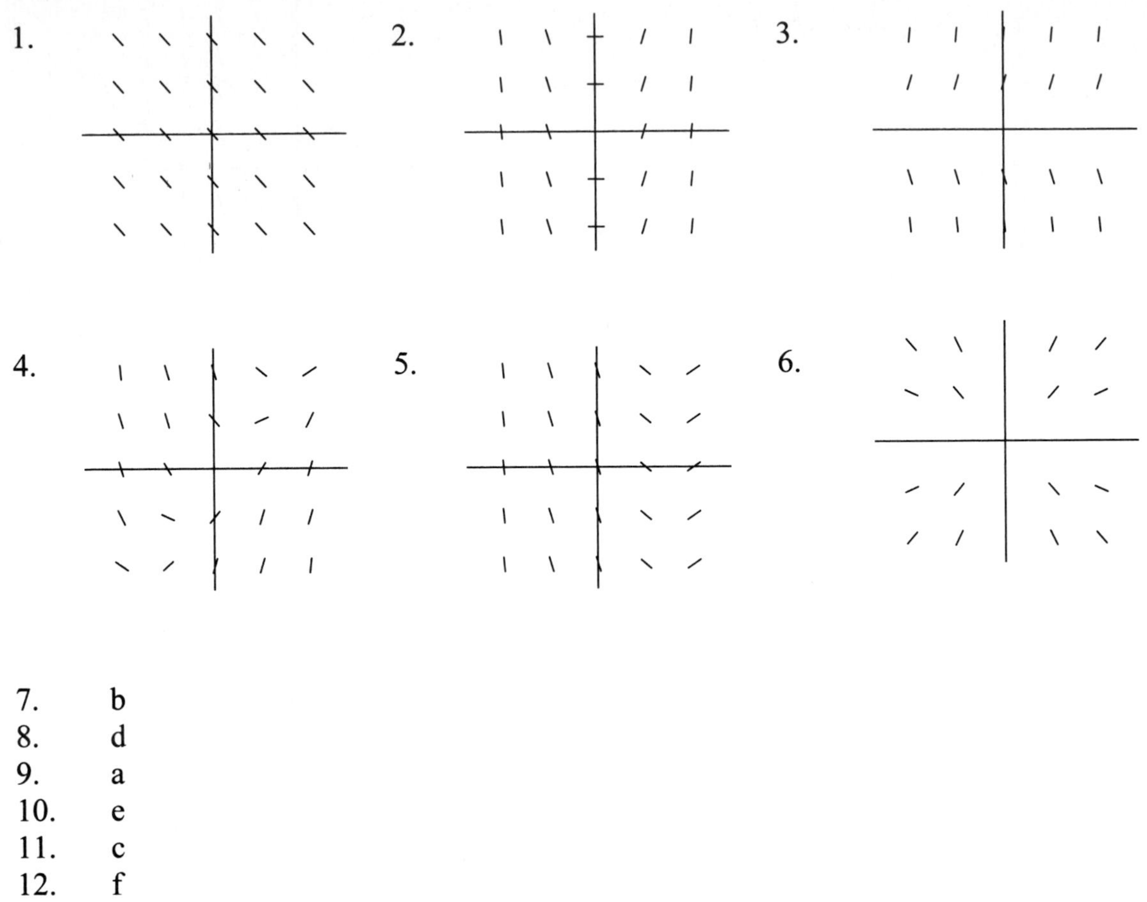

7. b
8. d
9. a
10. e
11. c
12. f
13. B
14. C
15. A
16. D

17.

Student Activity: Logistics Model–"She Said, He Said" (Calculus BC Topic)

Teacher's Notes:

This activity is designed to model a logistic growth curve. It is based on the premise that rumors spread quickly at first through a population. However, over time, the number of people who have heard the rumor grows more slowly.

1. Number each student in the classroom. Explain that one person will be chosen randomly to be the first person who hears the rumor. Explain that each person who hears the rumor will tell only two people per hour. Use a random number generator to select the initial person. Have this person stand. This is the value for hour 0. Record the value on the board.

2. Since this person will tell only two people, use the random number generator to select two more numbers representing people who have now heard the rumor. Have these people stand. Count the number of people who are now standing. This is the value for hour 1. Record the value on the board.

3. For each person standing, choose two random numbers. Some may be duplicates of those previously selected. Have all people who have heard the rumor stand. Record the value for hour 3.

4. Repeat step 3 as many times as necessary until all people in the class have heard the rumor. Record the value for each hour.

5. Make a plot of Hour (x-axis) vs. People who have heard the rumor (y-axis). Students should notice that the data appears to grow exponentially at first. But after a while, the number of people who have heard the rumor levels off. Use the curve fitting feature to fit a logistic model to the data.

6. Have students note where the growth rate seems slowest and fastest. Plot the derivative of the logistic function on the same axes. The maximum of the derivative should correspond to the location of the fastest growth. Students should know that the maximum growth of a logistic function occurs midway between the *y-value* of the function at $t = -\infty$ and $t = \infty$.

Applications

Social scientists use logistic models to track the spread of rumors or stories or jokes through a population. Epidemiologists use the same model to track the growth of a disease.

Large retailers like Wal-Mart use this model to determine when to stop reordering seasonal items. For example, in colder climates heavy coats usually appear in stores in the early fall. Stores track the week-to-week sales of coats. As long as the rate of change increases, managers will order more coats. As soon as the rate of change stops increasing, they will stop ordering more coats and sell only the ones that still remain in the store. As soon as most of the coats are gone, they use the space for the next seasonal item. This ensures that the store will maximize the income from that floor space.

Student Activity: Logistics Model–Popcorn (Calculus BC Topic)

Teacher's Notes:

The concept of the logistics growth function is usually unfamiliar to students, however, some biology classes discuss logistics population growth models so students may know about the function, but they have probably never studied its mathematical properties. If your school's biology course discusses logistic growth, a great interdisciplinary teaching unit could be developed.

The popcorn activity is a dramatic demonstration of logistic growth that makes it clear that logistic growth is all around us.

Give each student a bag or two (depends on class size) of microwavable popcorn. Assign each student a different length of time to pop his/her corn. Since most microwavable popcorn starts popping after about 1 minute and is finished in about 2 minutes, use 5 second intervals from 60 seconds to 120 seconds.

After the time has elapsed, each student should count the number of kernels popped. They can then enjoy the popped corn, but must remember to bring their result to class. Gather the student results and use the **STAT** features of the TI83/84 to analyze the collected data.

The keystrokes for the TI-83/84 follow.

1. Clear Lists $\mathbf{L_1}$ through $\mathbf{L_4}$.

2. Enter the time values, 60-120, in $\mathbf{L_1}$. The regression process requires all number of kernels popped to be greater than 0. If some of the quicker times, i.e. less than 70 seconds have no data eliminate them from the analysis.

3. Enter the number of popped kernels in $\mathbf{L_2}$.

4. Use **StatPlo**t to make a scatter plot of the student data. Let $\mathbf{L_1}$ be the X list and $\mathbf{L_2}$ be the Y List. Choose **Plot1**. The plot should look like the graph of a logistics function.

5. Go to **STAT, CALC, B: Logistic** and press ENTER. On the home screen, after the Logistic command select $\mathbf{L_1}$**,** $\mathbf{L_2}$**, Vars, Y-Vars, Function, Y1** and then press enter. The complete command, before you press enter, should look like **Logistic** $\mathbf{L_1}$**,** $\mathbf{L_2}$**, Y1**. The calculator will determine a best-fit logistics function for the data (this may take some time). The results will be displayed on the home screen and the equation will be placed in **Y1**. Use the results to complete the template for a logistics function. Press **GRAPH** and the resulting equation will be graphed with the students' popcorn data.

6. To display the graph of the derivative type the following command in **Y2=MATH,8 derive(Y1,X,X)**. You will probably have to adjust the **YMAX** value (much lower) to see the derivative graph (note the original **YMAX** value so it can be reentered for step 7). To determine the time when the number of kernels is increasing the fastest, either use **TRACE** on the derivative graph or use **(2ND CALC) MAX**, to find the maximum value of the derivative.

7. Restore **YMAX** to the original value and use **(2ND CALC) VALUE x=** the result from step 6 to locate the point on the graph where the number of popped kernels is increasing fastest.

8. After studying the properties of the logistics functions, the students should be able to answer these questions:

   a. Using the values supplied by the Logistic regression write the function that represents the relationship between elapsed time and the number of kernels popped. Round all values to 3 decimal places.

   b. What is the significance of the value of c in the calculator's logistic function?

   c. Using the logistics equation, how many kernels were popped at $t = 60, 80, 100, 120$ seconds? How do these values compare to the actual data collected?

   d. When was the corn popping the fastest? What was the time determined in step 6? How did you know this in the kitchen? How do you know this when you look at the graph?

Teacher's Notes: The Logistics Function (Calculus BC Topic)

The first references to the logistics function appear in section 3.9, on page 334. In the logistics equation $p(t)$ represents the fraction of the maximum sustainable population at time t. The rate of change of the fraction of the population is $p'(t) = r\,p(t)[1 - p(t)]$ and $p''(t) = \frac{d}{dt}p'(t)$ is used to find the fraction of the population when the growth rate of the population is a maximum.

$$\begin{aligned} p''(t) &= rp'(t)(1 - p(t)) + rp(t)(-p'(t)) \\ &= rp'(t)(1 - p(t) - p(t)) \\ &= rp'(t)(1 - 2p(t)) \end{aligned}$$

$p''(t) = 0$ when $rp'(t) = 0$ or $1 - 2p(t) = 0$

Since the graph of $p'(t)$ is a downward opening parabola, the critical point is a maximum value and $p'(t)$ reaches its maximum value when $p(t) = \frac{1}{2}$. Note: this time is the inflection point for p(t).

In other words, the rate of change of the population is fastest when the population level is $\frac{1}{2}$ of the maximum sustainable population.

Notice, the maximum rate of growth doesn't depend on the value of r.

The rate of change of a population, $p'(t) = r\,p(t)[1 - p(t)]$, is called the logistics equation.

Exercises 49-53 are related to this concept.

A more common representation is the differential equation $y'(t) = ky(M - y)$ where $y(t)$ is the actual population at time t and M is the maximum sustainable population.

$$\begin{aligned} y''(t) &= ky'(t)(M - y) + ky(-y'(t)) \\ &= ky'(t)(M - y - y) \\ &= ky'(t)(M - 2y) \end{aligned}$$

Again, the rate of growth is the largest when $y = \frac{1}{2}M$ and it doesn't depend on the value of k

This value is the inflection point for $y(t)$.

Students will find it useful to be able to identify when the rate of growth is the largest and that finding the value of $\lim_{t \to \infty} y(t)$ is the same as finding the value of M, the maximum sustainable population.

The idea of logistic growth reappears in section 7.2, on page 581. At this time, the authors solve the logistics equation $y'(t) = ky(M - y)$ to derive the general formula for the size of the population at any time t. Since the differential equation is separable, the integration technique, partial fractions, can be used to find the general formula $y = \dfrac{AMe^{kMt}}{1 + Ae^{kMt}}$ where M is the maximum sustainable population and A is a constant determined by the initial condition in the problem.

Most text books continue to simplify this equation:

$$y = \frac{AMe^{kMt}}{1 + Ae^{kMt}}$$

$$y = \frac{M}{\frac{1}{Ae^{kMt}} + 1}$$

$$y = \frac{M}{1 + \frac{1}{A}e^{-kMt}}$$

Two simplifying substitutions are usually made $a = \dfrac{1}{A}$ and $b = kM$

leading to this version of the formula for the population: $y = \dfrac{M}{1 + ae^{-bt}}$

The value for a can be calculated directly using $a = \dfrac{M - y_0}{y_0}$ and the time to the inflection point (when the population is increasing the fastest) can be calculated using $t = \dfrac{\ln\left(\frac{1}{a}\right)}{-b}$.

Related exercises (31-40) provide practice in computing a particular solution and for finding when a specific value of the population will occur. It is important that students learn to recognize the value (M) of the maximum carrying capacity of the population when the function is given in its differential equation form.

Properties of the graph of the logistic function are discussed in 7.2 and the important features of the rate of change of the population, $p'(t)$, are discussed in 3.9.

A typical multiple-choice question on this topic would probably ask either of these two questions:

a. The number of mice at Thomasville Lab grows according to the logistics differential equation $\frac{dM}{dt} = 16M - 4M^2$, where M is the number of hundreds of mice after t months. If $M(0) = \frac{1}{4}$, for what value of M is the number of mice increasing the fastest?

$$\frac{dM}{dt} = 4M(4 - M)$$

$$Max = 4$$

$$\frac{1}{2}Max = 2$$

The number of mice is growing the fastest when there are 200 mice

b. The number of mice at Thomasville Lab grows according to the logistics differential equation $\frac{dM}{dt} = 16M - 4M^2$, where M is the number of hundreds of mice after t months. If $M(0) = \frac{1}{4}$, find $\lim_{t \to \infty} M(t)$

$$\frac{dM}{dt} = 4M(4 - M)$$

$$Max = 4$$

The maximum number of mice in the lab is 400

Parts (a) and (b) question 5 on the 2004 Calculus BC Free-Response exam ask the student to provide the same type of information about the properties of a logistics differential equation. Please note that in parts (c) and (d) of this question, the differential equation is changed and it is no longer a logistics equation. Regular techniques for solving a separable differential equation can be applied to the solution of these questions.

Several multiple-choice and free-response questions at the end of this chapter can give students more practice with the logistics differential equation.

Multiple-Choice Questions–Calculus AB/BC Topics

1. Which of the following is a slope field for the differential equation $\frac{dy}{dx} = \frac{x+1}{y}$?

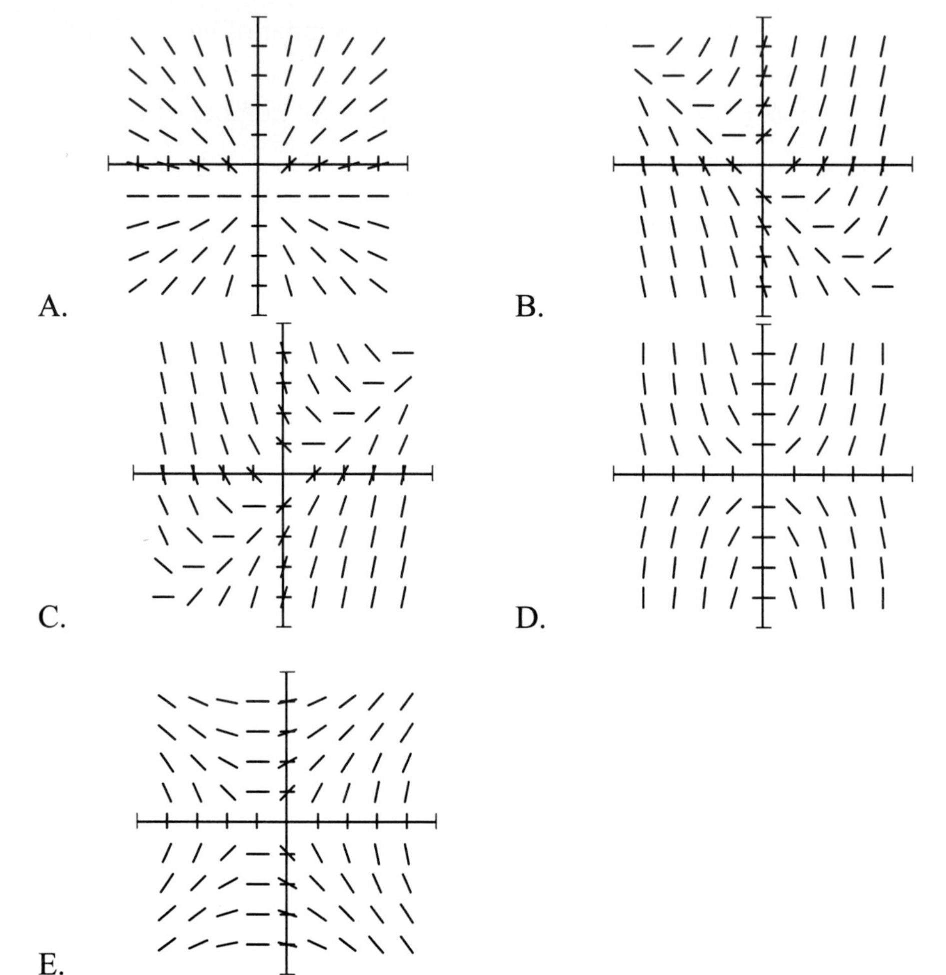

A. B. C. D. E.

2. The slope field for a certain differential equation is shown below. Which of the following could be a specific solution to that differential equation?

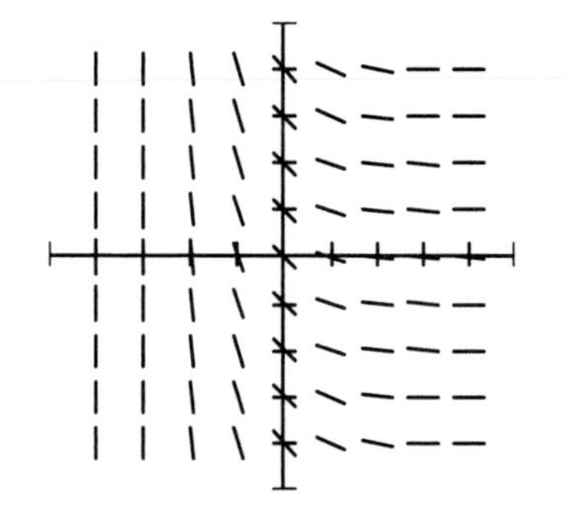

A. $y = x^2$ B. $y = e^{-x}$ C. $y = \sin(x)$ D. $y = \ln(x)$ E. $y = x^{\frac{2}{3}}$

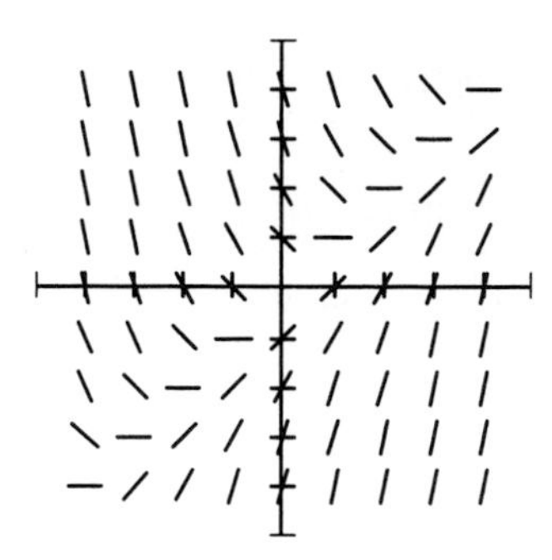

3. Shown above is the slope field for which of the following differential equations?

A. $\frac{dy}{dx} = \frac{y+1}{x}$ B. $\frac{dy}{dx} = x - y$ C. $\frac{dy}{dx} = 2x$

D. $\frac{dy}{dx} = \frac{2}{3\sqrt[3]{x}}$ E. $\frac{dy}{dx} = xy$

*4. The rate at which a bacteria population grows is proportional to the number of bacteria present. At 3 hours there are 400 bacteria present and at 7 hours there are 2000 bacteria present. Approximately how long does it take the population to double?

A. 1 hour
B. 1.3 hours
C. 1.4 hours
D. 1.7 hours
E. 2.7 hours

5. If $y\left(\sqrt{\pi}\right) = -2$, then a solution to the differentiable equation $\frac{dy}{dx} = \frac{x\cos\left(x^2\right)}{y}$ is

A. $y = -\sqrt{\sin\left(x^2\right)+5}$
B. $y = -\sqrt{\sin\left(x^2\right)+4}$
C. $y = \sin\left(x^2\right)$
D. $y = \sqrt{3-\sin\left(x^2\right)}$
E. $y = \sqrt{4-\sin\left(x^2\right)}$

Multiple-Choice Questions – 6-10 Calculus BC Topics

6. The number of mice at Thomasville Lab grows according to the logistics differential equation $\frac{dM}{dt}=12M-8M^2$, where M is number of hundreds of mice after t months. If $M(0)=\frac{1}{4}$, for what value of M is the number of mice increasing the fastest?
   A. $M=\frac{3}{4}$
   B. $M=\frac{4}{3}$
   C. $M=\frac{3}{2}$
   D. $M=12$
   E. $M=16$

7. The number of rats at Thomasville Lab grows according to the logistics differential equation $\frac{dR}{dt}=R-\frac{1}{8}R^2$, where R is number of hundreds of rats after t months. If $R(0)=10$, what is the fastest growth rate, in rats per month, for this population?
   A. 30
   B. 87.5
   C. 200
   D. 400
   E. 800

8. The number of rabbits at Thomasville Lab grows according to the logistics differential equation $\frac{dR}{dt}=15000R-50R^2$, where R represents the number of rabbits after t months. If $R(0)=100$, find $\lim_{t\to\infty} R(t)$.
   A. 150
   B. 250
   C. 300
   D. 400
   E. 3000

9. If $N(0)=20$ and $\frac{dN}{dt}=\frac{1}{4}N-\frac{1}{400}N^2$, what is $N(t)$?

A. $\frac{100}{1+4e^{-0.75t}}$

B. $\frac{100}{1+4e^{-0.25t}}$

C. $\frac{400}{1+19e^{-0.75t}}$

D. $\frac{400}{1+19e^{-0.25t}}$

E. $\frac{100}{1-4e^{-0.75t}}$

10. Suppose that a bee population grows according to the logistics differential equation $\frac{dB}{dt}=4B-0.0001B^2$, where B represents the number of bees after t months. Which of the following statements is true?

I. $\lim_{t\to\infty} B(t)=4000$

II. If $B(t)>4000$, then $\frac{dB}{dt}<0$.

III. If $B(0)=100$, then the greatest growth rate occurs when $B=4000$.

A. I only
B. III only
C. II and III only
D. I and II only
E. I, II, and III

11. The table below gives selected values for the derivative of function *f*. If $f(1)=-2$, approximate $f(2)$ using Euler's method with step size 0.5.

x	1	1.5	2
$f'(x)$	$\frac{4}{3}$	$\frac{2}{3}$	$-\frac{1}{3}$

A. $-\frac{10}{3}$
B. $-\frac{11}{3}$
C. -1
D. $-\frac{1}{3}$
E. 0

Free-Response Questions–Calculus AB/BC Topics

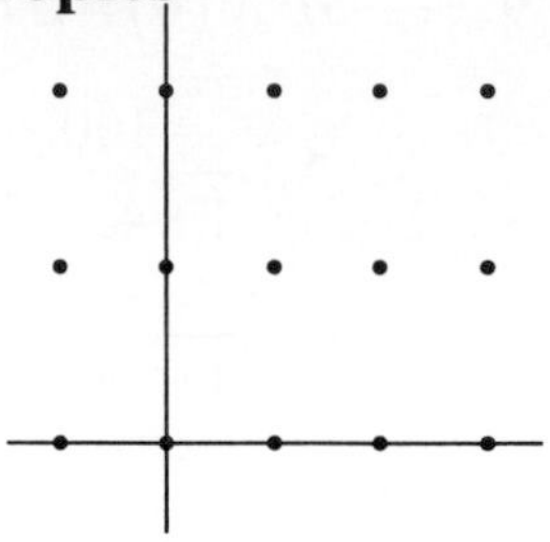

1. Consider the differential equation given by $\frac{dy}{dx} = y(2-x)$

   a. On the axes provided, sketch a slope field for the given differential equation at the fifteen points indicated.

   b. Let $y = f(x)$, $f(0) = 1$, be the particular solution. Write the equation of the line tangent to the function at $(0,1)$ and use it to approximate the value of $f(0.1)$.

   c. Find the particular solution $y = f(x)$ to the given differential equation with the initial condition $f(0) = 1$.

2. Consider the differential equation $\frac{dy}{dx} = \frac{y}{1+x^2}$.

   a. On the axes provided, sketch a slope field for the given differential equation at the twelve points indicated.

   b. Sketch the solution curve that passes through the point $(0,1)$.

   c. If $y > 0$, a solution curve is strictly increasing. Why?

   d. If $y(0) = 1$, find a particular solution $y(x)$ to the given differential equation.

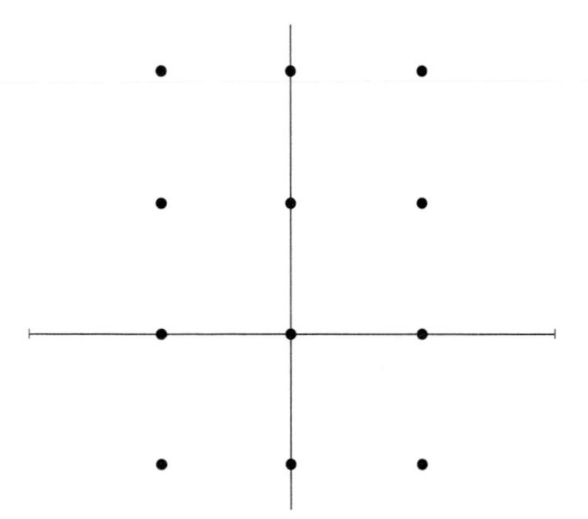

Free-Response Questions BC Topics

3. A population is modeled by a function P that satisfies the logistic differential equation $\frac{dP}{dt} = \frac{P}{4}\left(1 - \frac{P}{18}\right)$.

   a. If $P(0) = 6$, find $\lim_{t \to \infty} P(t)$.
   If $P(0) = 20$, find $\lim_{t \to \infty} P(t)$.

   b. If $P(0) = 6$, find a particular solution $P(t)$ to the given differential equation.
   For what value of P is the population growing the fastest?
   For what value of t, $t > 0$, is the population growing the fastest?

   c. If $P(0) = 20$, find a particular solution $P(t)$ to the given differential equation.

   d. If $P(0) = 6$, on the axes provided below, using the information from parts (a) and (b), sketch a graph for $P(t)$. If $P(0) = 20$, on the same axes, using the information from part (a) sketch a graph for $P(t)$.

*4. Consider the differential equation $\frac{dy}{dx} = 2x + y$.

   a. The slope field for the given differential equation is provided.
   Sketch the solution curve that passes through the point (0, 0) and
   Sketch the solution curve that passes through (-2, 1).

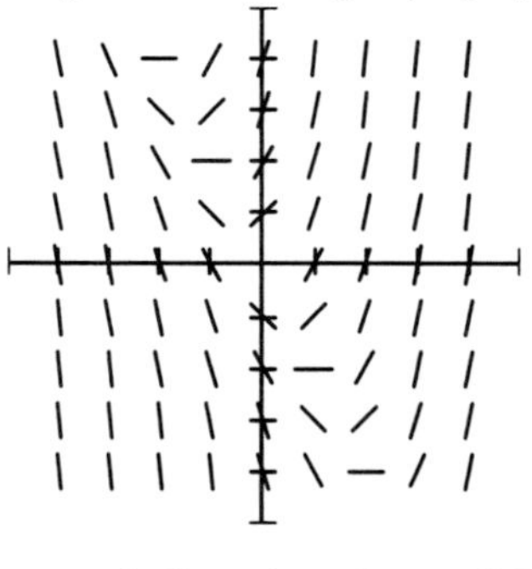

   b. Let f be the function that satisfies the given differential equation with the initial condition $f(-2) = 1$. Use Euler's method, starting at $x = -2$, with a step-size of 0.1 to approximate $f(-1.7)$. Show work that leads to your answer.

   c. Find $\frac{d^2y}{dx^2}$ in terms of x and y. Determine whether the approximation in part (b) is an over-estimate or an under-estimate. Explain your reasoning.

   d. Show that $y = -2x - 2 - e^2 e^x$ is a solution to the differential equation with the initial condition $f(-2) = 1$.

Solutions to Sample Questions

Solutions to Multiple-Choice Questions

1. E When $x = -1$, $y \neq 0$ the value of $\frac{dy}{dx}$ is 0. This is the only choice with this property.

2. B

3. B The slope field has slopes that equal 0 at points where $x = y$ and slopes that equal 1 when $x - y = 1$, so $\frac{dy}{dx} = x - y$

*4. D

$$\frac{dy}{dt} = ky \Rightarrow y = Ae^{kt}$$
$$400 = Ae^{3k}, 2000 = Ae^{7k}$$
$$\frac{400}{e^{3k}} = \frac{2000}{e^{7k}}$$
$$e^{4k} = 5$$
$$k = \tfrac{1}{4}\ln(5)$$
$$2A = Ae^{kt}$$
$$2 = e^{kt}$$
$$t = \frac{\ln(2)}{k}$$

5. B

$$\int y\,dy = \int x\cos(x^2)\,dx$$
$$\tfrac{1}{2}y^2 = \tfrac{1}{2}\sin(x^2) + C$$
$$y = \pm\sqrt{\sin(x^2) + C}$$
$$-2 = -\sqrt{\sin(\pi) + C}$$

6. A $\frac{dM}{dt} = 8M\left(\frac{3}{2} - M\right)$

$Max = \frac{3}{2}$

$\frac{1}{2}Max = \frac{3}{4}$

7. C $\frac{dR}{dt} = \frac{1}{8}R\left(8 - R\right)$

$M = 8$

$\frac{1}{2}M = 4$

$\left.\frac{dR}{dt}\right|_{R=4} = 2$

8. C $\frac{dR}{dt} = 50R\left(300 - R\right)$

$M = 300$

9. B $\frac{dN}{dt} = \frac{1}{400}\left(100 - n\right)$

$M = 100$

$a = \frac{M - y_0}{y_0} = \frac{100 - 20}{20} = 4$

$b = \frac{1}{400} \cdot M = 0.25$

10. D $\frac{dB}{dt} = 0.0001B\left(4000 - B\right)$

11. C $f(1) = -2$

$f(1.5) = -2 + \frac{4}{3}\left(\frac{1}{2}\right) = -\frac{4}{3}$

$f(2) = -\frac{4}{3} + \frac{2}{3}\left(\frac{1}{2}\right)$

Solutions to Free-Response Questions

1. Consider the differential equation given by $\frac{dy}{dx} = y(2-x)$

   a. On the axes provided, sketch a slope field for the given differential equation at the fifteen points indicated.

   b. Let $y = f(x)$, $f(0) = 1$, be the particular solution. Write the equation of the line tangent to the function at (0,1) and use it to approximate the value of $f(0.1)$.

   c. Find the particular solution $y = f(x)$ to the given differential equation with the initial condition $f(0) = 1$.

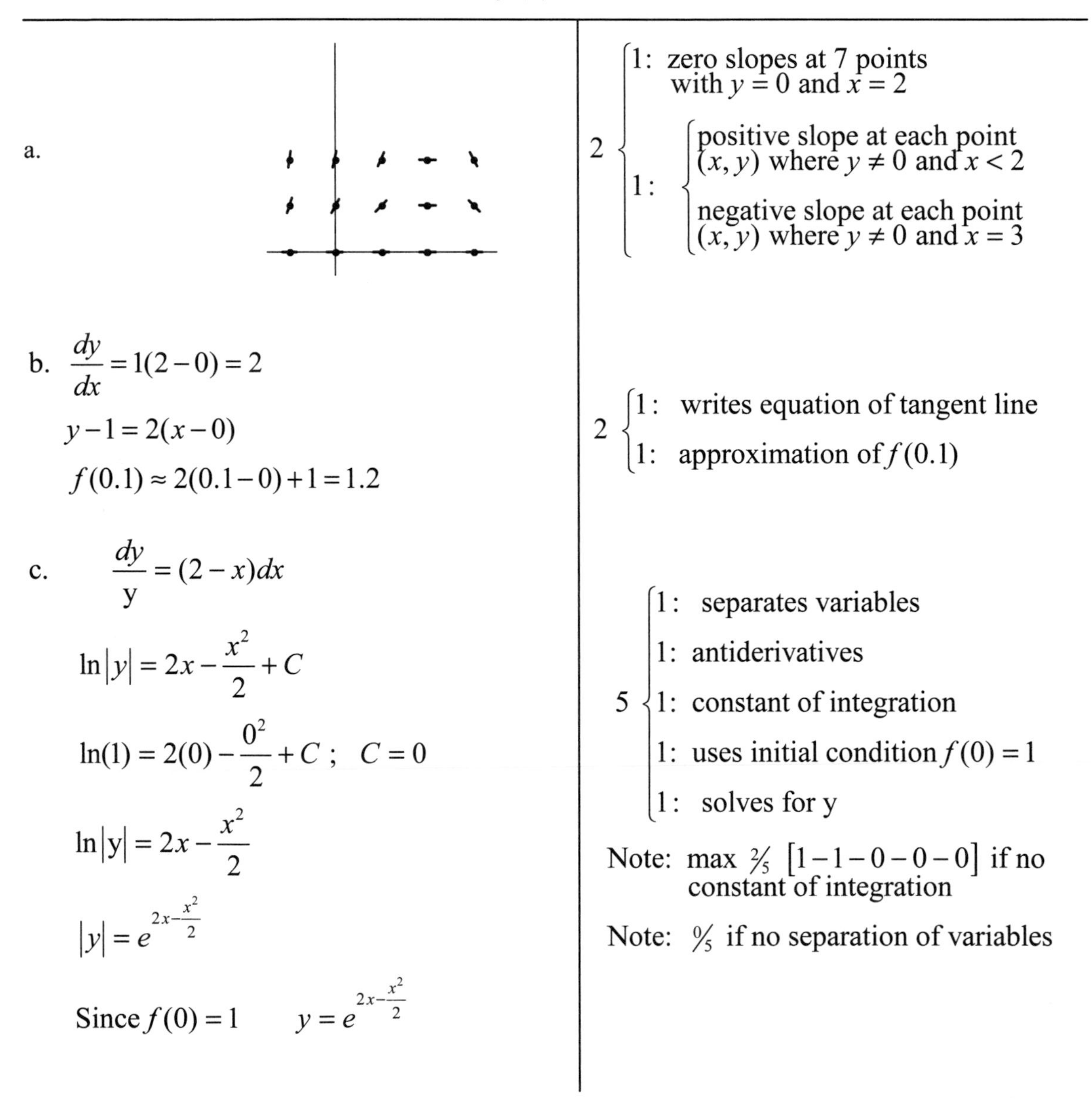

a.

2 points:
- 1: zero slopes at 7 points with $y = 0$ and $x = 2$
- 1: positive slope at each point (x, y) where $y \neq 0$ and $x < 2$; negative slope at each point (x, y) where $y \neq 0$ and $x = 3$

b. $\frac{dy}{dx} = 1(2-0) = 2$

$y - 1 = 2(x - 0)$

$f(0.1) \approx 2(0.1 - 0) + 1 = 1.2$

2 points:
- 1: writes equation of tangent line
- 1: approximation of $f(0.1)$

c. $\frac{dy}{y} = (2-x)dx$

$\ln|y| = 2x - \frac{x^2}{2} + C$

$\ln(1) = 2(0) - \frac{0^2}{2} + C$; $C = 0$

$\ln|y| = 2x - \frac{x^2}{2}$

$|y| = e^{2x - \frac{x^2}{2}}$

Since $f(0) = 1$ $\quad y = e^{2x - \frac{x^2}{2}}$

5 points:
- 1: separates variables
- 1: antiderivatives
- 1: constant of integration
- 1: uses initial condition $f(0) = 1$
- 1: solves for y

Note: max $2/5$ $[1-1-0-0-0]$ if no constant of integration

Note: $0/5$ if no separation of variables

2. Consider the differential equation $\dfrac{dy}{dx} = \dfrac{y}{1+x^2}$.

   a. On the axes provided, sketch a slope field for the given differential equation at the twelve points indicated.
   b. Sketch the solution curve that passes through the point $(0,1)$.
   c. If $y > 0$, a solution curve is strictly increasing. Why?
   d. If $y(0) = 1$, find a particular solution $y(x)$ to the given differential equation.

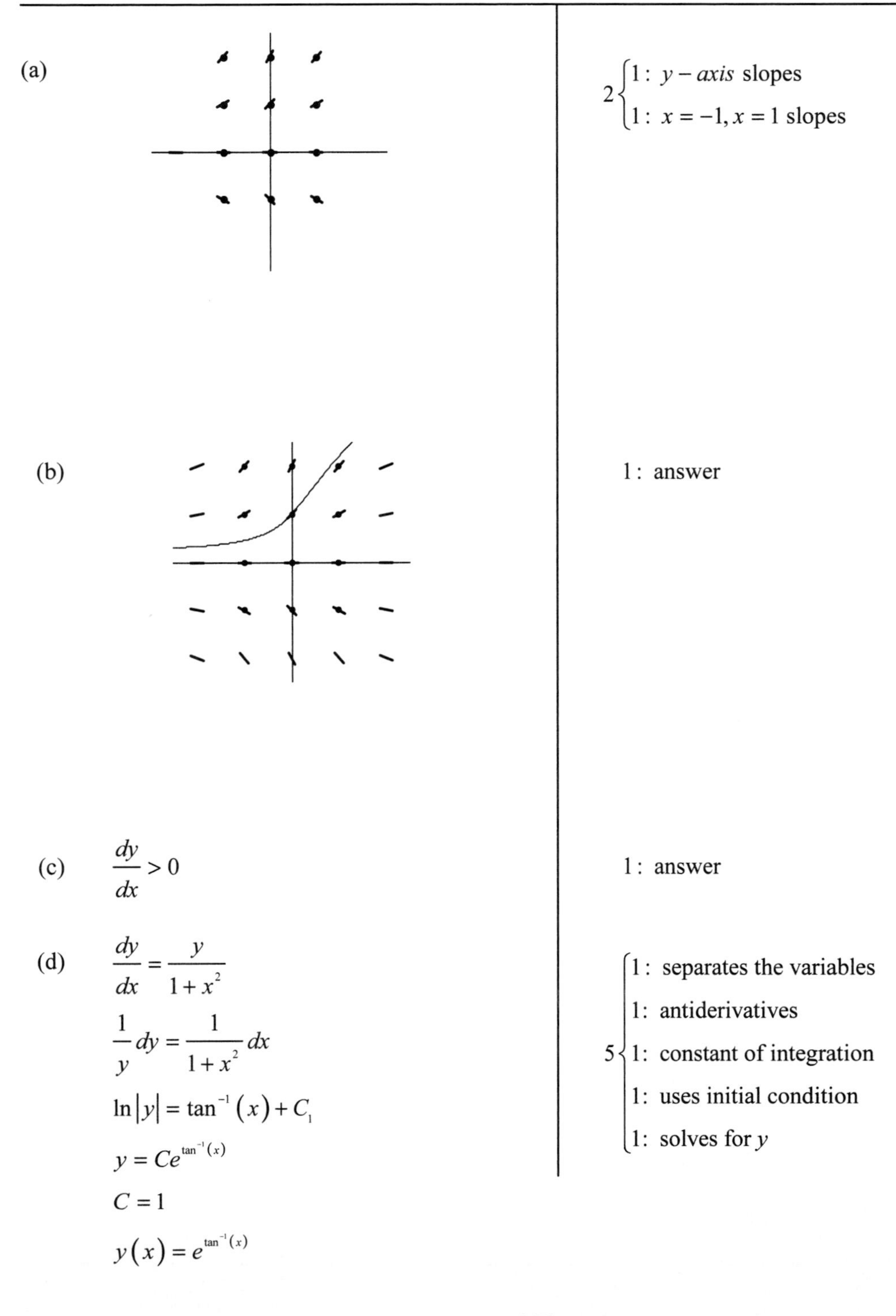

(a)

$2\begin{cases} 1: \ y-axis \text{ slopes} \\ 1: \ x = -1, x = 1 \text{ slopes} \end{cases}$

(b)

$1:$ answer

(c) $\dfrac{dy}{dx} > 0$

$1:$ answer

(d)

$$\frac{dy}{dx} = \frac{y}{1+x^2}$$

$$\frac{1}{y}dy = \frac{1}{1+x^2}dx$$

$$\ln|y| = \tan^{-1}(x) + C_1$$

$$y = Ce^{\tan^{-1}(x)}$$

$$C = 1$$

$$y(x) = e^{\tan^{-1}(x)}$$

$5\begin{cases} 1: \text{ separates the variables} \\ 1: \text{ antiderivatives} \\ 1: \text{ constant of integration} \\ 1: \text{ uses initial condition} \\ 1: \text{ solves for } y \end{cases}$

3. A population is modeled by a function P that satisfies the logistic differential equation $\frac{dP}{dt} = \frac{P}{4}\left(1 - \frac{P}{18}\right)$.

   a. If $P(0) = 6$, find $\lim_{t \to \infty} P(t)$.
      If $P(0) = 20$, find $\lim_{t \to \infty} P(t)$.

   b. If $P(0) = 6$, find a particular solution $P(t)$ to the given differential equation.
      For what value of P is the population growing the fastest?
      For what value of t, $t > 0$, is the population growing the fastest?

   c. If $P(0) = 20$, find a particular solution $P(t)$ to the given differential equation.

   d. If $P(0) = 6$, on the axes provided below, using the information from parts (a) and (b), sketch a graph for $P(t)$. If $P(0) = 20$, on the same axes, using the information from part (a) sketch a graph for $P(t)$.

(a) For this logistic differential equation, the carrying capacity is 18.
If $P(0) = 6$, $\lim_{t \to \infty} P(t) = 18$.
If $P(0) = 20$, $\lim_{t \to \infty} P(t) = 18$.

$2\begin{cases} 1: \text{ answer} \\ 1: \text{ answer} \end{cases}$

(b)
$$P(t) = \frac{M}{1 + ae^{-bt}}$$
$$P(t) = \frac{18}{1 + 2e^{-0.25t}}$$
Population is growing the fastest when $P = 9$ or $t = -4\ln\left(\frac{1}{2}\right)$.

$4\begin{cases} 2: \langle -1 \rangle \text{ each incorrect } M, a, b \\ 1: \text{ answer} \\ 1: \text{ answer} \end{cases}$

(c)
$$P(t) = \frac{18}{1 - 0.1e^{-0.25t}}$$

$1: \text{ answer}$

(d)

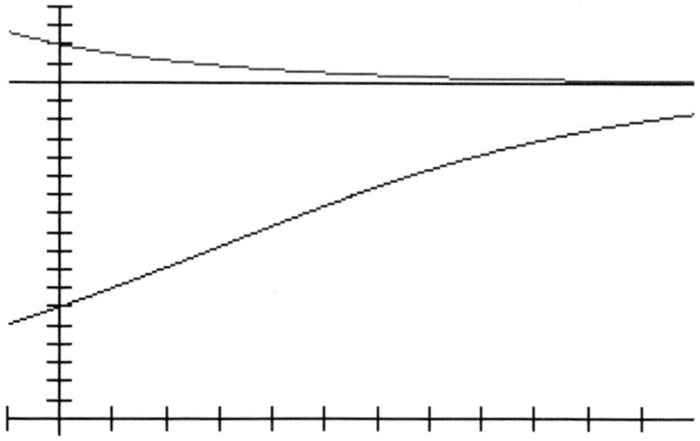

$2\begin{cases} 1: \text{ solution curve through } (0,6) \\ 1: \text{ solution curve through } (0,20) \end{cases}$

*4. Consider the differential equation $\frac{dy}{dx} = 2x + y$.

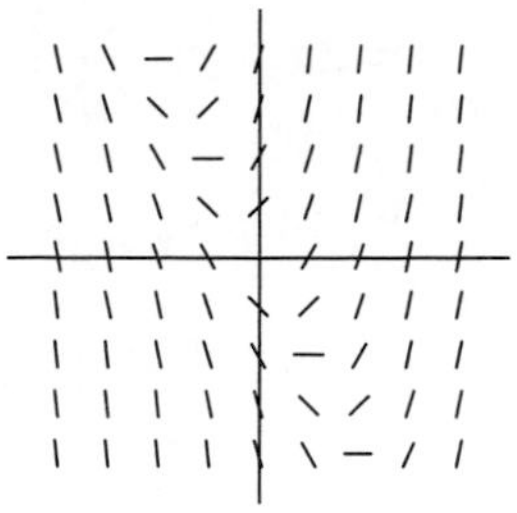

a. The slope field for the given differential equation is provided. Sketch the solution curve that passes through the point (0,0) and sketch the solution curve that passes through (-2,1).

b. Let f be the function that satisfies the given differential equation with the initial condition $f(-2) = 1$. Use Euler's method, starting at $x = -2$, with a step-size of 0.1 to approximate f(-1.7). Show work that leads to your answer.

c. Find $\frac{d^2y}{dx^2}$ in terms of x and y. Determine whether the approximation in part (b) is an over-estimate or an under-estimate. Explain your reasoning.

d. Show that $y = -2x - 2 - e^2e^x$ is a solution to the differential equation with the initial condition $f(-2) = 1$.

---

a.

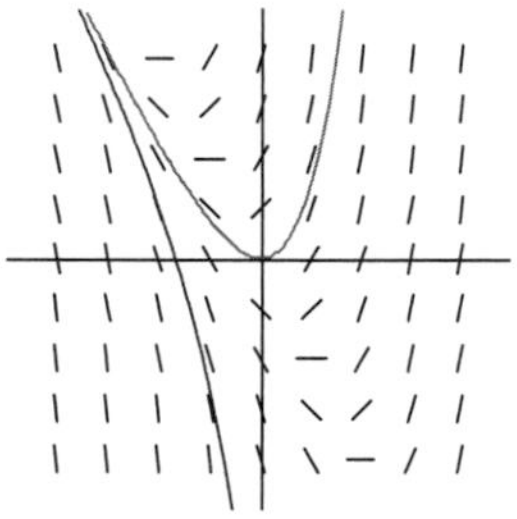

$$2 \begin{cases} 1: \text{ solution curve through } (0,0) \\ 1: \text{ solution curve through } (-2,1) \end{cases}$$

Curves must go through the indicated points, follow the given slope lines, and extend to the boundary of the slope field.

b. $f(-1.9) \approx f(-2) + f'(0)(0.1)$

$= 1 + (2(-2) + 1)(0.1) = 0.7$

$f(-1.8) \approx f(-1.9) + f'(-1.9)(0.1)$

$= 0.7 + (2(-1.9) + 0.7)(0.1) = 0.39$

$f(-1.7) \approx f(-1.8) + f'(-1.8)(0.1)$

$= 0.39 + (2(-1.8) + 0.39)(0.1) = .069$

2 { 1: Euler's Method equations or equivalent table
1: answer (not eligible without first point) }

c. $\frac{dy}{dx} = 2x + y$; $\frac{d^2y}{dx^2} = 2 + \frac{dy}{dx}$;

$\frac{d^2y}{dx^2} = 2 + 2x + y$

At $(-2,1)$ $\frac{d^2y}{dx^2}$ is < 0 so

the graph of the function is concave down and the approximation is an overestimate.

2 { 1: calculates $\frac{d^2y}{dx^2}$; 1: answer }

d. $y = -2x - 2 - e^2e^x$; $y' = -2 - e^2e^x$

$\frac{dy}{dx} = 2x + y$; $\frac{dy}{dx} = 2x + -2x - 2 - e^2e^x$

$\frac{dy}{dx} = -2 - e^2e^x$

3 { 1: finds y'; 1: substitutes y into $\frac{dy}{dx}$; 1: shows $\frac{dy}{dx} = y'$ }

Connect2Calculus Videos for Chapter 7

The Calculus Concepts Video's for Chapter 7: *(Calculus BC topics are in italic type)*
Some of the topics on the videos go beyond the scope of Calculus AB/BC, but would be worth watching as an application of calculus.

14.0 Differential Equations: The Language of Change
14.1 *Modeling the Spread of an Infection*
14.2 Direction Fields and Approximate Solutions to Differential Equations
14.3 *Numerical Solutions to Differential Equations*
4.0 Modeling with Derivatives
4.1 Derivatives and Motion: Distance, Velocity, and Acceleration (this topic is from Chapter 2)
4.2 Modeling with Exponential Functions (this topic also appears in Chapter 7)
4.3 The Derivative of a Product of Functions: Damped Oscillations

CHAPTER 8: INFINITE SERIES

Correlations

The section by section correspondence to the Topic Outline for Calculus BC (*Calculus BC topics are in italic type*) is:

AP Topic	Chapter.Section	Pages
II. Derivatives		
Applications of derivatives		
+ *L'Hopital's Rule, including its use in ... convergence of ... series*	*8.3, 8.5*	*636-648, 656-664*
IV. Polynomial Approximations and Series		
****Concept of series** A series is defined as a sequence of partial sums, and convergence is defined in terms of the limit of the sequence of partial sums. Technology can be used to explore convergence or divergence.*	*8.1, 8.2*	*612-626, 626-636*
***Series of constants**		
+ *Motivating examples, including decimal expansion*	*8.2*	*626-636*
+ *Geometric series with applications*	*8.2*	*626-636*
+ *The harmonic series*	*8.2*	*626-636*
+ *Alternating series with error bound*	*8.4*	*648-655*
+ *Terms of series as areas of rectangles and their relationship to improper integrals, including the integral test and its use in testing the convergence of p-series*	*8.3*	*636-648*
+ *The ratio text for convergence and divergence*	*8.5*	*656-664*
+ *Comparing series to test for convergence or divergence*	*8.3*	*636-648*

AP Topic	Chapter.Section	Pages
IV. Concept of series		
***Taylor Series**		
+ *Taylor polynomial approximation with graphical demonstration of convergence (for example, viewing* graphs *of various Taylor polynomials of the sine function approximating the sine curve)*	*8.7*	*672-685*
+ *Maclaurin series and the general Taylor series centered at* $x = a$	*8.7*	*672-685*
+ *Maclaurin series for the functions* e^x, $\sin(x)$, $\cos(x)$, *and* $\frac{1}{1-x}$	*8.7*	*672-685*
+ *Formal manipulation of Taylor series and shortcuts to computing Taylor series, including substitution, differentiation, antidifferentiation, and the formulation of new series from known series*	*8.6, 8.7, 8.8*	*664-672, 672-685, 685-694*
+ *Functions defined by power series*	*8.6*	*664-672*
+ *Radius and interval of convergence of power series*	*8.6,*	*664-672,*
+ *Lagrange error bound for Taylor polynomial*	*8.7*	*672-685*

Textbook Section	AP Topic
8.1 Sequences of Real Numbers	**IV. Polynomial Approximations and Series** ***Concept of series** A series is defined as a sequence of partial sums, and convergence is defined in terms of the limit of the sequence of partial sums. Technology can be used to explore convergence or divergence.*
8.2 Infinite Series	**IV. Polynomial Approximations and Series** ***Concept of series** A series is defined as a sequence of partial sums, and convergence is defined in terms of the limit of the sequence of partial sums. Technology can be used to explore convergence or divergence.* ***Series of constants** + *Motivating examples, including decimal expansion* + *Geometric series with applications* + *The harmonic series*
8.3 The Integral Test and Comparison Tests	**II. Derivatives** **Applications of derivatives** + *L'Hopital's Rule, including its use in ... convergence of ... series* **IV. Polynomial Approximations and Series** ***Series of constants** + *Terms of series as areas of rectangles and their relationship to improper integrals, including the integral test and its use in testing the convergence of p-series* + *Comparing series to test for convergence or divergence*
8.4 Alternating Series	**IV. Polynomial Approximations and Series** ***Series of constants** + *Alternating series with error bound*
8.5 Absolute Convergence and the Ratio Test	**II. Derivatives** **Applications of derivatives** + *L'Hopital's Rule, including its use in ... convergence of ... series* **IV. Polynomial Approximations and Series** ***Series of constants** + *The ratio text for convergence and divergence*

Textbook Section	AP Topic
8.6 Power Series	**IV. Concept of series** ***Taylor Series** + *Formal manipulation of Taylor series and shortcuts to computing Taylor series, including substitution, differentiation, antidifferentiation, and the formulation of new series from known series* + *Functions defined by power series* + *Radius and interval of convergence of power series*
8.7 Taylor Series	**IV. Concept of series** ***Taylor Series** + *Taylor polynomial approximation with graphical demonstration of convergence (for example, viewing* graphs *of various Taylor polynomials of the sine function approximating the sine curve)* + *Maclaurin series and the general Taylor series centered at* $x = a$ + *Maclaurin series for the functions* $e^x, \sin(x), \cos(x), \textit{and } \frac{1}{1-x}$ + *Formal manipulation of Taylor series and shortcuts to computing Taylor series, including substitution, differentiation, antidifferentiation, and the formulation of new series from known series* + *Lagrange error bound for Taylor polynomial*
8.8 Applications of Taylor Series	**IV. Concept of series** ***Taylor Series** + *Formal manipulation of Taylor series and shortcuts to computing Taylor series, including substitution, differentiation, antidifferentiation, and the formulation of new series from known series*

Vocabulary and Section Notes

Vocabulary used in the Topic Outline for Calculus BC (*Calculus BC topics are in italic type*) include:

Absolute convergence
Alternating Series Test
Bounded
Comparison Test
Conditional convergence
Geometric series
Harmonic series
Infinite series
Integral Test
Interval of convergence
k-th term test for divergence
LaGrange Error
Limit Comparison Test
Limit of sequence
Partial sum
Power series
p-series
Radius of convergence
Ratio Test
Remainder term
Sequence
Series converges
Series diverges
Squeeze Theorem
Sum of a series
Taylor polynomial
Taylor series
Taylor's Theorem
Telescoping or collapsing sum

Section notes for the Calculus BC Course:

Section 8.1(Sequences of Real Numbers): The convergence of sequences of real numbers is not part of the Topic Outline for Calculus BC, however, the concept of a sequence of partial sums and its role in the convergence of an infinite series is an important component of the rest of the chapter. Suggested Example 1.1 and Exercises 1 – 4.

Section 8.5 (Absolute Convergence and the Ratio Test): The Root Test is not part of the Topic Outline for Calculus BC.

Section 8.7 (Taylor Series): The error in the Taylor series, Example 7.6, is also called the LaGrange Error in the Topic Outline for Calculus BC.

Section 8.8 (Applications of Taylor Series): The Bessel function of order p and the Binomial Series are not part of the Topic Outline for Calculus BC.

Section 8.9 (Fourier Series): Fourier series is not part of the Topic Outline for Calculus BC.

Student Activity: Investigating the *p*-series

Teacher's Notes:

This statement: The *p*-series $\sum_{k=1}^{\infty}\frac{1}{k^p}$ converges if $p>1$ and diverges if $p\leq 1$ is simple, short, and an extremely powerful tool to use when determining if the sum of an infinite series of constants converges or diverges. The proof uses the Integral Test to establish the values of *p* in converging series and the values of *p* in diverging series. Before the formal proof, it might be helpful to have students investigate, through the calculation of partial sums, some *p*-series and form a hypothesis about the value of *p* and the convergence or divergence of the sum of the series of constants. First, students need to familiarize themselves with the *p*-series and what the series of constants looks like.

For $p=2$ the $p-$series looks like this: $\sum_{k=1}^{\infty}\frac{1}{k^2}=\frac{1}{1^2}+\frac{1}{2^2}+\frac{1}{3^2}+\frac{1}{4^2}+\ldots+\frac{1}{k^2}+\ldots$

For $p=-1$ the $p-$series looks like this: $\sum_{k=1}^{\infty}\frac{1}{k^{-1}}=\frac{1}{1^{-1}}+\frac{1}{2^{-1}}+\frac{1}{3^{-1}}+\frac{1}{4^{-1}}+\ldots+\frac{1}{k^{-1}}+\ldots$

Have the students enter this program into their calculators, either by typing it, or using the **LINK** feature of the calculator to share the program, which has been typed onto one other calculator. This program can be used for the TI83/84 calculator.

```
PARTSUM



ClrHome
Disp "PARTIAL SUMS"
Disp ""
Input "F(X)= ",Y1
Input "N= ",N
0→S
ClrHome
For(I,1,N)
Y1(I)+S→S
Disp S
End
Output(8,1,"")
```

Because the students are entering the expression for the *p*-series directly into the program, it is necessary to put quotation marks around the expression. Thus, the *p*-series for $p=2$, $\frac{1}{k^2}$, with the required quotes, would be entered into as "$1/x\wedge 2$". Students should be aware that computing the partial sum for 2000 terms could take a noticeable amount of time. In fact, the TI84-Plus Silver edition is much faster than a TI83 but all machines will calculate the requested partial sum. After completing the following tables, students should be comfortable with the convergence of the *p*-series and be ready for the formal proof of the convergence of the *p*-series.

Student Worksheet

Use these functions $\frac{1}{x^2}, \frac{1}{x^{\frac{3}{2}}}, \frac{1}{x^1}, \frac{1}{x^{\frac{1}{2}}}, \frac{1}{x^{-\frac{1}{2}}}, \frac{1}{x^{-1}}$ to represent some of the

possible p-series and use the **PARTSUM** program to determine their partial sums.

Remember to put your function in quotes when asked to enter it into the calculator.

Be sure to copy the calculator's complete answer for each partial sum.

$\frac{1}{x^2}$	S_{20}	S_{100}	S_{200}	S_{500}	S_{1000}	S_{2000}
Partial sums						

$\frac{1}{x^{\frac{3}{2}}}$	S_{20}	S_{100}	S_{200}	S_{500}	S_{1000}	S_{2000}
Partial sums						

$\frac{1}{x^1}$	S_{20}	S_{100}	S_{200}	S_{500}	S_{1000}	S_{2000}
Partial sums						

$\frac{1}{x^{\frac{1}{2}}}$	S_{20}	S_{100}	S_{200}	S_{500}	S_{1000}	S_{2000}
Partial sums						

$\frac{1}{x^{-\frac{1}{2}}}$	S_{20}	S_{100}	S_{200}	S_{500}	S_{1000}	S_{2000}
Partial sums						

$\frac{1}{x^{-1}}$	S_{20}	S_{100}	S_{200}	S_{500}	S_{1000}	S_{2000}
Partial sums						

Now, select two more $p-$series, one with $p>1$ and one with $p<1$ and complete these tables:

	S_{20}	S_{100}	S_{200}	S_{500}	S_{1000}	S_{2000}
Partial sums						

	S_{20}	S_{100}	S_{200}	S_{500}	S_{1000}	S_{2000}
Partial sums						

Fill in the following blanks:

When $p>$ _______________ the series converges. Explain your reasoning.

When $p\le$ _______________ the series diverges. Explain your reasoning.

Student Activity: Power Series Representation of ln(x)

Teacher's Notes

The purpose of this activity is to help students develop a number sense about the interval of convergence between $\ln(x)$ and its Taylor Series polynomial approximations. Both graphical and numerical representations are used to support the analytic results.

It is helpful for the teacher to demonstrate the first and second degree Taylor polynomials so that students can better understand what they are to do. Students should note that, as the number of terms in the polynomial increases, the values for the function and the polynomial converge. They are to "eyeball" and trace the intervals of convergence as they increase the number of terms in the polynomial. Students should notice that the graphs diverge whenever $x < 0$ or $x > 2$. You can direct them to figures 8.41 and 8.42 (in the text) to see a more accurate graph of the convergence. You can also draw their attention to figures 8.40a-d to show how the sine wave can also be approximated by a Taylor polynomial.

The last part of the activity shows how the error is measured. Let **Y₄**=0.001 and $\text{Y}_3 = |\text{Y}_1 - \text{Y}_2|$ (**Y_3** is the error that arises by using the Taylor's polynomial to approximate the values of the function $\ln(x)$). As students draw the graph of **Y_3** and **Y_4**, they should find the interval of convergence to be $(0.5428, 1.5191)$. This means that the 6th degree Taylor polynomial is within 0.001 of the actual value of $\ln(x)$ whenever $0.5428 < x < 1.5191$. It is a good time to explain why the interval is not symmetric about $x = 1$ (because $\ln(x)$ is not symmetric about $x = 1$).

In Example 7.6 in Section 8.7 of the text the authors "leave it as an exercise to show that the series converges to $f(x) = \ln(x)$ for the interval $0 < x < 2$." The proof would be:

For any fixed x there exists a z between x and 1 such that

$$|R_n(x)| = \left| \frac{f^{(n+1)}(z)(x-1)^{(n+1)}}{(n+1)!} \right|$$

Observe that for all n, $\left|f^{(n+1)}(z)\right| = \dfrac{n!}{|z|^{(n+1)}}$, so

$$|R_n(x)| = \left| \frac{n!(x-1)^{(n+1)}}{|z|^{(n+1)}(n+1)!} \right| = \left| \frac{x-1}{z} \right|^{(n+1)} \cdot \frac{1}{(n+1)} \to 0 \text{ as } n \to \infty$$

Since $|R_n(x)| = 0$, by Theorem 7.2, the Taylor's Series for $\ln(x)$ converges to $\ln(x)$

Another question to ask students would be:

Why, according to the text, is the interval of convergence $0 < x \leq 2$?

Recall: $\ln(x) = (x-1) - \frac{(x-1)^2}{2} + \frac{(x-1)^3}{3} - \frac{(x-1)^4}{4} + \ldots + \frac{(-1)^{n+1}(x-1)^n}{n}$

The Ratio Test says:

$$\lim_{x\to\infty}\left|\frac{(-1)^{n+2}(x-1)^{n+1}}{n+1}\cdot\frac{n}{(-1)^{n+1}(x-1)^n}\right| = \lim_{x\to\infty}\left|(x-1)\cdot\frac{n}{n+1}\right| = |x-1|$$

and the series will converge as long as $|x-1| < 1$

$-1 < x-1 < 1$

$0 < x < 2$

at $x = 0$ the series becomes $(-1) - \frac{(-1)^2}{2} + \frac{(-1)^3}{3} - \frac{(-1)^4}{4} + \ldots + \frac{-1}{n}$

which is the harmonic series and it diverges.

at $x = 2$ the series becomes $(1) - \frac{(1)^2}{2} + \frac{(1)^3}{3} - \frac{(1)^4}{4} + \ldots + \frac{(-1)^{n+1}}{n}$

which is the alternating harmonic series and it converges.

Therefore the interval of convergence is $0 < x \leq 2$

Student Activity Worksheet

The first power series is the geometric series

$$\frac{1}{1-x} = 1 + x + x^2 + x^3 + \ldots + x^n + \ldots$$

which is valid for $|x| < 1$. By substituting $1-x$ for x, we create another power series

$$\frac{1}{1-(1-x)} = 1 + (1-x) + (1-x)^2 + (1-x)^3 + \ldots + (1-x)^n + \ldots$$

which simplifies to

$$\frac{1}{x} = 1 + (1-x) + (1-x)^2 + (1-x)^3 + \ldots + (1-x)^n + \ldots.$$

This is valid for $|1-x| < 1$.

Now integrate both sides $\int \frac{1}{x} dx = \int (1 + (1-x) + (1-x)^2 + (1-x)^3 + \ldots + (1-x)^n + \ldots) dx$

$$u = 1-x; \quad du = -dx; \quad dx = -du$$

$$\ln(x) = -((1-x) + \frac{(1-x)^2}{2} + \frac{(1-x)^3}{3} + \ldots + \frac{(1-x)^n}{n} + \ldots)$$

$$\ln(x) = (x-1) - \frac{(x-1)^2}{2} + \frac{(x-1)^3}{3} - \frac{(x-1)^4}{4} + \ldots + \frac{(-1)^{n+1}(x-1)^n}{n}$$

We want to look at graphical and numerical representations of nth order Taylor polynomials of $\ln(x)$ to see how closely the right-hand side of the equation approximates the left-hand side.

Case 1: $P_1 = x - 1$

Using your calculator, graph $Y_1 = \ln(x)$ and $Y_2 = x - 1$ in the window below. Notice the **XSCL** value of 0.5

Sketch both graphs on the axes below.

```
WINDOW
 Xmin=-.5
 Xmax=2.5
 Xscl=.5
 Ymin=-3.1
 Ymax=2
 Yscl=1
 Xres=1
```

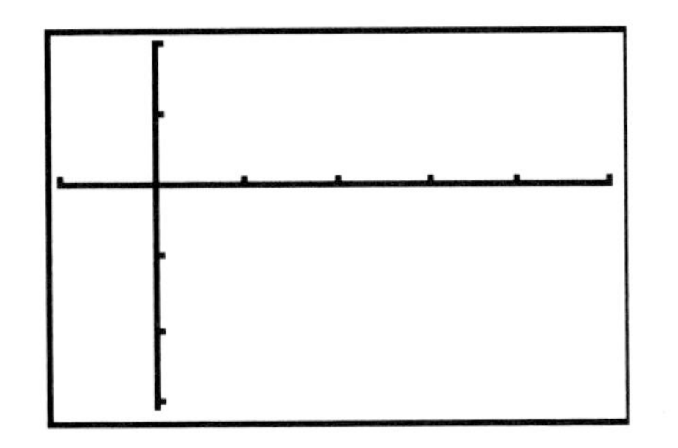

Notice this is the tangent line to Y_1 at $x = 1$. Notice the graphs seem to coincide only briefly around $x = 1$. We can look at this more closely using the **TABLE** feature. Use **TBLSET** with the following parameters.

Then press **TABLE** to see the following table of values

X	Y1	Y2
.7	-.3567	-.3
.8	-.2231	-.2
.9	-.1054	-.1
1	0	0
1.1	.09531	.1
1.2	.18232	.2
1.3	.26236	.3

X=.7

Notice that the values are equal only at $x = 1$. Scroll up and down the x-column. How do the two columns of y-values seem to compare to each other? (Use complete sentences.)

Case 2: $P_2 = (x-1) - \dfrac{(x-1)^2}{2}$

Now update $Y_2 = (x-1) - \dfrac{(x-1)^2}{2}$. Sketch both graphs in the window below

Mark the interval where the graphs seem to coincide (remember the **XSCL** value is 0.5). Write the interval in algebraic notation.

Look once again at the **TABLE** of values

X	Y1	Y2
.7	-.3567	-.345
.8	-.2231	-.22
.9	-.1054	-.105
1	0	0
1.1	.09531	.095
1.2	.18232	.18
1.3	.26236	.255

X=.7

Scroll up and down the x-column. How do the two columns of y-values seem to compare to each other? (Use complete sentences.)

Let's look at the next case.

Case 3: $P_3 = (x-1) - \frac{(x-1)^2}{2} + \frac{(x-1)^3}{3}$

Update $Y_2 = (x-1) - \frac{(x-1)^2}{2} + \frac{(x-1)^3}{3}$. Sketch both graphs in the window below

Mark the interval where the graphs seem to coincide.
Write the interval in algebraic notation.

Look at the **TABLE** to compare the values of the two functions. Scroll up and down the x-column. How do the two columns of y-values seem to compare to each other? (Use complete sentences.)

What has happened to the apparent interval of convergence as the number of terms in the Taylor polynomial has increased?
We want to look at one more case before we try to generalize the results.

Case 4: $P_6 = (x-1) - \frac{(x-1)^2}{2} + \frac{(x-1)^3}{3} - \frac{(x-1)^4}{4} + \frac{(x-1)^5}{5} - \frac{(x-1)^6}{6}$

Update $Y_2 = (x-1) - \frac{(x-1)^2}{2} + \frac{(x-1)^3}{3} - \frac{(x-1)^4}{4} + \frac{(x-1)^5}{5} - \frac{(x-1)^6}{6}$.

Sketch both graphs in the window below.

Mark the interval where the graphs seem to coincide.
Write the interval in algebraic notation.

Look at the **TABLE** to compare the values of the two functions. Scroll up and down the x-column. How do the two columns of y-values seem to compare to each other? (Use complete sentences.)

It seems that the x-interval of convergence to is $0 < x < 2$. Try adding several more terms to the Taylor polynomial. Once again, sketch your result in the window below.

Has the interval of convergence gone beyond $x = 2$?

Using your text, list the interval of convergence for the power series representation of $\ln(x)$.

Explain what this means in terms of the graphs of the function and the Taylor polynomial as the number of terms increase?

Explain what this means in terms of the table of values of the function and the Taylor polynomial as the number of terms increase?

Notice that the values for the two functions appeared to converge as the number of terms in the polynomial increased. Mathematicians are often concerned with how closely a Taylor Series approximates a function. We can look at how closely the two functions match up in the interval $0 < x < 2$.

First, deselect functions $\mathbf{Y_1}$ and $\mathbf{Y_2}$ by placing the cursor over the equal sign and pressing **ENTER**. Next enter $\mathbf{Y_3 = abs(Y_1 - Y_2)}$ as shown below. $\mathbf{Y_3}$ is the error in using the P_6 Taylor's polynomial to approximate the value of $\ln(x)$.

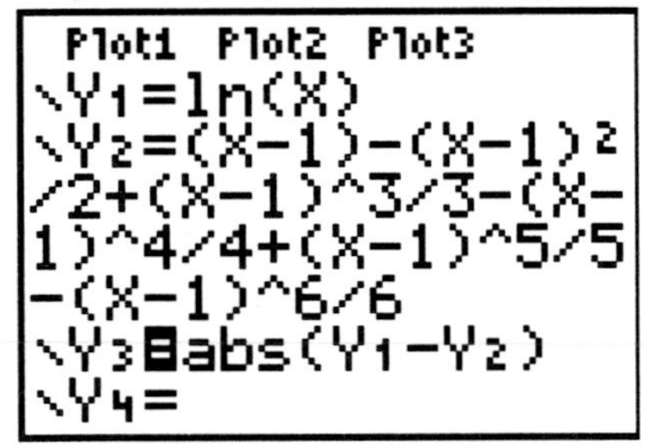

Finally, let $\mathbf{Y_4 = 0.001}$ and set your window as shown.

WINDOW
Xmin=⁻.5
Xmax=2.5
Xscl=1
Ymin=⁻.001
Ymax=.002
Yscl=.001
Xres=1

Sketch the graphs in the window below and find the points of intersection (Notice the **XSCL** and **YSCL** values in the **WINDOW**).

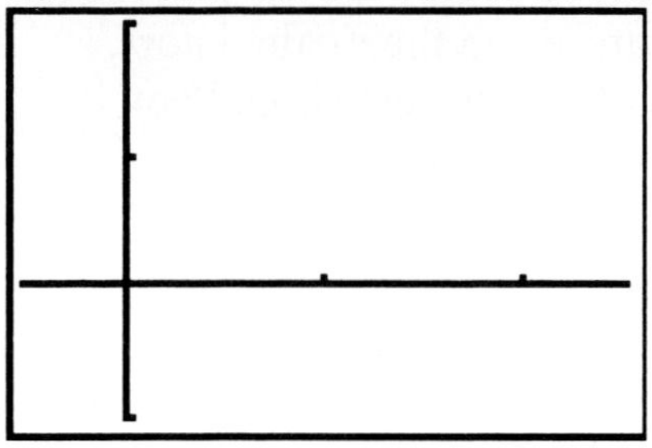

What does this picture say about the accuracy of the Taylor Polynomial approximation and the value of $\ln(x)$?

Complete this chart:

x	$\ln(x)$	$P_6(x)$	Error
0.5428			
1.5191			

Solutions: Student Worksheet

Note: Since students are using the TRACE and TABLE features on their calculators, there could be variations in their answers. However, the student answers should not differ significantly from those in the solutions. Answers are in **bold** type.

Case 1: $P_1 = x - 1$

Using your calculator, graph $Y_1 = \ln(x)$ and $Y_2 = x - 1$ in the window below. Notice the **XSCL** value of 0.5

Sketch both graphs on the axes below.

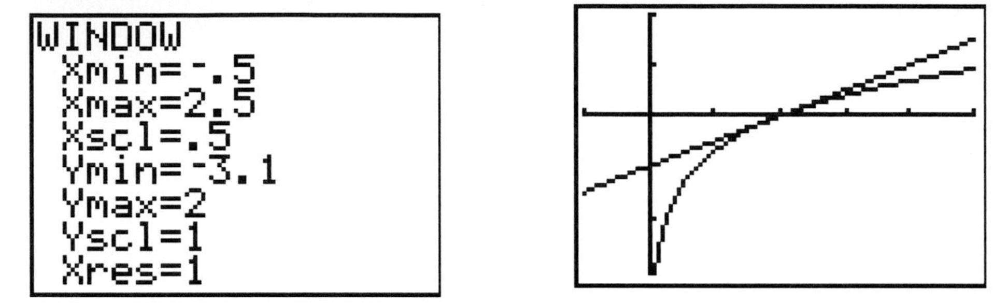

Notice that the values are equal only at $x = 1$. Scroll up and down the x-column. How do the two columns of y-values seem to compare to each other? (Use complete sentences.) **For $.9 < x < 1.1$, the values are close to each other.**

Case 2: $P_2 = (x-1) - \frac{(x-1)^2}{2}$

Now update $Y_2 = (x-1) - \frac{(x-1)^2}{2}$. Sketch both graphs in the window below.

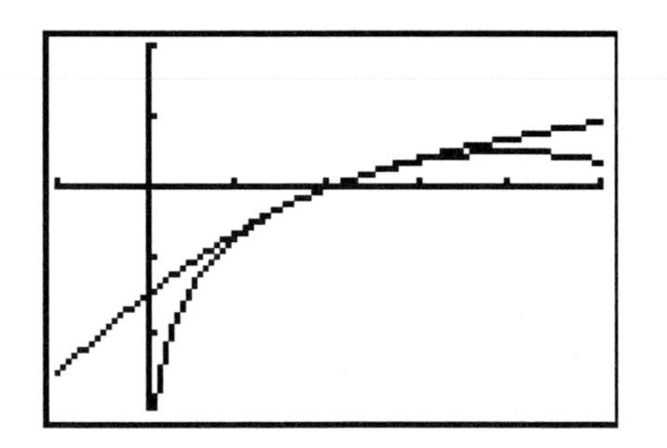

Mark the interval where the graphs seem to coincide (remember the **XSCL** value is 0.5). Write the interval in algebraic notation. $.8 < x < 1.1$

Scroll up and down the x-column. How do the two columns of y-values seem to compare to each other? (Use complete sentences.) **When $.8 < x < 1.1$, the values are close to each other.**

Let us look at the next case.

Case 3: $P_3 = (x-1) - \frac{(x-1)^2}{2} + \frac{(x-1)^3}{3}$

Update $Y_2 = (x-1) - \frac{(x-1)^2}{2} + \frac{(x-1)^3}{3}$. Sketch both graphs in the window below.

Mark the interval where the graphs seem to coincide.
Write the interval in algebraic notation: $.7 < x < 1.3$

Look at the **TABLE** to compare the values of the two functions. Scroll up and down the x-column. How do the two columns of y-values seem to compare to each other? (Use complete sentences.) **When $.7 < x < 1.3$, the y-values are almost identical.**

What has happened to the apparent interval of convergence as the number of terms in the Taylor polynomial has increased? **The interval is getting wider.**
We want to look at one more case before we try to generalize the results.

Case 4: $P_6 = (x-1) - \frac{(x-1)^2}{2} + \frac{(x-1)^3}{3} - \frac{(x-1)^4}{4} + \frac{(x-1)^5}{5} - \frac{(x-1)^6}{6}$

Update $Y_2 = (x-1) - \frac{(x-1)^2}{2} + \frac{(x-1)^3}{3} - \frac{(x-1)^4}{4} + \frac{(x-1)^5}{5} - \frac{(x-1)^6}{6}$. Sketch both graphs in the window below.

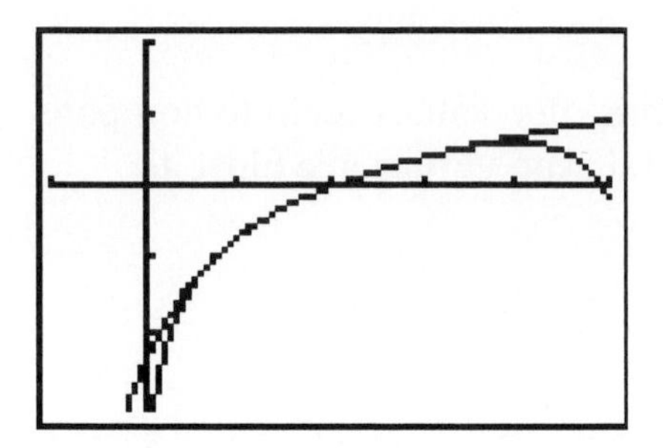

Mark the interval where the graphs seem to coincide.
Write the interval in algebraic notation. $.5 < x < 1.5$

Look at the **TABLE** to compare the values of the two functions. Scroll up and down the x-column. How do the two columns of y-values seem to compare to each other? (Use complete sentences.) **When $.5 < x < 1.5$, the y-values appear to be very close together.**

It seems that the x-interval of convergence to is $0 < x < 2$. Try adding several more terms to the Taylor polynomial. Once again, sketch your result in the window below.

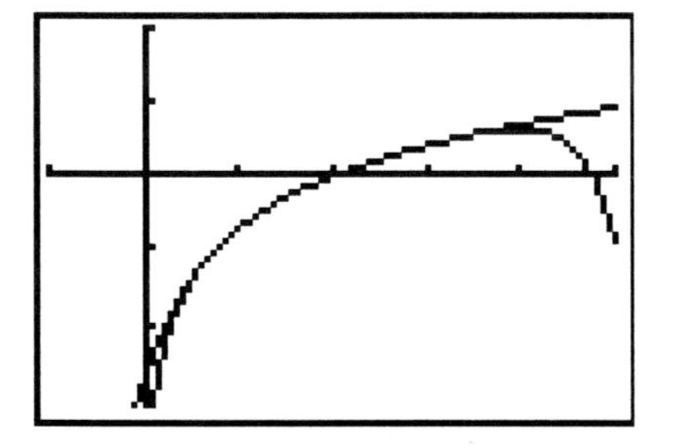

Has the interval of convergence gone beyond $x = 2$? **NO**

Using your text, list the interval of convergence for the power series representation of $\ln(x)$. $0 < x \leq 2$

Explain what this means in terms of the graphs of the function and the Taylor polynomial as the number of terms increase? **As the number of terms increases, the graph of the polynomial and the graph of the function coincide**.

Explain what this means in terms of the table of values of the function and the Taylor polynomial as the number of terms increase? **As the number of terms increases, the value of the polynomial evaluated at any $0 < x \leq 2$ is very close to the value of the function.**

Notice that the values for the two functions appeared to converge as the number of terms in the polynomial increased. Mathematicians are often concerned with how closely a Taylor Series approximates a function. We can look at how closely the two functions match up in the interval $0 < x < 2$.

Sketch the graphs in the window below and find the points of intersection (Notice the **XSCL** and **YSCL** values in the **WINDOW**). **The points of intersection are 0.5428 and 1.5191.**

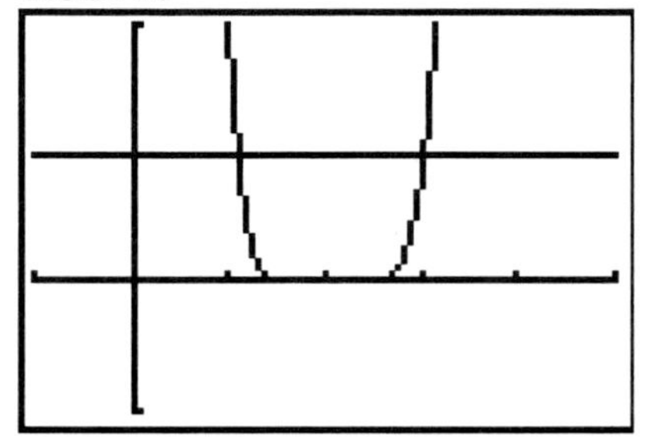

What does this picture say about the accuracy of the Taylor Polynomial approximation and the value of $\ln(x)$? **For any $0.5428 < x < 1.5191$, the error in the Taylor Polynomial approximation is less than 0.001.**

Complete this chart:

x	$\ln(x)$	$P_6(x)$	Error
0.5428	**-0.611014**	**-0.61001**	**0.001**
1.5191	**0.4181180**	**0.4171186**	**0.001**

Teacher's Notes: Series Error

Every truncation splits a Taylor series into two equally significant pieces: The Taylor polynomial $P_n(x)$ that gives us the approximation and the remainder $R_n(x)$ that tells us the accuracy of that approximation. Taylor's Theorem is about both pieces.

Theorem 7.1: **Taylor's Theorem with Remainder**

Suppose that function f has $(n+1)$ derivatives on the interval $(c-r, c+r)$, for some $r>0$. Then, for $x \in (c-r, c+r), f(x) \approx P_n(x)$ and the error in using $P_n(x)$ to approximate $f(x)$ is

$$R_n(x) = f(x) - P_n(x) = \frac{f^{(n+1)}(z)}{(n+1)!}(x-c)^{(n+1)}$$, for some number z between x and c.

The function $R_n(x)$ is the **remainder of order n** or the **error term** for the approximation of f by $P_n(x)$ over the interval $(c-r, c+r)$, for some $r>0$. It is also called the **Lagrange form** of the remainder, and bounds on $R_n(x)$ found using this form are **Lagrange error bounds**.

If $R_n(x) \to 0$ as $n \to \infty$ for all x in the interval $(c-r, c+r)$, for some $r>0$, we say that the Taylor's series generated by f at x = c converges to f on the interval $(c-r, c+r)$, for some $r>0$, and we write

$$f(x) = \sum_{k=0}^{\infty} \frac{f^{(k)}(c)}{k!}(x-c)^k .$$

The relationship between the values of $f(x)$, $P_n(x)$, and $R_n(x)$ at a particular value of x, near c, can be seen: $f(x) = P_n(x) + R_n(x)$

The error at a particular value of x, near c, is: $|f(x) - P_n(x)| = |R_n(x)|$

$$|f(x) - P_n(x)| = \left| \frac{f^{n+1}(z)}{(n+1)!}(x-c)^{n+1} \right|$$

The values of x, c, and n are known, but the value of z cannot usually be determined, so the exact value of the error cannot be determined. Generally, f^{n+1} is continuous and differentiable and seldom has a critical point in the interval so it has a maximum value at either of the endpoints of the interval under consideration. The maximum value of f^{n+1}, (call it M), is used to put an upper bound on the value of $f^{n+1}(z)$. Therefore:

$$|f(x) - P_n(x)| \le \left|\frac{M}{(n+1)!}(x-c)^{n+1}\right|$$

$$-\left|\frac{M}{(n+1)!}(x-c)^{n+1}\right| \le f(x) - P_n(x) \le \left|\frac{M}{(n+1)!}(x-c)^{n+1}\right|$$

The expression $-\left|\frac{M}{(n+1)!}(x-c)^{n+1}\right| + P_n(x) \le f(x) \le \left|\frac{M}{(n+1)!}(x-c)^{n+1}\right| + P_n(x)$

creates an interval of values that includes the true value of f(x).

The following problems ask students to consider the differing bounds on the error incurred when using a Taylor's polynomial to approximate the value of an unknown function:

The Maclaurin series for the function f is given by

$$f(x) = 1 + x + \frac{x^2}{2!} + \frac{x^3}{3!} + ... + \frac{x^n}{n!} = \sum_{n=0}^{\infty} \frac{x^n}{n!} \text{ and } f^n(x) = e^x$$

a. Use the Lagrange Error bound to put a bound on the error if $P_2(x)$ is used to approximate the value of the function $f(.9)$.

$$|f(.9) - P_2(.9)| = \left|\frac{f^3(z)(.9)^3}{3!}\right|$$

On the interval $0 \le x \le .9$ $f^3(x) = e^x$ is an increasing function (graph it) and its maximum occurs at $x = .9$ but we are approximating the value of $f(.9) = e^{.9}$ so we must use a known, larger value to put a bound on $f^3(z)$. On the interval $0 \le x \le .9$ it is true that $|f^3(z)| \le e^1$, so use e^1 as the bound.

$$|f(.9) - P_2(.9)| = \left|\frac{f^3(z)(.9)^3}{3!}\right| \le \left|\frac{e(.9)^3}{3!}\right| = 0.33027$$

b. If $f(x) = e^x$ calculate the exact error if $P_2(x)$ is used to approximate the value of $f(.9)$.

$$\left|e^{.9} - (1 + .9 + \frac{(.9)^2}{2!})\right| = 0.1546$$

The actual error is less than the bound on the error calculated using the Lagrange error bound.

The Maclaurin series for the function f is given by

$$f(x)=\sum_{n=1}^{\infty}(-1)^{n-1}\frac{x^n}{n}= x-\frac{x^2}{2}+\frac{x^3}{3}-\frac{x^4}{4}+...(-1)^{n-1}\frac{x^n}{n} \text{ and } f^n(x)=\frac{(-1)^{n-1}(n-1)!}{(1+x)^n}$$

a. Use the Lagrange error bound to put a bound on the error if $P_3(x)$ is used to approximate the value of $f(.8)$.

$$|f(.8)-P_3(.8)|=\left|\frac{f^4(z)(.8)^4}{4!}\right|$$

On the interval $0\le x\le .8$, $|f^4(z)|=\left|\frac{(-1)^{4-1}(4-1)!}{(1+z)^4}\right|$ is a decreasing function (graph it)

and its maximum value occurs at $x=0$ so $|f^4(z)|\le\left|\frac{(-1)^{4-1}(4-1)!}{(1+0)^4}\right|=6$

$$|f(.8)-P_3(.8)|=\left|\frac{f^4(z)(.8)^4}{4!}\right|\le\frac{6(.8)^4}{4!}=.1024$$

b. When a polynomial is an alternating series with decreasing terms the error is always less than the first omitted term, and these calculations do not require a bound on the derivative. Since this Maclaurin series is an Alternating Series, put a bound on the error if $P_3(x)$ is used to approximate the value of $f(.8)$

$$|f(x)-P_3(x)|\le\left|(-1)^{4-1}\frac{x^4}{4}\right|$$

$$|f(.8)-P_3(.8)|\le\left|(-1)^{4-1}\frac{.8^4}{4}\right|=0.1024$$

c. If $f(x)=\ln(1+x)$ calculate the exact error if $P_3(x)$ is used to approximate the value $f(.8)$

$$|f(.8)-P_3(.8)|=\left|\ln(1+.8)-(.8-\frac{.8^2}{2}+\frac{.8^3}{3})\right|=0.06288$$

The exact error is less than the bound on the error calculated using either the Lagrange bound or the Alternating Series bound.

Question 1 from the free-response questions at the end of this chapter is an example of another way to use the error in an approximation.

The function f has derivatives of all orders for all real numbers x. Assume that $f(0)=1,\ f'(0)=-2,\ f''(0)=6,\ f'''(0)=3$.

a. Write the third-degree Taylor polynomial for f about $x=0$ and use it to approximate $f(0.5)$.

b. The fourth derivative of f satisfies the inequality $\left|f^{(4)}(x)\right| \le 8$ for all x in the closed interval $[0,0.5]$. Use the LaGrange error bound on the approximation to $f(0.5)$ found in part (a) to determine if $f(0.5)$ could be 0.8

a. $P_3(x)=1+\dfrac{-2x^1}{1!}+\dfrac{6x^2}{2!}+\dfrac{3x^3}{3!}$

$f(0.5)\approx P_3(0.5)=1-2(0.5)+3(0.5)^2+\dfrac{1}{2}(0.5)^3=$
0.8125

b. $\left|f(0.5)-P_3(0.5)\right|=\dfrac{f^4(z)(0.5)^4}{4!}$

$\left|f(0.5)-P_3(0.5)\right|\le\dfrac{8(0.5)^4}{4!}$

$-0.208333\le f(0.5)-P_3(0.5)\le 0.0208333$

$.7916\le f(0.5)\le .8333$

Since 0.8 is in the interval, $f(0.5)$ could be 0.8

The Lagrange error bound is used to estimate the error in approximations on questions in 1999 BC4 and 2004 BC6. The Alternating Series Error Estimation is used in questions from 2000 BC3 and 2003 BC6. Several questions at the end of this chapter ask students to use one of these methods to estimate the error in approximations.

Multiple-Choice Questions–Calculus BC Topics

1. $\sum_{n=0}^{\infty} \frac{e^{n+1}}{(-\pi)^n} =$

   A. $\frac{\pi e}{\pi + e}$

   B. $\frac{e}{1+e}$

   C. $\frac{e}{\pi + e}$

   D. $\frac{e}{1-e}$

   E. $\frac{\pi e}{\pi - e}$

2. The radius of convergence for the power series $\sum_{n=0}^{\infty} \frac{(2x)^n}{n^2}$ is

   A. $\frac{1}{4}$
   B. $\frac{1}{2}$
   C. 1
   D. 2
   E. 4

3. The power series $1 - \frac{1}{3}x + \frac{1}{9}x^2 - \frac{1}{27}x^3 \cdots$ converges for what values of x?

   A. $-\frac{1}{3} \le x \le \frac{1}{3}$
   B. $-\frac{1}{3} < x < \frac{1}{3}$
   C. $-3 \le x \le 3$
   D. $-3 < x < 3$
   E. all real numbers x

4. The power series $\sum_{n=1}^{\infty} \frac{x^n}{n}$ converges for what values of x?

   A. $-1 < x < 1$
   B. $-1 < x \le 1$
   C. $-1 \le x < 1$
   D. $-1 \le x \le 1$
   E. all real numbers x

5. If $f(x)=\sum_{n=0}^{\infty}\frac{(\cos x)^n}{n!}$, then $f''(\pi)=$

A. -1
B. $-\frac{1}{e}$
C. 0
D. $\frac{1}{e}$
E. 1

6. A function *f* has a Maclaurin series given by $x-x^2+\frac{x^3}{2!}-\cdots+\frac{(-1)^n x^{n+1}}{n!}+\cdots$. Which of the following is an expression for $f(x)$?

A. $\frac{\sin(x)}{x}$
B. xe^{-x}
C. $\frac{-\cos(x)}{x}$
D. $\frac{e^x}{x}$
E. $\frac{x}{1+x}$

*7. The error from using the first five terms to approximate the series $\frac{1}{3!}-\frac{2}{4!}+\frac{3}{5!}-\frac{4}{6!}+\cdots$ is

A. 0.00014
B. 0.00099
C. 0.00555
D. 0.02500
E. 0.08333

8. The Maclaurin series for $\frac{1}{1-x}$ is $\sum_{n=0}^{\infty}x^n$. What is the power series expansion for $\frac{x}{1+x^3}$?

A. $1+x+x^2+x^3+x^4+\ldots$
B. $1-x^3+x^6-x^9+x^{12}+\ldots$
C. $x-x^4+x^7-x^{10}+x^{13}+\ldots$
D. $1+x^3+x^6+x^9+x^{12}+\ldots$
E. $x+x^4+x^7+x^{10}+x^{13}+\ldots$

9. Which of the following series converges?

I. $\sum_{n=1}^{\infty} \frac{1}{n^2}$ II. $\sum_{n=1}^{\infty} \frac{n}{2n-1}$ III. $\sum_{n=1}^{\infty} \frac{3^n}{4^{n+1}}$

A. I only B. II only C. III only D. I, III E. I, II, III

*10. Let $p(x)$ be the sum of the first 2 non-zero terms of the Taylor series for $\sin(x)$ centered at $x = 0$. The maximum value of $|\sin(x) - p(x)|$ for $1.2 \le x \le 1.7$ is

A. -0.562 B. 0.020 C. 0.060 D. 0.110 E. 0.992

11. Let $P(x) = 6 - 5x - 3x^2 + 2x^3 - 8x^4$ be the fourth-degree Taylor polynomial for the function $f(x)$ about $x = 0$. What is the value of $f'''(0)$?

A. $\frac{1}{3}$ B. $\frac{2}{3}$ C. 2 D. 6 E. 12

Free-Response Questions–Calculus BC Topics

*1. The function f has derivatives of all orders for all real numbers x. Assume $f(0)=1,\ f'(0)=-2,\ f''(0)=6,\ f'''(0)=3$.

a. Write the third-degree Taylor polynomial for f about $x=0$ and use it to approximate $f(0.5)$.

b. The fourth derivative of f satisfies the inequality $\left|f^{(4)}(x)\right|\leq 8$ for all x in the closed interval $[0,0.5]$. Use the LaGrange error bound on the approximation to $f(0.5)$ found in part (a) to determine if $f(0.5)$ could be 0.8

c. Find $\lim\limits_{x\to 0}\dfrac{f(x)-1}{x}$

d. Write the fourth–degree Taylor polynomial for g, where $g(x)=f(x^2)$.

2. The Maclaurin series for the function f is given by

$$f(x)=\sum_{n=0}^{\infty}\frac{(3x)^{n+1}}{n+1}=3x+\frac{9x^2}{2}+\frac{27x^3}{3}+\frac{81x^4}{4}+....+\frac{(3x)^{n+1}}{n+1}+...$$

a. Find the interval of convergence of the Maclaurin series for f. Justify your answer.

b. Find the first four terms and the general term for the Maclaurin series for $f'(x)$.

c. Use the Maclaurin series you found in part (b) to find the value of $f'(-\frac{1}{6})$.

3. The Taylor series about $x = 2$ for a certain function f converges to $f(x)$ for all x in the interval of convergence. The nth derivative of f at $x = 2$ is given by $f^{(n)}(2) = \frac{(-1)^n (n-1)!}{3^n}$ and $f(2) = 0$.

   a. Write a fourth-degree Taylor polynomial for f about $x = 2$.

   b. Find the radius of convergence of the Taylor series for f about $x = 2$.

   c. Show that the second-degree Taylor polynomial for f about $x = 2$ approximates $f(2.1)$ with an error less than $\frac{1}{1000}$.

4. Function f is defined by $f(x) = \frac{2}{2-x}$ for all real numbers x for which the series converges. Let $g(x) = f'(x)$ and $h(x) = \int_0^x f(t)\,dt$.

   a. Find the first four terms and the general term for the Maclaurin series for f.

   b. Find the first four terms and the general term for the Maclaurin series for g.

   c. Find the first four terms and the general term for the Maclaurin series for h.

   d. If function $y(x) = f(x) - g(x)$, find $y'(0)$ and $y''(0)$. Determine whether y has a relative minimum, relative maximum, or neither at $x = 0$. Justify your answer.

Solutions to Sample Questions

Solutions to Multiple-Choice Questions

1. A $\quad e-\frac{e^2}{\pi}+\frac{e^3}{\pi^2}-\frac{e^4}{\pi^3}+\cdots=\frac{e}{1+\frac{e}{\pi}}=\frac{e}{1}\cdot\frac{\pi}{\pi+e}$

2. B $\quad \lim_{n\to\infty}\left|\frac{(2x)^{n+1}}{(n+1)^2}\cdot\frac{n^2}{(2x)^n}\right|=\lim_{n\to\infty}\left|\frac{(2x)^{n+1}}{(2x)}\cdot\frac{n^2}{(n+1)^2}\right|$

$|2x\cdot 1|<1$

$|x|<\frac{1}{2}$

3. D $\quad$ Geometric with $r=-\frac{1}{3}x$.

$\left|-\frac{1}{3}x\right|<1$

$\left|\frac{1}{3}x\right|<1$

4. C $\quad \lim_{n\to\infty}\left|\frac{x^{n+1}}{n+1}\cdot\frac{n}{x^n}\right|=\lim_{x\to\infty}\left|\frac{n}{n+1}\cdot\frac{x^{n+1}}{x}\right|$

$|1\cdot x|<1$

At $x=-1$.

$\sum_{n=1}^{\infty}\frac{(-1)^n}{n}$

$\lim_{n\to\infty}\frac{1}{n}=0$ and $\frac{1}{n+1}<\frac{1}{n}$

Converges by alternating series test.

At $x=1$.

$\sum_{n=1}^{\infty}\frac{(1)^n}{n}$

Diverges by p-test

5. D $\quad \sum_{n=0}^{\infty}\frac{(\cos x)^n}{n!}=e^{\cos x}$

$f(x)=e^{\cos x}$

$f'(x)=-\sin x\cdot e^{\cos x}$

$f''(x)=-\cos x\cdot e^{\cos x}+(\sin x)^2 e^{\cos x}$

$f''(\pi)=1\cdot e^{-1}+0\cdot e^{-1}$

6. B

$$e^x = 1 + x + \frac{x^2}{2!} + \frac{x^3}{3!} + \frac{x^4}{4!} + \cdots + \frac{x^n}{n!} + \cdots$$

$$e^{-x} = 1 - x + \frac{x^2}{2!} - \frac{x^3}{3!} + \frac{x^4}{4!} \cdots + \frac{(-1)^n x^n}{n!} + \cdots$$

$$xe^{-x} = x - x^2 + \frac{x^3}{2!} - \frac{x^4}{3!} + \frac{x^5}{4!} \cdots + \frac{(-1)^n x^{n+1}}{n!} + \cdots$$

*7. A

This is a decreasing-alternating series. The error from the first five terms is the sixth term $= \frac{6}{8!}$

8. C

$$\frac{1}{1-x} = 1 + x + x^2 + x^3 + x^4 + \ldots$$

$$\frac{1}{1-(-x^3)} 1 + (-x^3) + (-x^3)^2 + (-x^3)^3 + (-x^3)^4 + \ldots$$

$$\frac{x}{1+x^3} = x(1 - x^3 + x^6 - x^9 + x^{12} + \ldots) + x - x^4 + x^7 - x^{10} + x^{13} + \ldots$$

9. D

I. converges, p-series, $n > 1$

II. diverges, $\lim_{n\to\infty} \frac{n}{2n-1} = \frac{1}{2} \neq 0$

III. converges, geometric, $r = \frac{3}{4}, |r| < 1$

*10. D

$$p(x) = x - \frac{x^3}{3!}$$

graph $\left| \sin(x) - \left(x - \frac{x^3}{3!} \right) \right|$ on the interval $1.2 \le x \le 1.7,\ 0 \le y \le 0.5$

11. E

$$\frac{f'''(0)x^3}{3!} = \frac{2x^3}{1};\ f'''(0) = 3! \cdot 2 = 12$$

Solutions to Free-Response Questions

*1. The function f has derivatives of all orders for all real numbers x. Assume $f(0)=1,\ f'(0)=-2,\ f''(0)=6,\ f'''(0)=3$.

a. Write the third-degree Taylor polynomial for f about $x=0$ and use it to approximate $f(0.5)$.

b. The fourth derivative of f satisfies the inequality $\left|f^{(4)}(x)\right| \le 8$ for all x in the closed interval $[0,0.5]$. Use the LaGrange error bound on the approximation to $f(0.5)$ found in part (a) to determine if $f(0.5)$ could be 0.8

c. Find $\lim\limits_{x\to 0}\dfrac{f(x)-1}{x}$

d. Write the fourth–degree Taylor polynomial for g, where $g(x)=f(x^2)$.

---

a. $P_3(x)=1+\dfrac{-2x^1}{1!}+\dfrac{6x^2}{2!}+\dfrac{3x^3}{3!}$

$f(0.5)\approx P_3(0.5)=1-2(0.5)+3(0.5)^2+\dfrac{1}{2}(0.5)^3=$
0.8125

3 points:
- 2: $1-2x+3x^2+\dfrac{1}{2}x^3$
  <−1> each incorrect term, extra term, or +...
- 1: approximates $f(0.5)$

b. $\left|f(0.5)-P_3(0.5)\right|=\dfrac{f^4(z)(0.5)^4}{4!}$

$\left|f(0.5)-P_3(0.5)\right|\le\dfrac{8(0.5)^4}{4!}$

$-0.208333\le f(0.5)-P_3(0.5)\le 0.0208333$

$.7916\le f(0.5)\le .8333$

Since 0.8 is in the interval, $f(0.5)$ could be 0.8

3 points:
- 1: $\dfrac{f^4(z)(0.5)^4}{4!}\le\dfrac{8(0.5)^4}{4!}$
- 1: interval
- 1: conclusion

c. $\dfrac{f(x)-1}{x}=\dfrac{1}{x}\left(-1+1-2x+3x^2+\dfrac{1}{2}x^3+...\right)=$

$-2+3x+\dfrac{1}{2}x^2+...$

$\lim\limits_{x\to 0}\dfrac{f(x)-1}{x}=\lim\limits_{x\to 0}\left(-2+3x+\dfrac{1}{2}x^2+...\right)=-2$

2 points:
- 1: $\dfrac{f(x)-1}{x}$
- 1: answer

d. $g(x)=f(x^2)=1-2(x^2)+3(x^2)^2=1-2x^2+3x^4$

1: answer

2. The Maclaurin series for the function f is given by

$$f(x) = \sum_{n=0}^{\infty} \frac{(3x)^{n+1}}{n+1} = 3x + \frac{9x^2}{2} + \frac{27x^3}{3} + \frac{81x^4}{4} + ... + \frac{(3x)^{n+1}}{n+1} + ...$$

a. Find the interval of convergence of the Maclaurin series for f. Justify your answer.

b. Find the first four terms and the general term for the Maclaurin series for $f'(x)$.

c. Use the Maclaurin series you found in part (b) to find the value of $f'(-\frac{1}{6})$.

---

a. $\lim_{n\to\infty} \left| \frac{\frac{(3x)^{n+1}}{n+1}}{\frac{(3x)^n}{n}} \right| = \lim_{n\to\infty} \left| \frac{(3x)n}{n+1} \right| = |3x| < 1$

at $x = -\frac{1}{3}$, the series is $\sum_{n=0}^{\infty} \frac{(-1)^{n+1}}{n+1}$, which converges

at $x = \frac{1}{3}$, the series is $\sum_{n=0}^{\infty} \frac{(1)^{n+1}}{n+1}$, which diverges

Therefore, the interval of convergence is $-\frac{1}{3} \le x < \frac{1}{3}$

5 {
1: sets up ratio test
1: computes limit
1: conclusion of ratio test
2: analysis/conclusion at endpoints
  1: right endpoint
  1: left endpoint
}

b. $f'(x) = 3 + 9x + 27x^2 + 81x^3 + ... + \sum_{n=0}^{\infty} (3)^{n+1} x^n$

2 {
1: first 4 terms
1: general term
}

c. $f'(-\frac{1}{6}) = 3 + 9\left(-\frac{1}{6}\right) + 27\left(-\frac{1}{6}\right)^2 + 81\left(-\frac{1}{6}\right)^3 + ...$

geometric series, $a = 3$, $r = -\frac{1}{2}$; sum $= \frac{3}{1 - \left(-\frac{1}{2}\right)} = 2$

2 {
1: substitues $x = -\frac{1}{6}$ into infinite series from (b) or expresses series from (b) in closed form
1: answer
}

3. The Taylor series about $x = 2$ for a certain function f converges to $f(x)$ for all x in the interval of convergence. The nth derivative of f at $x = 2$ is given by

$f^{(n)}(2) = \frac{(-1)^n (n-1)!}{3^n}$ and $f(2) = 0$.

a. Write a fourth-degree Taylor polynomial for f about $x = 2$.

b. Find the radius of convergence of the Taylor series for f about $x = 2$.

c. Show that the second-degree Taylor polynomial for f about $x = 2$ approximates $f(2.1)$ with an error less than $\frac{1}{1000}$.

(a)

$$P_3(x) = 0 - \tfrac{1}{1!}\cdot\tfrac{1}{3}(x-2) + \tfrac{1}{2!}\cdot\tfrac{1}{3^2}(x-2)^2 - \tfrac{1}{3!}\cdot\tfrac{2!}{3^3}(x-2)^3 + \tfrac{1}{4!}\cdot\tfrac{3!}{3^4}(x-2)^4$$

$$P_3(x) = -\tfrac{1}{3}(x-2) + \tfrac{1}{18}(x-2)^2 - \tfrac{1}{81}(x-2)^3 + \tfrac{1}{324}(x-2)^4$$

$3\begin{cases} 1: \text{ correct } \dfrac{1}{n!} \text{ in first four terms} \\ 1: \text{ correct } f^{(n)}(2) \text{ in first four terms} \\ 1: \text{ powers of } (x-2) \text{ in first four terms} \end{cases}$

(b)

$$a_n = \frac{1}{n!}\cdot\frac{(n-1)!(x-2)^n}{3^n} = \frac{(x-2)^n}{n3^n}$$

$$\lim_{n\to\infty}\left|\frac{(x-2)^{n+1}}{(n+1)\cdot 3^{n+1}}\cdot\frac{n\cdot 3^n}{(x-2)^n}\right| = \lim_{n\to\infty}\left|\frac{n}{n+1}\cdot\frac{3^n}{3^{n+1}}\cdot\frac{(x-2)^{n+1}}{(x-2)^n}\right|$$

$$\left|\tfrac{1}{3}(x-2)\right| < 1$$

$$|x-2| < 3$$

Radius of convergence is 3.

$4:\begin{cases} 1: \text{ finds } a_n \\ 1: \text{ sets up ratio} \\ 1: \text{ limit} \\ 1: \text{ answer} \end{cases}$

(c)

$$f(2.1) = -\tfrac{1}{3}\left(\tfrac{1}{10}\right) + \tfrac{1}{18}\left(\tfrac{1}{100}\right) - \tfrac{1}{81}\left(\tfrac{1}{1000}\right) + \cdots$$

This is an alternating series whose these decrease in absolute value with limit 0.

Error $= \tfrac{1}{81}\left(\tfrac{1}{1000}\right) < \tfrac{1}{1000}$.

$2:\begin{cases} 1: \text{ decreasing terms with limit 0} \\ 1: \text{ error bound } < \dfrac{1}{1000} \end{cases}$

4. Function f is defined by $f(x)=\dfrac{2}{2-x}$ for all real numbers x for which the series converges. Let $g(x)=f'(x)$ and $h(x)=\int_0^x f(t)\,dt$.

a. Find the first four terms and the general term for the Maclaurin series for f.
b. Find the first four terms and the general term for the Maclaurin series for g.
c. Find the first four terms and the general term for the Maclaurin series for h.
d. If function $y(x)=f(x)-g(x)$, find $y'(0)$ and $y''(0)$. Determine whether y has a relative minimum, relative maximum, or neither at $x=0$. Justify your answer.

(a) $\dfrac{2}{2-x}=\dfrac{1}{1-\frac{1}{2}x}$

$f(x)=1+\frac{1}{2}x+\frac{1}{4}x^2+\frac{1}{8}x^3+\cdots+\left(\frac{1}{2}x\right)^n+\cdots$

$2:\begin{cases}1: \text{first four terms}\\ 1: \text{general term}\end{cases}$

(b) $g(x)=\frac{1}{2}+\frac{1}{2}x+\frac{3}{8}x^2+\frac{1}{4}x^3+\cdots+\frac{1}{2}n\left(\frac{1}{2}x\right)^{n-1}+\cdots$

$2:\begin{cases}1: \text{first four terms}\\ 1: \text{general term}\end{cases}$

(c) $h(x)=x+\frac{1}{2}x^2+\frac{1}{12}x^3+\frac{1}{32}x^4+\cdots+\frac{1}{2^n(n+1)}x^{n+1}+\cdots$

$2:\begin{cases}1: \text{first four terms}\\ 1: \text{general term}\end{cases}$

(d) $y(x)=\frac{1}{2}-\frac{1}{8}x^2-\frac{1}{8}x^3-\frac{3}{32}x^4-\cdots$

$y'(x)=-\frac{1}{4}x-\frac{3}{8}x^2-\frac{12}{32}x^3-\cdots$

$y''(x)=-\frac{1}{4}-\frac{6}{8}x-\frac{36}{32}x-\cdots$

$y'(0)=0$

$y''(0)=-\frac{1}{4}$

y has a relative maximum at $x=0$.

$3:\begin{cases}1: y'(0)\\ 1: y''(0)\\ 1: \text{answer}\end{cases}$

Connect2Calculus Videos for Chapter 8

The Calculus Concepts Video's for Chapter 8: *(Calculus BC topics are in italic type)*
Some of the topics in the videos go beyond the scope of Calculus AB/BC, but would be worth watching as an application of calculus.

15.0 Sequences and Series: Taking the Sum Ad Infinitum
15.1 *Partial Sums and Infinite Series*
15.2 *Series Convergence*
15.3 *Taylor Series*

CHAPTER 9: PARAMETRIC EQUATIONS AND POLAR COORDINATES
CHAPTER 10: VECTORS AND THE GEOMETRY OF SPACE
CHAPTER 11: VECTOR-VALUED FUNCTIONS

Correlations

The section by section correspondence to the Topic Outline for Calculus BC (*Calculus BC topics are in italic type*) is:

AP Topic	Chapter.Section	Pages
I. Functions, Graphs, and Limits ***Parametric, polar, and vector functions** *The analysis of planar curves includes those given in parametric form, polar form and vector form.*	*9.1, 9.4, 10.1, 11.1*	*716-725, 742-754, 786-796, 854-864*
II. Derivatives **Applications of derivatives** + *Analysis of planar curves given in parametric form, polar form, and vector form, including velocity and acceleration*	*9.2, 9.5, 11.2, 11.3, 11.5*	*726-734, 755-763, 864-875, 876-877, 895-896*
II. Derivatives **Computation of derivatives** + *Derivatives of parametric, polar, and vector functions*	*9.2, 9.5, 11.2*	*726-734, 755-764, 864-875*
III. Integrals **Applications of integrals** *Appropriate integrals are used in a variety of applications to model physical, biological, or economics situations. Although only a sampling of applications can be included in any specific course, students should be able to adapt their knowledge and techniques to solve other similar application problems. Whatever applications are chosen, the emphasis is on using the method of setting up an*	*9.3 9.5*	*734-742, 755-764*

approximating Riemann sum and representing its limit as a definite integral. To provide a common foundation, specific applications should include ..., finding the area of a region (including a region bounded by polar curves), and the length of a curve (including a curve given in parametric form).		

Textbook Section	AP Topic
9.1 Plane Curves and Parametric Equations	**I. Functions, Graphs, and Limits** ***Parametric, polar, and vector functions** *The analysis of planar curves includes those given in parametric form, polar form and vector form.*
9.2 Calculus and Parametric Equations	**II. Derivatives** **Applications of derivatives** + *Analysis of planar curves given in parametric form, polar form, and vector form, including velocity and acceleration* **Computation of derivatives** + *Derivatives of parametric, polar, and vector functions*
9.3 Arc Length and Surface Area in Parametric Equations	**III. Integrals** **Applications of integrals** *Appropriate integrals are used in a variety of applications to model physical, biological, or economics situations. Although only a sampling of applications can be included in any specific course, students should be able to adapt their knowledge and techniques to solve other similar application problems. Whatever applications are chosen, the emphasis is on using the method of setting up an approximating Riemann sum and representing its limit as a definite integral. To provide a common foundation, specific applications should include ..., finding the area of a region (including a region bounded by polar curves), and the length of a curve (including a curve given in parametric form).*
9.4 Polar Coordinates	**I. Functions, Graphs, and Limits** ***Parametric, polar, and vector functions** *The analysis of planar curves includes those given in parametric form, polar form and vector form.*

Textbook Section	AP Topic
9.5 Calculus and Polar Coordinates	**II. Derivatives** **Applications of derivatives** + *Analysis of planar curves given in parametric form, polar form, and vector form, including velocity and acceleration* **Computation of derivatives** + *Derivatives of parametric, polar, and vector functions* **III. Integrals** **Applications of integrals** *Appropriate integrals are used in a variety of applications to model physical, biological, or economics situations. Although only a sampling of applications can be included in any specific course, students should be able to adapt their knowledge and techniques to solve other similar application problems. Whatever applications are chosen, the emphasis is on using the method of setting up an approximating Riemann sum and representing its limit as a definite integral. To provide a common foundation, specific applications should include ..., finding the area of a region (including a region bounded by polar curves), and the length of a curve (including a curve given in parametric form).*
10.1 Vectors in the Plane	**I. Functions, Graphs, and Limits** ***Parametric, polar, and vector functions*** *The analysis of planar curves includes those given in parametric form, polar form and vector form.*
11.1 Vector-Valued Functions	**I. Functions, Graphs, and Limits** ***Parametric, polar, and vector functions*** *The analysis of planar curves includes those given in parametric form, polar form and vector form.*
11.2 The Calculus of Vector-Valued Functions	**II. Derivatives** **Applications of derivatives** + *Analysis of planar curves given in parametric form, polar form, and vector form, including velocity and acceleration* **Computation of derivatives** + *Derivatives of parametric, polar, and vector functions*
11.3 Motion in Space	**II. Derivatives** **Applications of derivatives** + *Analysis of planar curves given in parametric form, polar form, and vector form, including velocity and acceleration*
11.5 Tangent and Normal Vectors	**II. Derivatives** **Applications of derivatives** + *Analysis of planar curves given in parametric form, polar form, and vector form, including velocity and acceleration*

Vocabulary and Sections Notes

Vocabulary used in the Topic Outline for Calculus BC (*Calculus BC topics are in italic type*) include:

Chapter 9

Arc length
Area in polar coordinates
Horizontal component of velocity
Parametric equations
Polar coordinates
Slope in parametric equations
Slope in polar equations
Vertical component of velocity

Chapter 10

Component
Horizontal component
Initial Point
Magnitude
Position vector
Resultant vector
Scalar
Terminal point
Triangle Inequality
Unit vector
Vector
Vertical component

Chapter 11

Acceleration vector
Antiderivative of a vector function
Arc length
Continuous vector function
Definite integral of a vector function
Derivative of a vector function
Indefinite integral of a vector function
Normal component
Position vector
Principal unit normal
Speed
Tangent vector
Tangential component
Vector-valued function
Velocity vector

Section notes for the Calculus BC Course:

Section 9.2 (Calculus and Parametric Equations): Area enclosed by a curve defined parametrically is not part of the Topic Outline for Calculus BC.

Section 9.3 (Arc Length and Surface Area in Parametric Equations): Surface area is not part of the Topic Outline for Calculus BC.

Section 9.5 (Calculus and Polar Coordinates): Arc length of a polar curve is not part of the Topic Outline for Calculus BC.

Section 9.6 (Conic Sections): Conic sections are not explicitly part of the Topic Outline for Calculus BC; however, this section is a thorough review of topics discussed in most precalculus courses.

Section 9.7 (Conic Sections in Polar Coordinates): This topic is not part of the Topic Outline for Calculus BC.

Section 10.1(Vectors in the Plane): Only section 10.1 with its introduction to the concept of a vector and the horizontal and vertical components of a vector are necessary to the study of vector valued functions that are a part of the Topic Outline for Calculus BC.

Section 11.1 (Vector-Valued Functions): The authors use 3-dimensional vectors in many of their discussions. The Topic Outline for Calculus BC limits itself to 2-dimensional vectors. The topics discussed are pertinent to the Calculus BC Course, as long as one limits the discussion to 2-dimensional vectors.

Section 11.2 (The Calculus of Vector-Valued Functions): As long as one limits the discussion to 2-dimensional vectors, all topics in this section are part of the Topic Outline for Calculus BC.

Section 11.3 (Motion in Space): Only examples 3.1 and 3.2, finding position, velocity or acceleration vectors (2-dimensions) are part of the Topic Outline for Calculus BC. Pertinent exercises would be 1-14. The other topics in this section are not part of the Topic Outline for Calculus BC.

Section 11.4 (Curvature): This topic is not part of the Topic Outline for Calculus BC.

Section 11.5 (Tangent and Normal Vectors): Only Example 5.1, Finding Unit Tangent and Principal Unit Normal Vectors (in 2-dimensions) is part of the Topic Outline for Calculus BC.

Student Activity: Vector Functions and Parametric Equations

Teacher's Notes:

This activity summarizes, for the teacher and student, the important features of vector functions and provides a teaching example and two exercises to evaluate student learning.

1. Some of the acceptable, but different, notations used for vectors are

$$r(t) = \vec{v} = (2,3) \text{ or}$$

$$r(t) = \vec{v} = <2,3> \text{ or}$$

$$r(t) = \vec{v} = 2i + 3j.$$

If $\vec{v} = (2,3)$, then the vector's horizontal displacement is 2 and its vertical displacement is 3. The 2 and 3 are called the vector's *components*.

2. When a particle moves in the *xy*-plane, the coordinates of its position are usually given as $x = x(t)$ and $y = y(t)$ for some time interval $a \le t \le b$. These parametric equations, $x = x(t)$ and $y = y(t)$, can be thought of as the particle's horizontal and vertical displacement. The particle's position vector, $r(t) = (x(t), y(t))$, is called a **vector function** of time *t*. The coordinates of the particle's positions at time *t* are the same as the components of $r(t)$ at time *t*. A **vector function** is just a different notation used for a **parametric relation**.

3. The graph below shows several position vectors for the vector-valued function

$$r(t) = \left\langle 6 - t^2, \frac{1}{2}t \right\rangle.$$

t	$x(t)$	$y(t)$
-2	2	-1
-1.5	3.75	-0.75
-1	5	-0.5
-0.5	5.75	-0.25
0	6	0
0.5	5.75	0.25
1	5	0.5
1.5	3.75	0.75
2	2	1
2.5	-0.25	1.25
3	- 3	1.5
3.5	-6.25	1.75

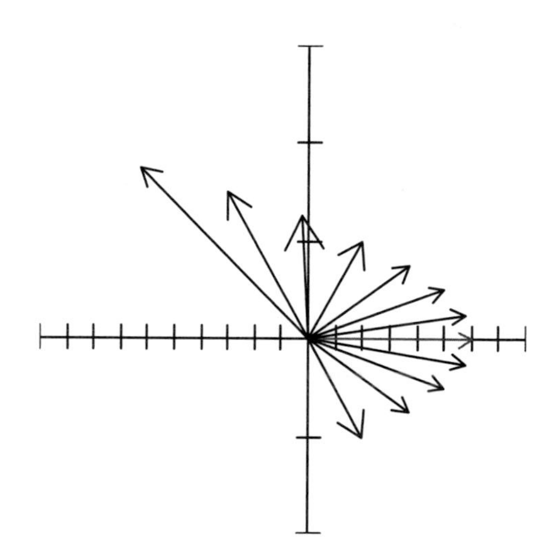

The graph of the path of the particle is generated by connecting the points located at the ends (tips) of the different position vectors.

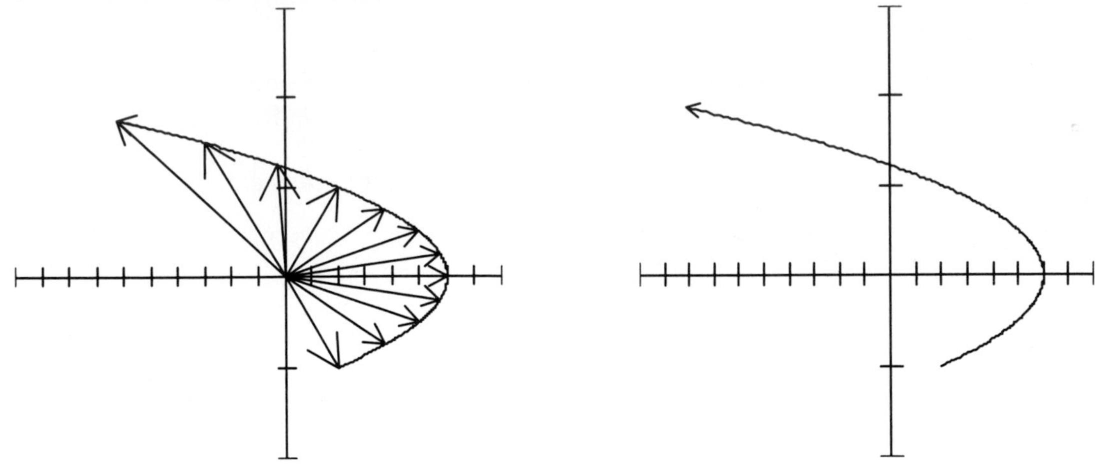

When graphing the parametric motion of a particle, be sure to use the "ball" option. Not only is the path clearly delineated, but also, the viewer can literally see the particle's speed decrease as it rounds a "corner" and then increase as it follows a "straighter" path.

4. A vector function, $r(t) = \left(x(t), y(t)\right)$, is differentiable at t if x and y have derivatives at t.

   The derivative of $r(t), \frac{d}{dt}r(t)$, is defined as the velocity vector: $v(t) = \left(x'(t), y'(t)\right)$.

   The derivative of $v(t), \frac{d}{dt}v(t)$, is defined as the acceleration vector: $a(t) = v'(t) = (x''(t), y''(t))$.

5. **Position vector**
   a. The initial point of the position vector is the *origin*. The terminal point of the vector lies on the *curve*.
   b. The length of the vector equals the *distance* the object is from the origin.

6. **Velocity vector**
   a. The initial point of the velocity vector lies on the *position curve.*
   b. The vector points in the direction the object is *moving*.
   c. The length of the vector equals the *speed* of the object at that instant.
   d. The velocity vector is the *derivative* of the position vector.

7. **Acceleration vector**

   a. The initial point of the acceleration vector lies on the *position curve*.

   b. The acceleration vector changes the object's *speed* and *direction*.

   c. The acceleration vector is the derivative of the *velocity* vector.

8. **Increasing/Decreasing Speed (these concepts are not needed for the AP Calculus Exam)**

   a. If the velocity vector and the acceleration vector point in the same direction, the object has *increasing* speed.

   b. If the two vectors point in opposite directions, the object has *decreasing* speed.

   c. If the two vectors form an *acute* angle, the object is speeding up.

   d. If the two vectors form an *obtuse* angle, the object is slowing down.

9. **Stopped**

   a. If $r(t)=(x(t),y(t))$, then, at time t, a particle is stopped if $x'(t)$ and $y'(t)$ are simultaneously zero.

10. **Speed** $=\|\vec{v}\|=\sqrt{(x'(t))^2+(y'(t))^2}$

11. **Net distance traveled** = arc length $=\int_{t\,\min}^{t\,\max}\sqrt{\left(\frac{dx}{dt}\right)^2+\left(\frac{dy}{dt}\right)^2}\,dt$. Remember, this formula works only if the path is traveled *once* and the path is *smooth*.

12. The position, in feet, of a particle moving in the $xy-$plane is given by the vector-value function $r(t)=\left(t^2-1,2t\right)$ for time $t,-2\le t\le 3$, in seconds.

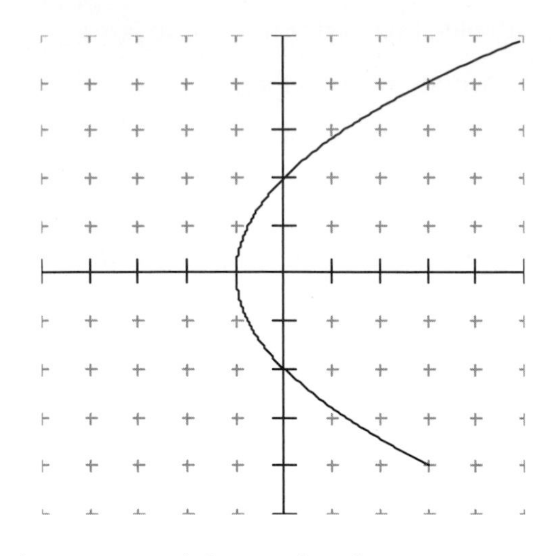

a. Find the velocity vector and the acceleration vector.

b. Find $r\left(-1.5\right),v\left(-1.5\right),a\left(-1.5\right)$ Plot each vector on the graph at its correct position.

c. Based on the graphs of the vectors, is the particle speeding up or slowing down?

d. Find the speed of the object at time $t=-1.5$ seconds.

e. Find the distance traveled by the particle from time $t=-1.5$ to $t=0$ seconds.

Solutions:

a. $v(t)=\langle 2t,2\rangle;\ a(t)=\langle 2,0\rangle$

b. $r(-1.5)=\langle 1.25,-3\rangle;\ v(-1.5)=\langle -3,2\rangle;\ a(t)=\langle 2,0\rangle$

c. The object is slowing down (obtuse angle).

d. speed $=\sqrt{(-3)^2+(2)^2}=\sqrt{13}$ ft per sec

e. distance $=\int_{-1.5}^{0}\sqrt{(2t)^2+(2)^2}\,dt=3.89892$ feet

Student Worksheet

1. The position, in feet, of a particle moving in the xy-plane is given by the vector-value function $r(t) = \left\langle \frac{1}{3}t^3 - 4t, 4\cos\left(\frac{1}{2}t\right) \right\rangle$ for time t, $t \geq 0$, in seconds.

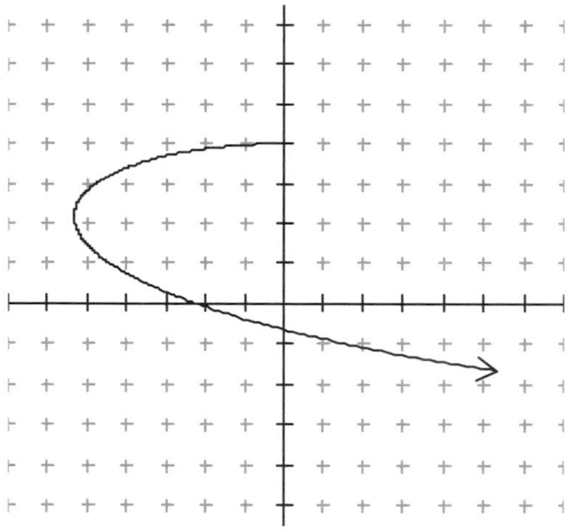

a. Find the velocity vector and the acceleration vector.
b. Find $r(1.5), v(1.5), a(1.5)$. Plot each vector on the graph at its correct position.
c. Based on the graphs of the vectors, is the particle speeding up or slowing down?
d. Find the speed of the object at time $t = 1.5$ seconds.
e. Find the distance traveled by the particle from time $t = 0$ to $t = 1.5$. seconds.

2. The position, in feet, of a particle moving in the $xy-$plane is given by the vector-value function $r(t)=\left\langle \frac{1}{3}t^3-4t, 4\cos\left(\frac{1}{2}t\right)\right\rangle$ for time t, $t\geq 0$, in seconds.

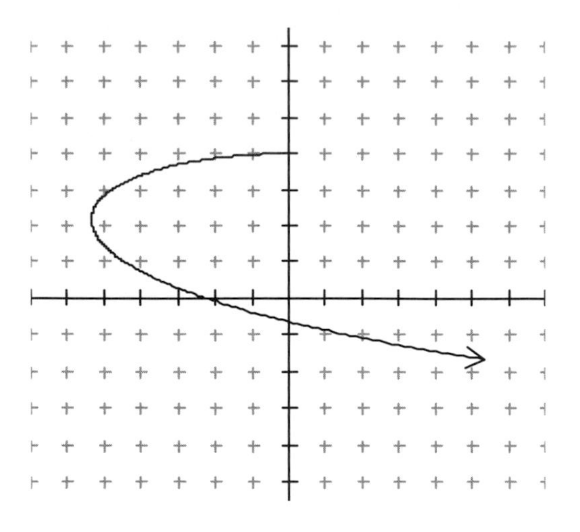

a. Find the velocity vector and the acceleration vector.

b. Find $r(2.5), v(2.5), a(2.5)$. Plot each vector on the graph at its correct position.

c. Based on the graphs of the vectors, is the particle speeding up or slowing down?

d. Find the speed of the object at time $t = 2.5$ seconds.

e. Find the distance traveled by the particle from time $t = 0$ to $t = 2.5$ seconds.

Solutions: Student Worksheet

1. The position, in feet, of a particle moving in the $xy-$plane is given by the vector-value function $r(t)=\left\langle \frac{1}{3}t^3-4t, 4\cos\left(\frac{1}{2}t\right)\right\rangle$ for time t, $t\geq 0$, in seconds.

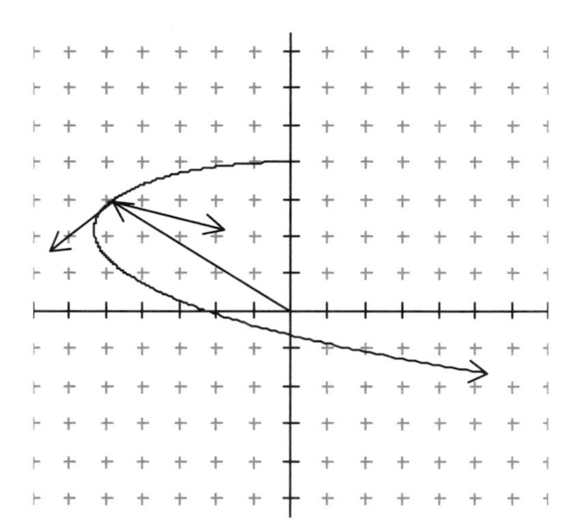

a. Find the velocity vector and the acceleration vector.
b. Find $r(1.5), v(1.5), a(1.5)$. Plot each vector on the graph at its correct position.
c. Based on the graphs of the vectors, is the particle speeding up or slowing down?
d. Find the speed of the object at time $t=1.5$.
e. Find the distance traveled by the particle from time $t=0$ to $t=1.5$. seconds.

a. $v(t)=\left\langle t^2-4, -2\sin\left(\frac{1}{2}t\right)\right\rangle$; $a(t)=\left\langle 2t, -\cos\left(\frac{1}{2}t\right)\right\rangle$

b. $r(1.5)=\langle -4.875, 2.9268\rangle, v(1.5)=\langle -1.75, -1.363\rangle,$
$a(1.5)=\langle 3, -0.7317\rangle.$

c. The particle is slowing down (obtuse angle).

d. speed $=\sqrt{(-1.75)^2+(-1.363)^2}=2.218167$ feet per second

e. distance $=\int_0^{1.5}\sqrt{(t^2-4)^2+(-2\sin(\frac{1}{2}t))^2}\,dt=5.0613$ feet

2. The position, in feet, of a particle moving in the $xy-$plane is given by the vector-value function $r(t)=\left\langle \frac{1}{3}t^3-4t, 4\cos\left(\frac{1}{2}t\right)\right\rangle$ for time t, in seconds.

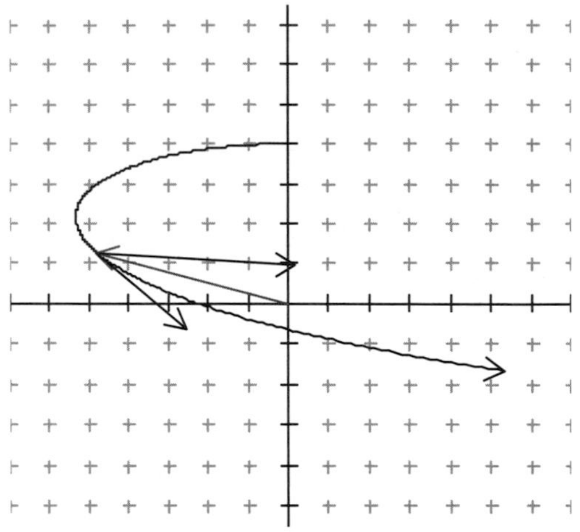

a. Find the velocity vector and the acceleration vector.
b. Find $r(2.5), v(2.5), a(2.5)$. Plot each vector on the graph at its correct position.
c. Based on the graphs of the vectors, is the particle speeding up or slowing down?
d. Find the speed of the object at time $t = 2.5$
e. Find the distance traveled by the particle from time $t=0$ to $t=2.5$ seconds

a. $v(t)=\left\langle t^2-4, -2\sin\left(\frac{1}{2}t\right)\right\rangle$; $a(t)=\left\langle 2t, -\cos\left(\frac{1}{2}t\right)\right\rangle$

b. $r(2.5)=\langle -4.792, 1.2613\rangle, v(2.5)=\langle 2.25, -1.898\rangle,$
$a(2.5)=\langle 5, -.3153\rangle.$

c. The particle is speeding up (acute angle).

d. speed $=\sqrt{(2.25)^2+(-1.898)^2}=2.9436$ feet per second

e. distance $=\int_0^{2.5}\sqrt{(t^2-4)^2+(-2\sin(\frac{1}{2}t))^2}\,dt=7.06945$ feet

Multiple-Choice Questions–Calculus BC Topics

*1. The area enclosed by the polar curve $r = 4 + 2\cos(2\theta)$ is

A. 36π
B. 18π
C. 9π
D. 8π
E. 4π

2. Which of the following equals the area of region inside the polar curve $r = 3\sin\theta$ and outside the polar curve $r = \sin\theta$?

A. $8\int_0^{\pi} \sin^2\theta\, d\theta$
B. $\frac{9}{2}\int_0^{\pi} \sin^2\theta\, d\theta$
C. $\frac{5}{2}\int_0^{\frac{\pi}{2}} \sin^2\theta\, d\theta$
D. $4\int_0^{\frac{\pi}{2}} \sin^2\theta\, d\theta$
E. $8\int_0^{\frac{\pi}{2}} \sin^2\theta\, d\theta$

3. What is the slope of the polar curve $r = \frac{1}{2}\theta^2$ at $\theta = \pi$?

A. $-\frac{\pi}{2}$
B. -1
C. 1
D. $\frac{\pi}{2}$
E. π

*4. A particle moves along the curve defined by the equations $x = \sin(t)$ and $y = \ln(t)$. The length of the path traveled over the interval $1 \le t \le 2\pi$ is

A. 0.486 B. 2.021 C. 3.937 D. 7.599 E. doesn't exist

5. A particle moves in the *xy*-plane so that its position at any time *t* is given by $x'(t) = t^2 - 4$ and $y'(t) = t + 3$. What is the speed of the particle when $t = 1$?

A. $\sqrt{3}$ B. $\sqrt{5}$ C. 1 D. 5 E. 25

6. The position of a particle moving in the *xy*-plane is given by the parametric equations $x(t)=t-t^2$ and $y(t)=\sin(t)$. When $t=\pi$, the particle is

A. moving right and up.
B. moving right and down.
C. moving left and up.
D. moving left and down.
E. stopped.

7. A particle moves in the *xy*-plane so that its position vector at time *t* is $\left(2\sin\left(\frac{1}{2}t\right),\cos(t)\right)$. Find its acceleration vector when the particle is at rest and $0<t<2\pi$.

A. $(1,0)$
B. $\left(-\frac{1}{2},1\right)$
C. $(-1,0)$
D. $\left(\frac{1}{2},-1\right)$
E. $(0,-1)$

8. The position of a particle moving in the *xy*-plane is given by the parametric equations $x(t)=\frac{1}{3}t^3-4t$ and $y(t)=\frac{1}{3}t^3-\frac{3}{2}t^2+2t$. Which of the following statements are true?

I. The particle's path has a vertical tangent line at $t=-2$.
II. The particle's path has a horizontal tangent line at $t=1$.
III. The particle's path forms a cusp at $t=2$.

A. I only
B. II only
C. I and III only
D. II and III only
E. I, II, and III

9. A curve in the plane is defined parametrically by the equations $x(t)=t^3-12t$ and $y=t^2-4t$. An equation for the line tangent to the curve at $t=2$ is

A. $x=-16$
B. $y+4=\frac{1}{3}(x+16)$
C. $y+4=\frac{1}{4}(x+16)$
D. $y+4=\frac{1}{6}(x+16)$
E. $y=-4$

10. If $x = e^{\cos t}$ and $y = (\sin t)^2$, then $\frac{d^2 y}{dx^2}$ at $x = \pi$ is

A. $-4e^2$
B. $4e^{-2}$
C. 0
D. 1
E. $4e^2$

11. If $x(t) = 3e^{-t} - 2t$ and $y(t) = 3t - 2e^{-2t}$, find $\lim_{t\to\infty}\left(\frac{dy}{dx}\right)$.

A. $-\frac{3}{2}$
B. $-\frac{2}{3}$
C. 0
D. $\frac{2}{3}$
E. $\frac{3}{2}$

12. If a curve in the plane is defined parametrically by the equations $x(t) = 2t$ and $y(t) = \sin(2t)$, $0 \le t \le \pi$, then the curve changes concavity at

A. $\frac{\pi}{6}$
B. $\frac{\pi}{4}$
C. $\frac{\pi}{3}$
D. $\frac{\pi}{2}$
E. π

Free-Response Questions–Calculus BC Topics

*1. The curve at the right is drawn in the *xy*-plane and is described by the polar equation $r = \sin\theta + \cos\theta$ for $0 \le \theta \le \pi$, where r is measured in centimeters and θ is measured in radians. The derivative of r with respect to θ is given by $\frac{dr}{d\theta} = \cos\theta - \sin\theta$.

a. Find the area of the region enclosed by the polar curve.

b. Find the angle $\theta, 0 \le \theta \le \frac{\pi}{2}$, that corresponds to the point on the curve with *x*-coordinate $\frac{1}{2}$.

c. At what value r in the interval $0 \le \theta \le \frac{\pi}{2}$ is the curve the furthest distance from the origin? Justify your answer.

d. Show that the polar curve has a vertical tangent line at $\theta = \frac{\pi}{8}$.

2. A particle moves in the *xy*-plane so that its position vector at time t is $\left(\frac{1}{3}t^3 - t, 2t - t^2\right)$.

a. Find the slope of the particle's path at $t = 1$.

b. Find all points on the particle's path that have a vertical tangent line.

c. When is the particle moving to the right? Justify.

d. Set up, but do not evaluate, an integral expression that represents the length of the path the particle traveled from $2 \le t \le 6$.

3. An object is moving along a path in the *xy*-plane defined by $y = x^2 + x$. For time

$$t \ge 0, \frac{dx}{dt} = te^t \text{ and when } t = 0, \quad x = -1.$$

a. Find $x(t)$ in terms of t.

b. Find $\frac{dy}{dt}$ in terms of t.

c. Find the slope of the line tangent to the path of the particle at $t = 1$.

d. Find the speed of the particle at $t = 1$.

*4. An object is moving along a path in the *xy*-plane. For $t \geq 0$, $\frac{dx}{dt} = \frac{-2}{\sqrt{t^2+1}}$ and $\frac{dy}{dt} = \frac{1}{\sqrt{3t+1}}$. At $t = 3$ the position of the object is $(1, 5)$.

a. Find the *x*-coordinate of the position of the object at time $t = 3.2$.

b. Write an equation for the line tangent to the curve when $t = 3$ and use it to approximate the *y*-value of the function when $x = 0.9$.

c. Are the *x*- and *y*-coordinates of the particle increasing or decreasing at $t = 3$? Justify your answer.

d. Find the *y*-coordinate of the position of the object at time $t = 3.2$.

Solutions to Sample Questions

Solutions to Multiple-Choice Questions

*1. B $\frac{1}{2}\int_0^{2\pi}\left(4+2\cos(2\theta)\right)^2\,d\theta = 18\pi$

2. E $2\left[\frac{1}{2}\int_0^{\frac{\pi}{2}}(3\sin\theta)^2-(\sin\theta)^2\right]d\theta$

$\int_0^{\frac{\pi}{2}}\left(9\sin^2\theta-\sin^2\theta\right)d\theta$

3. D $\dfrac{dr}{d\theta}=\theta$

$\dfrac{dy}{dx}=\dfrac{\theta\sin\theta+\frac{1}{2}\theta^2\cos\theta}{\theta\cos\theta-\frac{1}{2}\theta^2\sin\theta}$

$\left.\dfrac{dy}{dx}\right|_{\theta=\pi}=\dfrac{\pi\cdot 0-\frac{1}{2}\pi^2}{-\pi-\frac{1}{2}\pi^2\cdot 0}$

*4. C $\dfrac{dx}{dt}=\cos(t);\ \dfrac{dy}{dt}=\dfrac{1}{t};\ \int_1^{2\pi}\sqrt{(\cos(t))^2+\left(\dfrac{1}{t}\right)^2}\,dt=3.937$

5. D $\sqrt{((1)^2-4)^2+(1+3)^2}=\sqrt{9+16}=5$

6. D $x'(t)=1-2t$

$x'(\pi)<0$

$y'(t)=\cos(t)$

$y'(\pi)<0$

7. B Let $\vec{r}(t)=\left(2\sin\left(\frac{1}{2}t\right),\cos(t)\right)$.

$\vec{r}'(t)=\left(\cos\left(\frac{1}{2}t\right),-\sin(t)\right)$

$\cos\left(\frac{1}{2}t\right)=0 \qquad -\sin(t)=0$

$t=\pi \qquad t=\pi$

$\vec{r}''(t)=\left(-\frac{1}{2}\sin\left(\frac{1}{2}t\right),-\cos(t)\right)$

$\vec{r}''(\pi)=\left(-\frac{1}{2}\cdot 1,-1\cdot -1\right)$

8. E $x'(t)=t^2-4$ $y'(t)=t^2-3t+2$

$$t^2-4=0 \qquad t^2-3t+2=0$$

$$t=\pm 2 \qquad t=2 \text{ or } t=1$$

9. D $\frac{dy}{dx}=\frac{2t-4}{3t^2-12}=\frac{2(t-2)}{3(t-2)(t+2)}$

$$\lim_{t\to 2}\left(\frac{dy}{dx}\right)=\frac{1}{6}$$

$$x(2)=-16$$

$$y(2)=-4$$

10. A $\frac{dy}{dx}=\frac{2\sin t\cos t}{-\sin t\cdot e^{\cos t}}=\frac{-2\cos t}{e^{\cos t}}$

$$\frac{d^2y}{dx^2}=\frac{2\sin t\cdot e^{\cos t}-2\cos t\cdot\sin t\cdot e^{\cos t}}{e^{2\cos t}}\cdot\frac{-1}{\sin t\cdot e^{\cos t}}=\frac{2\cos t-2}{e^{2\cos t}}$$

$$\left.\frac{d^2y}{dx^2}\right|_{t=\pi}=\frac{2\cdot -1-2}{e^{2\cdot -1}}$$

11. A $\lim_{t\to\infty}\left(\frac{3+4e^{-2t}}{-3e^{-t}-2}\right)=\frac{3+0}{0-2}$

12. D $\frac{dy}{dx}=\frac{2\cos(2t)}{2}=\cos(2t)$

$$\frac{d^2y}{dx^2}=\frac{-2\sin(2t)}{2}=-\sin(2t)$$

$$-\sin(2t)=0$$

$$t=\tfrac{\pi}{2}$$

$$\frac{d^2y}{dx^2}<0 \text{ when } 0<t<\tfrac{\pi}{2}, \frac{d^2y}{dx^2}>0 \text{ when } \tfrac{\pi}{2}<t<\pi$$

Solutions to Free-Response Questions

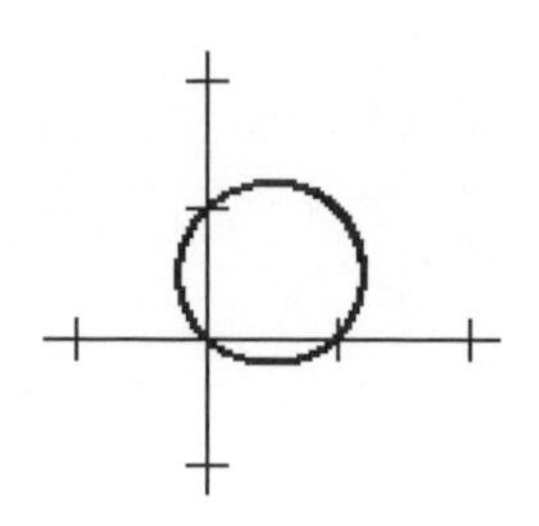

*1. The curve at the right is drawn in the xy-plane and is described by the polar equation $r = \sin\theta + \cos\theta$ for $0 \le \theta \le \pi$, where r is measured in centimeters and θ is measured in radians. The derivative of r with respect to θ is given by $\frac{dr}{d\theta} = \cos\theta - \sin\theta.$

a. Find the area of the region enclosed by the polar curve.

b. Find the angle $\theta, 0 \le \theta \le \frac{\pi}{2}$, that corresponds to the point on the curve with x-coordinate $\frac{1}{2}$.

c. At what value r in the interval $0 \le \theta \le \frac{\pi}{2}$ is the curve the furthest distance from the origin? Justify your answer.

d. Show that the polar curve has a vertical tangent line at $\theta = \frac{\pi}{8}$.

(a) $\frac{1}{2}\int_0^{\pi}(\sin\theta + \cos\theta)^2\, d\theta = \frac{\pi}{2} = 1.570 \text{ or } 1.571$

1: answer

(b) $\frac{1}{2} = r\cos(\theta) = (\sin(\theta) + \cos(\theta))\cos(\theta)$

$\theta = 1.178$

$2\begin{cases}1: \text{ equation}\\ 1: \text{ answer}\end{cases}$

(c) $\cos\theta - \sin\theta = 0$

$\theta = \frac{\pi}{4} = 0.785$

$r(0) = 1$

$r\left(\frac{\pi}{4}\right) = \sqrt{2} = 1.414$

$r\left(\frac{\pi}{2}\right) = 1$

The curve is furthest from the origin at $r = \frac{\pi}{4}$.

$3\begin{cases}1: \ \theta = \frac{\pi}{4}\\ 1: \ r(0), r\left(\frac{\pi}{4}\right), r\left(\frac{\pi}{2}\right)\\ 1: \text{ answer}\end{cases}$

(d) $\frac{dy}{dx} = \frac{(\cos\theta - \sin\theta)\sin\theta + (\sin\theta + \cos\theta)\cos\theta}{(\cos\theta - \sin\theta)\cos\theta - (\sin\theta + \cos\theta)\sin\theta}$

$\frac{dy}{d\theta} = (\cos\theta - \sin\theta)\sin\theta + (\sin\theta + \cos\theta)\cos\theta$

$\left.\frac{dy}{d\theta}\right|_{\theta=\frac{\pi}{8}} = \sqrt{2} \ne 0$

$\frac{dx}{d\theta} = (\cos\theta - \sin\theta)\cos\theta - (\sin\theta + \cos\theta)\sin\theta$

$\left.\frac{dx}{d\theta}\right|_{\theta=\frac{\pi}{8}} = 0$

$3\begin{cases}1: \ \frac{dy}{dx}\\ 1: \left.\frac{dy}{d\theta}\right|_{\theta=\frac{\pi}{8}} \ne 0\\ 1: \left.\frac{dx}{d\theta}\right|_{\theta=\frac{\pi}{8}} = 0\end{cases}$

2. A particle moves in the xy-plane so that its position vector at time t is $\left(\frac{1}{3}t^3 - t, 2t - t^2\right)$.

   a. Find the slope of the particle's path at $t = 1$.
   b. Find all points on the particle's path that have a vertical tangent line.
   c. When is the particle moving to the right? Justify.
   d. Set up, but do not evaluate, an integral expression that represents the length of the path the particle traveled from $2 \le t \le 6$.

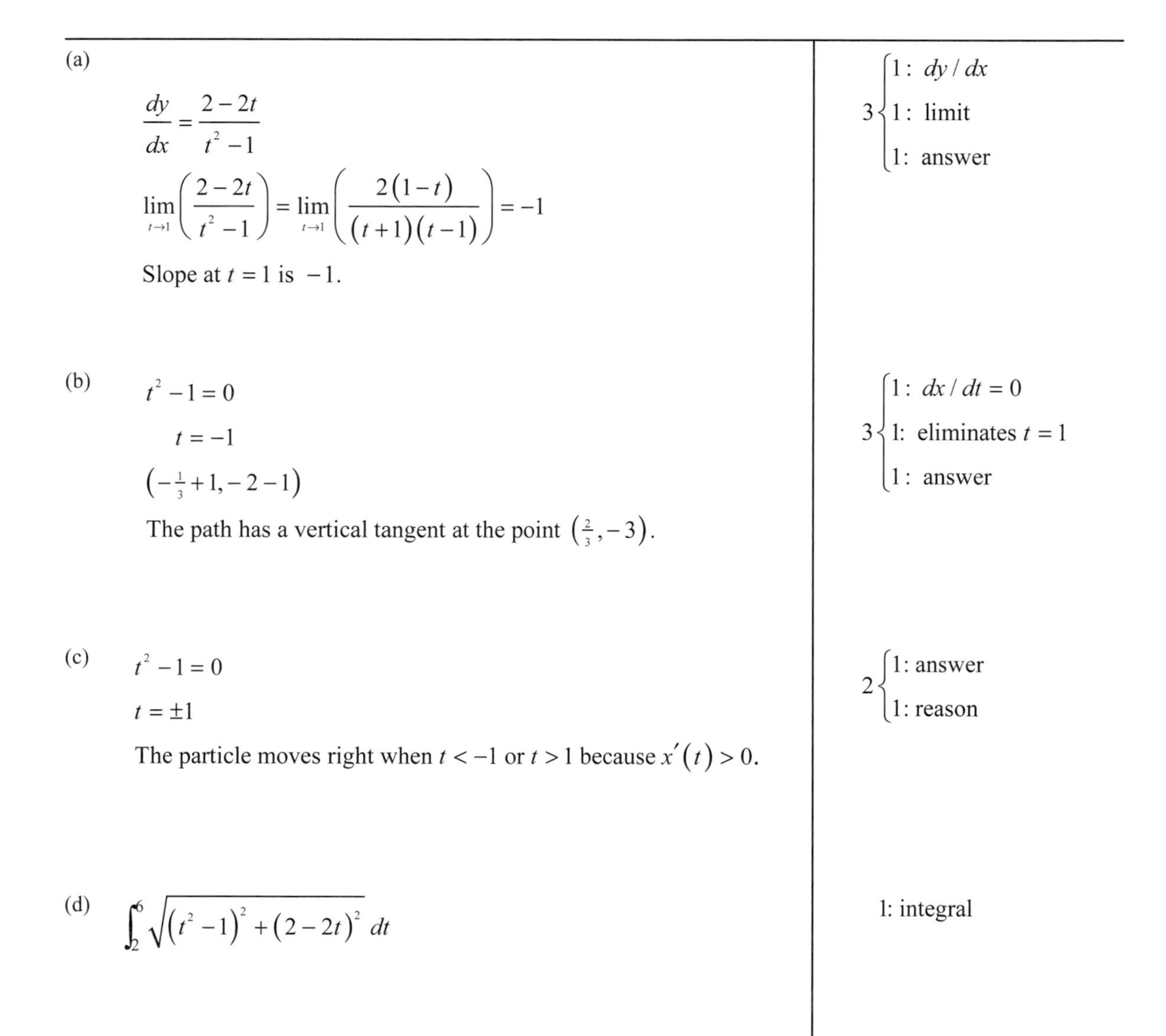

(a)

$$\frac{dy}{dx} = \frac{2-2t}{t^2-1}$$

$$\lim_{t \to 1}\left(\frac{2-2t}{t^2-1}\right) = \lim_{t \to 1}\left(\frac{2(1-t)}{(t+1)(t-1)}\right) = -1$$

Slope at $t = 1$ is -1.

$3\begin{cases} 1:\ dy/dx \\ 1:\ \text{limit} \\ 1:\ \text{answer} \end{cases}$

(b)

$$t^2 - 1 = 0$$
$$t = -1$$
$$\left(-\tfrac{1}{3}+1, -2-1\right)$$

The path has a vertical tangent at the point $\left(\frac{2}{3}, -3\right)$.

$3\begin{cases} 1:\ dx/dt = 0 \\ 1:\ \text{eliminates } t = 1 \\ 1:\ \text{answer} \end{cases}$

(c)

$$t^2 - 1 = 0$$
$$t = \pm 1$$

The particle moves right when $t < -1$ or $t > 1$ because $x'(t) > 0$.

$2\begin{cases} 1:\ \text{answer} \\ 1:\ \text{reason} \end{cases}$

(d)

$$\int_2^6 \sqrt{\left(t^2-1\right)^2 + \left(2-2t\right)^2}\, dt$$

1: integral

3. An object is moving along a path in the xy-plane defined by $y = x^2 + x$. For time $t \geq 0, \frac{dx}{dt} = t\,e^t$ and when $t = 0, \quad x = -1$.

a. Find $x(t)$ in terms of t.

b. Find $\frac{dy}{dt}$ in terms of t.

c. Find the slope of the line tangent to the path of the particle at $t = 1$.

d. Find the speed of the particle at $t = 1$.

---

a. $x(t) = te^t - e^t + C$

$x(0) = -1 = 0e^0 - e^0 + C; C = 0$

$x(t) = te^t - e^t$

$$3\begin{cases} 1:\ \text{antiderivative} \\ 1:\ C = 0 \\ 1:\ x(t) \end{cases}$$

b. $y = (te^t - e^t)^2 + (te^t - e^t)$

$\frac{dy}{dt} = 2(te^t - e^t)(te^t) + (te^t)$

$\frac{dy}{dt} = (2(te^t - e^t) + 1)(te^t)$

$$2\begin{cases} 1:\ \frac{dy}{dt} = 2x\frac{dx}{dt} + \frac{dx}{dt} \\ 1:\ \frac{dy}{dt} \text{ in terms of } t \end{cases}$$

c. $\frac{dy}{dx} = 2x + 1; \left.\frac{dy}{dx}\right|_{t=1} = 1$

$$2\begin{cases} 1:\ \frac{dy}{dx} \\ 1:\ \text{answer} \end{cases}$$

d. speed $= \sqrt{\left(\frac{dx}{dt}\right)^2 + \left(\frac{dy}{dt}\right)^2}$

$\sqrt{(1e^1)^2 + ((2(1e^1 - e^1) + 1)(1e^1))^2} = e\sqrt{2}$

$$2\begin{cases} 1:\ \text{speed} \\ 1:\ \text{answer} \end{cases}$$

*4. An object is moving along a path in the xy-plane. For $t \geq 0$, $\frac{dx}{dt} = \frac{-2}{\sqrt{t^2+1}}$ and $\frac{dy}{dt} = \frac{1}{\sqrt{3t+1}}$.

At $t = 3$ the position of the object is $(1, 5)$.

a. Find the x-coordinate of the position of the object at time $t = 3.2$.

b. Write an equation for the line tangent to the curve when $t = 3$ and use it to approximate the y-value of the function when $x = 0.9$.

c. Are the x- and y-coordinates of the particle increasing or decreasing at $t = 3$? Justify your answer.

d. Find the y-coordinate of the position of the object at time $t = 3.2$.

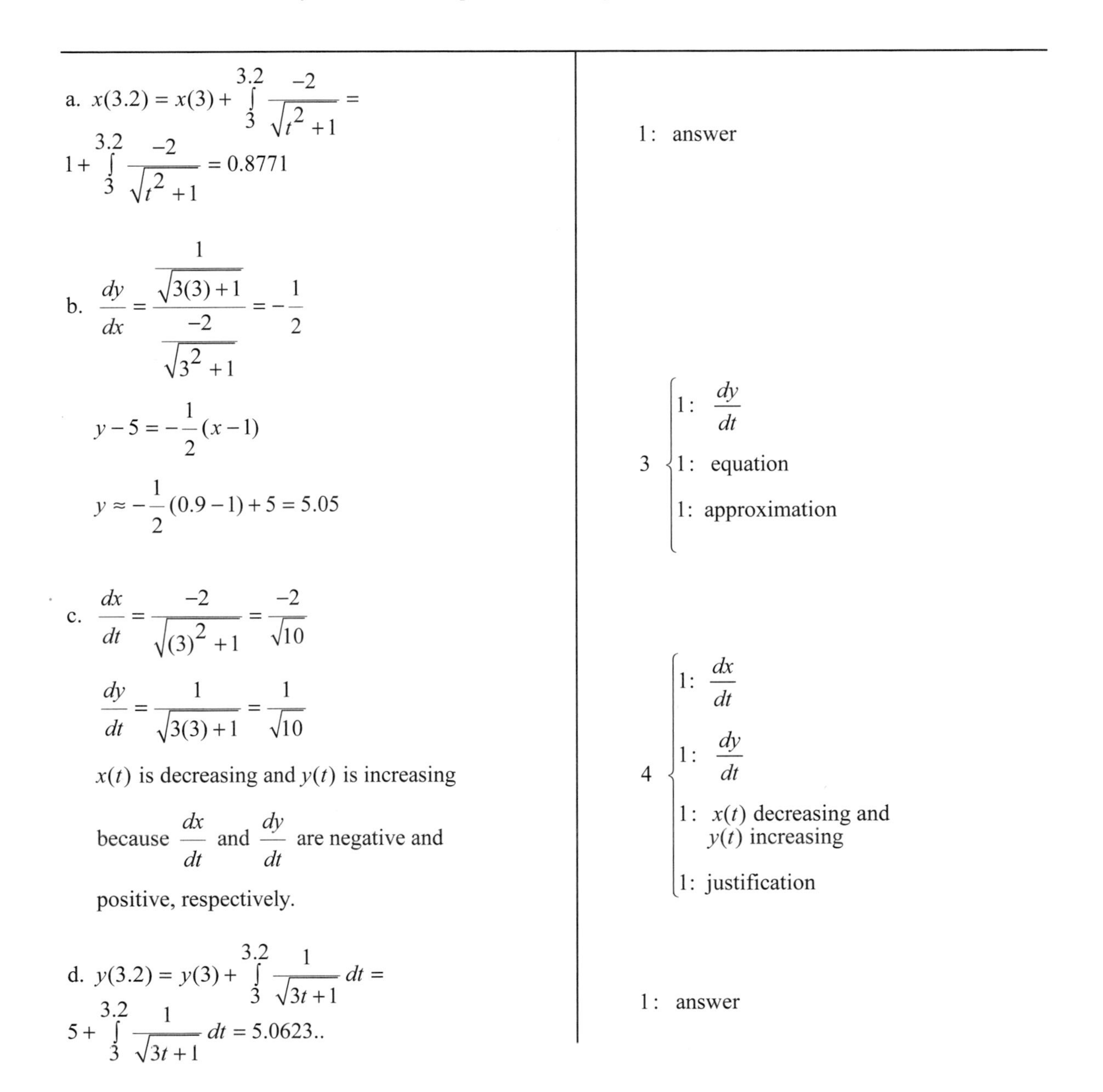

Solution	Scoring
a. $x(3.2) = x(3) + \int_3^{3.2} \frac{-2}{\sqrt{t^2+1}} =$ $1 + \int_3^{3.2} \frac{-2}{\sqrt{t^2+1}} = 0.8771$	1: answer
b. $\frac{dy}{dx} = \frac{\frac{1}{\sqrt{3(3)+1}}}{\frac{-2}{\sqrt{3^2+1}}} = -\frac{1}{2}$ $y - 5 = -\frac{1}{2}(x-1)$ $y \approx -\frac{1}{2}(0.9-1) + 5 = 5.05$	3: 1: $\frac{dy}{dt}$; 1: equation; 1: approximation
c. $\frac{dx}{dt} = \frac{-2}{\sqrt{(3)^2+1}} = \frac{-2}{\sqrt{10}}$ $\frac{dy}{dt} = \frac{1}{\sqrt{3(3)+1}} = \frac{1}{\sqrt{10}}$ $x(t)$ is decreasing and $y(t)$ is increasing because $\frac{dx}{dt}$ and $\frac{dy}{dt}$ are negative and positive, respectively.	4: 1: $\frac{dx}{dt}$; 1: $\frac{dy}{dt}$; 1: $x(t)$ decreasing and $y(t)$ increasing; 1: justification
d. $y(3.2) = y(3) + \int_3^{3.2} \frac{1}{\sqrt{3t+1}}\,dt =$ $5 + \int_3^{3.2} \frac{1}{\sqrt{3t+1}}\,dt = 5.0623..$	1: answer

Connect2Calculus Videos for Chapters 9, 10, and 11

The Calculus Concepts Video's for Chapter 9-10-11: *(Calculus BC topics are in italic type).* Some of the topics on the videos go beyond the scope of Calculus AB/BC, but would be worth watching as an application of calculus

Chapter 9

16.0 Parametric Equations: When the Curve is Not a Function
16.1 *Modeling: x and y as Functions of t*
16.2 *Arc Length*
16.3 Surface Area (not in the Topic Outline for Calculus AB/BC)

17.0 Polar Coordinates: When the Curve is Circular
17.1 *Constructing Circular Shapes with Polar Coordinates*
17.2 *Polar Coordinates and Calculus*
17.3 Limit Cycles: Heart Dynamics (not in the Topic Outline for Calculus AB/BC)

Chapter 10

18.0 Understanding Vectors and the Geometry of Space
18.1 *Vector Components and Operations*
18.2 Projection and Dot Products (not in Topic Outline for Calculus AB/BC)
18.3 Surfaces and Vectors, Cross Products (not in Topic Outline for Calculus AB/BC)

Chapter 11

19.0 Choosing The Vector Model: Vector-Valued Functions
19.1 Vector-Valued Functions: Velocity and Direction
19.2 Curvature (not in Topic Outline for Calculus AB/BC)
19.3 Tangent and Normal Vectors

Preparing for the AP Calculus Exam

To prepare students for the AP Calculus Exam, it is important that teachers understand the format of the exams. The authors also present some strategies and tips to help students prepare for the exams.

Format of the AP Calculus Exam

The AP Calculus Exam is split into two major sections. Each section is further split into calculator and non-calculator parts. Section I contains 45 multiple-choice questions. Section II has six essay questions, or free-response questions. Each free-response question is usually presented in parts. Students can earn partial credit on each part.

Fifty-four of the 108 possible points on the exam come from Section II (six essay questions worth nine points each). The scoring process for Section I is slightly more complicated. First, to correct for guessing, one-fourth the number of questions marked incorrectly is subtracted from the number of questions answered correctly. This total is then multiplied by 1.2 so that the Section I score is a weighted proportion of the remaining fifty-four possible points. (If all multiple-choice questions were correct then $45(1.2) = 54$ points.)
The actual test takes three hours and 15 minutes. It will take about another hour to take care of administrative details like distributing the exam, gridding in personal information on the multiple-choice answer sheet, and collecting the exam. There is a short break between the two sections. Students should plan on four hours from start to finish.

Section I—Multiple-Choice

The first section of the test is multiple-choice. These are the multiple-choice questions that are the lifeblood of any exam. For each question, students are given five options and must choose the one correct answer. The questions can be presented in analytic, graphical, or tabular form.

Part A of Section I is the non-calculator portion. Students have 55 minutes to answer 28 questions. Part B has 17 questions. Students will have 50 minutes to answer them. Students can use a graphing calculator on any of the questions in Part B, but only about six to eight questions in Part B will *require* a calculator. At the end of 105 minutes, students are asked to seal their multiple-choice answer sheet in the question booklet. Students are not allowed to have any scratch paper. However, there is ample space in the test booklet for any work needed to solve the problems. *None of the work in the test booklet will be graded on the multiple-choice section. Students should make sure to bubble in all their answers on the answer sheet.*

Section II—Free-Response

The second part of the exam is the free-response section. Again, the questions may be presented in analytic, graphical, or tabular form. At first glance, the free-response section seems like the more intimidating part of the test because there is so much work to do. However, it can actually be easier than the multiple-choice question section, as students are free to show their answer in any logical form. Each question is worth nine points. The scoring rubric is designed to allow students to earn partial credit.

Each of the six questions asks students to answer several questions about some functions. Several ideas are often combined. For example, there might be two functions that enclose a region. Part (a) of the question might be to find the area of the region bounded by the functions. Part (b) may ask for the volume if the region is revolved about the x-axis. Part (c) could ask for the volume of the solid formed by squares that are perpendicular to the region. The test can use the same question to measure students' knowledge of several different ideas.

Part A of Section II consists of three questions that will allow the use of a graphing calculator, although not all parts will need it. Students have 45 minutes for these three questions. After putting their calculator away, they can proceed to Part B of Section II. These three questions will be similar to those in Part A but no calculator is required. All work can and must be done by hand. Students have 45 minutes to finish this section and to complete any additional work on Part A. However, they cannot use their calculator any more to help on Part A. Section II of the test lasts 90 minutes.

The questions on this part of the test are designed so students can show their understanding of the concepts of calculus. The functions will be relatively simple, but they will have to show their work or justify their answer. Any justification must use analytic methods instead of a graph or a table of values.

Students may be asked to interpret the answer to a free-response question in terms of the context of the problem. For example, the answer to a related rate question about a ladder sliding down a wall might be -10 feet/second. Students must explain in complete sentences that the top of the ladder is sliding *down* the wall *at the rate* of 10 feet per second *at the moment* indicated in the problem.

It is important that students understand some of the requirements for presenting their work on the free-response sections. The Calculus Course Description booklet, beginning on page 15, discusses expectations such as showing enough work so that AP Exam Readers can follow student-reasoning, use of proper calculus notation, and justification of answers as a mathematical process and not a reporting of things observed when using a calculator. There are two important articles all teachers should read, "Calculus FRQ Instruction Commentary" and "On the Role of Sign Charts in AP Calculus Exams for Justifying Local or Absolute Extrema". Both are available on the home pages for Calculus AB and Calculus BC at AP Central (apcentral.collegeboard.com).

Things to Remember About the Free-Response Section

1. There is no need to simplify arithmetic. It will not make the answer any more correct ($2(1.5)+3$ does not need to be simplified).
2. Do not spend time erasing large amounts of work that need to be changed. Instead, cross it out and begin again. However, do not cross out work unless it can be replaced with a better solution.
3. Be sure to label answers and use correct units.
4. Even if unsure about the accuracy of a result in one part, use it anyway to finish the problem.
5. When using a calculator to solve a problem, describe the solution clearly in mathematical terms, not in calculator speak

   (use $\int_{-1}^{3}(2x-5)dx$ not $\text{fnInt}(2x-5,x,-1,3)$.)
6. Do not write bad math. ("Slope of the derivative" or "6.2368 = 6.237" or "-17.21 = 17.21".)
7. Remember: three decimal places, rounded or truncated. (More is ok.)
8. Do not write $f(x)=2(1.5)+3$ when you really mean $f(1.5)=2(1.5)+3$.
9. Every pronoun needs an antecedent. Use the name of the function when referring to the function. Do not say, "The slope is ...." Say, "The slope of g is ...," especially when discussing more than one function.
10. When asked to write an integral, start with the limits and any constants of multiplication. Then write the correct or most correct integrand.
11. Know the difference between increasing and positive. (f is increasing when f' is positive.)
12. Calculator work will be limited to the four required functionalities: graphing, zeros, numerical derivative, and numerical integration. Students will not be required to do anything else with the calculator and no question will be asked where using an additional feature would give an advantage (e.g., curve fitting).
13. Know the difference between local and global extrema.

14. Know the difference between the extreme value (y -coordinate) and the location of the extreme value (x- and y-coordinate).
15. When justifying local extrema or points of inflection, be sure to label the number line or chart. The number line or chart is not enough to justify local extrema or points of inflection. Students must summarize the results in complete sentences.
16. When asked to approximate the value of a function use $\approx$ not $=$ ($f(1.2) \approx 2.34678$, not $f(1.2) = 2.34678$)
17. Be sure the calculator is in radian mode.
18. The answers to properly organized area of a region or volume of a solid problems are positive numbers. If a result is negative, something is wrong and all work should be reviewed for errors.
19. Do not round intermediate answers in calculations (-7/(3 + cos(4)) = -2.983349, but -7/(3 - 0.653) = -2.982530, which is not correct to three decimal points).

Suggestions for preparing students for the exam

The myriad of schedules used in high schools precludes creating an ideal schedule of topics to follow when teaching either a Calculus AB or Calculus BC course. However, experienced teachers try to complete instruction by April 1, if possible, so that students have about five weeks to review and prepare for the exam. Please note that each section in this text is rich with topics and most Calculus AB teachers choose to spend more than one day developing the topics and completing the exercises. Calculus BC teachers, of necessity, must choose a slightly faster pace if they are to have adequate time to discuss all the topics in their course outline.

Suggestions for "testing" student readiness for exam

Each year the free-response questions and the scoring rubrics for evaluating student responses are released after the student papers have been scored. Teachers should develop a file of these questions and rubrics and use them, whenever appropriate in their course, to help students become familiar with the format and wording of the questions and to help students learn how to present their solutions to the problems. Suggested uses include solving a question with the students as part of the instruction on a topic, assigning them as homework problems or using them on tests or quizzes. Teachers can download the questions and rubrics from 1998 through the current year at the AP Central site (apcentral.collegeboard.com). The free-response questions and solutions from 1969-1997 are available in electronic format that can be purchased and downloaded from the College Board Store.

Appendix A contains a table of topics that analyzes the content of each part of each free-response question (1999-2006) and correlates it to a specific topic in the Topic Outline for Calculus AB and the Topic Outline for Calculus BC. Thus, a teacher searching for a free-response question that requires the calculation of a derivative using implicit differentiation would find that topic addressed in several questions.

The multiple-choice questions are not released every year. However, the complete 1998 and 2003 AP Calculus Exams (multiple-choice and free-response questions) have been released so that teachers can gain insight into the format and style of the questions. The released exams also include an analysis of student performance on each question as well as information about the scoring and detailed statistics about the overall student performance.

Many teachers use these two exams to assess their students' readiness for the actual exam. If possible, have the students attempt the questions in a testing situation so that their results can be compared with those of the students who actually took the exams in 1998 and 2003. An analysis of questions students left blank or their errors can help identify topics for further study and review.

Appendix B contains a table of topics correlated to specific questions on the multiple-choice portions of the 2003 Calculus AB and Calculus BC Exams.

Most students do not have any experience in taking a test that lasts for more than one class period. The AP Calculus Exams require three hours and fifteen minutes of actual testing time as well as time for necessary paperwork and a short break between the multiple-choice and free-response parts of the exam. If possible, it is recommended that students take practice exams in a setting that would allow a reasonable approximation to the conditions they might encounter when they take the actual exam.

Appendix A

AP Calculus AB Examination
Free-Response Question Topic Frequency

Functions

	‘06	‘05	‘04	‘03	‘02	‘01	‘00	‘99
Domain	X						X	
Range							X	
Continuity				X	X			

Differential Calculus

	‘06	‘05	‘04	‘03	‘02	‘01	‘00	‘99
Analyze a function given table of values	X	X		X				X
Tangent line equation	X	X		X	X	X	X	X
Evaluation of a derivative				X	X	X		X
Increasing and decreasing functions			X	X	X	X		
Relative extrema – local and global		X	X		X	X	X	X
Concavity		X		X	X	X		
Inflection points		X				X		X
Average rate of change	X	X	X			X		
Using the graph of f’(x) to analyze behavior of f(x)	X		X	X	X		X	
Using a table of values of f(x), f’(x), and f’’(x) to analyze the behavior of f(x)		X			X			
Sketching a curve or analyzing data using the graph of f’(x) or tables of values of of f(x), f’(x), and f’’(x)	X	X			X			
Mean Value Theorem for Derivative		X			X			
Implicit derivatives			X				X	
Linear approximation		X		X	X			
Related rates				X	X			X

Integral Calculus

	'06	'05	'04	'03	'02	'01	'00	'99
Area and/or interpretation	X	X	X	X	X	X	X	X
Riemann sums using left, right, and midpoint evaluations	X			X				X
Properties of integrals				X	X	X		X
Trapezoidal Rule/ approximations		X				X		
Fundamental Theorem of Calculus		X		X	X	X		X
Average Value	X	X	X	X		X		X
Volumes of solids of revolution	X	X	X	X	X	X	X	X
Volumes of solids with known cross sections			X	X			X	
Separable differential equations	X	X		X		X	X	X
Slope fields	X	X	X					
Rectilinear motion from equations		X					X	
Rectilinear motion from graphs		X				X	X	
Definite integral as an accumulator	X	X	X	X	X		X	X

Calculator Skills

	'06	'05	'04	'03	'02	'01	'00	'99
Draw a graph in a given window		X			X			
Zeros of a function					X			
Intersection points of two graphs	X	X	X	X		X	X	
Evaluation of a definite integral	X	X	X	X	X		X	X
Evaluation of a derivative		X	X	X	X	X		X

AP Calculus BC Examination
Free-Response Question Topic Frequency

Functions

	'06	'05	'04	'03	'02	'01	'00	'99
Domain & range							X	
Finite limits						X		
Limits involving infinity	X						X	

Differential Calculus

	'06	'05	'04	'03	'02	'01	'00	'99
Analyze a function given table of values		X				X		
Tangent line equation		X		X		X	X	X
Chain Rule						X		
Increasing and decreasing functions				X	X	X		X
Critical values	X				X	X	X	X
Concavity		X		X	X	X		x
Inflection points				X				X
Average rate of change	X	X	X		X			X
Extreme values	X	X			X	X		X
Higher order derivatives	X							
Sketching a curve or analyzing data using the graph of f'(x) or tables of values of of f(x), f'(x), and f''(x)		X			X	X		X
Mean Value Theorem for Derivative		X			X	X		X
Implicit derivatives	X	X	X				X	
Linear approximation						X		X
Related rates				X				

Integral Calculus

	'06	'05	'04	'03	'02	'01	'00	'99
Area and/or interpretation	X	X	X	X	X		X	X
Riemann sums using left, right, and midpoint evaluations	X							X
Properties of integrals				X	X			X
Trapezoidal Rule/ approximations		X				X		
Fundamental Theorem of Calculus		X		X	X			X
Average Value	X	X	X		X	X		X
Volumes of solids of revolution	X	X	X	X	X		X	X
Volumes of solids with known cross sections				X			X	
Separable differential equations	X			X		X	X	
Slope fields		x			X		X	
Rectilinear motion from equations		X					X	
Rectilinear motion from graphs		X				X	X	
Definite integral as an accumulator	X	X	X	X	X		X	X
Euler's Method	X	X			X	X		X
Logistic growth functions			X					

Calculator Skills

	'06	'05	'04	'03	'02	'01	'00	'99
Intersection points of two graphs	X	X		X			X	
Evaluation of a definite integral	X	X		X	X		X	X
Evaluation of a derivative			X		X	X		X

Sequences and Series

	'06	'05	'04	'03	'02	'01	'00	'99
Tests for convergence		X						
Geometric series						X		
Alternating series and error approximation				X			X	
Manipulation of a power series	X		X	X	X	X		
Radius of convergence of a power series							X	
Interval of convergence of a power series	X	X			X	X		
Maclaurin series				X	X			
Taylor series	X	X	X		X		X	X
Lagrange error bound			X					X

Parametric, Polar, and Vector Functions

	'06	'05	'04	'03	'02	'01	'00	'99
Parametrically defined curves			X	X	X	X		X
Derivatives of vector and parametric curves	X		X	X	X	X	X	X
Tangent lines to parametric curves			X	X		X	X	
Curvilinear motion on parametric curves	X		X		X		X	X
Polar coordinate graphs		X		X				
Areas of polar curves		X		X				

Appendix B

Alignment of 2003 Calculus AB Multiple-Choice Exam with the Topic Outline for Calculus AB

Question #	Topic	Question #	Topic	Question #	Topic
1	Computation of Derivatives	16	Derivative at a point	78	Applications of derivative
2	Techniques of antidifferentiation	17	Computation of a derivative, 2nd derivative	79	Limits of a function
3	Asymptotic behavior, derivative at a point	18	Derivative of a function	80	Derivative of a function
4	Computation of a derivative	19	Applications of antidifferentiation	81	Applications of derivative; calculator
5	Techniques of antidifferentiation	20	Concept of derivative; limits of functions	82	Concept of derivative; applications of integrals
6	Limits of functions	21	Second derivative	83	Concept of derivative; calculator
7	Derivative as a function; applications of derivative	22	Interpretation of definite integrals	84	Applications of antidifferentiation; calculator
8	Techniques of antidifferentiation	23	Fundamental Theorem of Calculus; computation of derivative	85	Numerical approximation to an integral
9	Computation of derivative	24	Derivative at a point	86	Applications of integrals; calculator
10	Second derivative	25	Applications of derivative	87	Second derivative; calculator
11	Techniques of antidifferentiation	26	Computation of derivative	88	Applications of integrals
12	Concept of derivative	27	Applications of derivative	89	Computation of derivative; derivative at a point
13	Concept of derivative; continuity as a property	28	Second derivative	90	Derivative of a function

14	Computation of derivativc	76	Applications of derivative; calculator	91	Applications of antidifferentiation; applications of derivative; calculator
15	Derivative as a function	77	Applications of integrals; interpretation of definite integrals	92	Fundamental Theorem of Calculus, antidifferentiation

Alignment of 2003 Calculus BC Multiple-Choice Exam with the Topic Outline for Calculus BC

Question #	Topic	Question #	Topic	Question #	Topic
1	Computation of Derivatives	16	Derivative at a point	78	Related rates
2	Indeterminant limits of functions	17	Tangent line from parametric function	79	Chain Rule from tabular values
3	Techniques of antidifferentiation	18	Fundamental Theorem of Calculus	80	Integral as an accumulator; calculator
4	Slope of a parametrically defined function	19	Applications of antidifferentiation	81	Limits; calculator
5	Euler's Method	20	Maclaurin Series	82	Applications of definite integrals; calculator
6	Convergence of an improper integral	21	Logistic growth function	83	Rolle's Theorem
7	Particle motion with parametric functions	22	Convergence of p-series	84	Speed of a parametric function; calculator
8	Techniques of antidifferentiation	23	Integration by Parts	85	Numerical approximation to an integral
9	Computation of derivative	24	Divergence of a series	86	Applications of derivatives; calculator
10	Limit of a series	25	Riemann Sum approximation	87	Particle from velocity; calculator
11	Manipulation of a Maclaurin series	26	Techniques of integration: partial fractions	88	Applications of integrals, Average Value Theorem

12	Differential equation	27	Fundamental Theorem of Calculus	89	Volume of solid with known cross-section; calculator
13	Concept of derivative; continuity as a property	28	Taylor series expansion	90	Analysis of graph of the derivative of a function
14	Slope field	76	Continuity and limits	91	Applications of antidifferentiation; applications of derivative; calculator
15	Derivative from arc length	77	Derivative of Taylor polynomial	92	Mean value Theorem; calculator

Notes